FAMILY PROCESSES AND SCHIZOPHRENIA

Family Processes and Schizophrenia

EDITED BY

*Elliot G. Mishler and
Nancy E. Waxler*

HARVARD MEDICAL SCHOOL
and
MASSACHUSETTS MENTAL HEALTH CENTER

SCIENCE HOUSE

New York

CONTRIBUTORS

Gregory Bateson, Ph.D.
Professor of Anthropology, University of Hawaii

Arnold Bernstein, Ph.D.
Associate Professor of Psychology, Queens College of the City University of New York

Maurice R. Beaulieu, M.D.
Chief, Highland Psychiatric Inpatient Service
Alameda County Medical Institutions

Daniel V. Caputo, Ph.D.
Assistant Professor of Psychology, Queens College of the City University of New York

Frances E. Cheek, Ph.D.
Chief, Experimental Sociology, State of New Jersey Bureau of Research in Neurology and Psychiatry

Amerigo Farina, Ph.D.
Professor, Department of Psychology, University of Connecticut

Henry L. Lennard, Ph.D.
Associate Professor of Medical Sociology (Psychiatry), San Francisco Medical Center, University of California

Paul M. Lerner, Ed.D.
Assistant Chief, Psychological Services, Sinai Hospital of Detroit

Theodore Lidz, M.D.
Chairman, Department of Psychiatry, Yale University

Elliot G. Mishler, Ph.D.
Associate Clinical Professor of Psychology, Department of Psychiatry, Harvard Medical School

William Pollin, M.D.
Chief, Section on Twin and Sibling Studies, Adult Psychiatry Branch, National Institute of Mental Health

David Reiss, M.D.
Clinical Associate, Adult Psychiatry Branch, National Institute of Mental Health

Shlomo Sharan (Singer), Ph.D.
Lecturer, Departments of Education and Psychology, Tel-Aviv University

John Spiegel, M.D.
Professor of Social Psychiatry, Florence Heller Graduate School for Advanced Studies in Social Welfare, Brandeis University

James R. Stabenau, M.D.
Research Psychiatrist, Section on Twin and Sibling Studies, Adult Psychiatry Branch, National Institute of Mental Health

Joe Tupin, M.D.
Assistant Professor, Director of Psychiatric Research, University of Texas Medical Branch

Nancy E. Waxler, Ph.D.
Associate in Social Psychology, Department of Psychiatry, Harvard Medical School

Martha Werner, M.A.
Research Psychologist, Section on Twin and Sibling Studies, Adult Psychiatry Branch, National Institute of Mental Health

Lyman Wynne, M.D.
Chief, Section on Family Studies, National Institute of Mental Health

CONTENTS

Part III   Commentaries

A SET OF formulations about relationships between family interaction processes and schizophrenia is rapidly being subjected to
experimental investigation. The seminal theoretical articles, drawn
primarily from clinical observations and clinical research, first
began to appear in professional journals in 1956. Hardly more
than a decade later, it is possible to assemble a group of papers
that report interesting and relevant results from systematic experimental studies of a number of the initial hypotheses.

New methods have been developed for collecting and analyzing
data on interaction in families. Some of the clinically based
hypotheses have proved more useful and viable than others, and
there are new findings that will have to be taken into account
in theories of family and personality pathology. Although there is
a common focus and objective in this work—the determination
of specific ways in which families of schizophrenic patients differ
from other families in how they interact together—there is great
diversity in the methods and concepts used. It seemed appropriate
at this time to bring some of these studies together in order to
assess their relationships to clinical observations, to compare their
findings, to indicate promising developments, and to suggest
theoretical issues that require further elaboration and clarification.

The theoretical overview with which the volume begins ex-
amines some of the main features of three formulations about
the relationships between schizophrenia and certain aspects of
family life. These alternative theoretical orientations are compared
with each other by focusing on their respective answers to four
critical questions: which family processes are considered to be
pathogenic, what is the nature of schizophrenia, what are the

mechanisms through which family patterns exert their pathogenic effect, and why are not all of the children schizophrenic?

This review of theories had been prepared with little attention to the experimental studies included in this volume; many of them had not appeared until after work on the review had been completed. Despite this lack of direct influence, there are striking parallels, reflecting their common points of origin, between the questions discussed in the review and the hypotheses and aims of the different studies. Although the experimenters vary in the degree of clarity and explicitness with which they connect their work with particular concepts and ideas, they all begin with questions drawn from clinical observations and associated theories. However, this only provides the initial stimulus and context for the research. The findings lead to new questions not only for researchers but for clinicians as well.

Of the eight experimental studies reprinted here, six were published in 1965 or later. They appeared in seven different journals. These are signs both of the contemporaneity and diversity of interest in this area. These studies have in common an experimental research approach in which family members are directly observed and recorded in a nontherapeutic interaction situation. We have grouped the papers together according to the interpersonal unit that is the object of direct study and analysis.

The three foci that form the basis of organization are the parental dyad, the pathogenic triad, and the family tetrad. In the first, attention is directed toward interaction between the parents, who are the only members of the family on whom direct observations are made; in the second, the schizophrenic child is included in the experimental situation; in the third, a well sibling of the patient is added to the family group.

Clearly, patterns of interaction will reflect in part the number and character of persons present. Theories about the pathogenic effects of family interaction will have to be specified in such a way that findings from studies of parental pairs can be related to findings from studies of family triads and tetrads and each in turn related to problems of socialization and personality development.

We are far from this stage of theorizing at this time; by organizing the volume around these different sub-groupings within the family we hoped that the findings within and between different sets could be more easily compared. In addition, problems of data analysis and interpretation become increasingly complex as one moves to the study of groups with three or four members with differentiated role structures. Some of these problems will be explored in the section introductions.

Each group of papers is preceded by an introduction, where an attempt is made to relate the methods, approaches, and findings of the several studies to each other. It will be seen that the studies share some of the important and noteworthy features of experimental work—control group designs, quantification of measures, statistical analysis of data. The reliability and validity of findings from experimental studies depend closely on the care that is exercised in dealing with a number of difficult methodological problems. This necessitates limiting the scope of the problem; thus, in comparison to clinical investigations, these studies are narrow in focus. However, what they lose in breadth of generalization is more than made up for, we believe, by the confidence that can be placed in their findings.

One final word. There are many useful approaches to the study of families and the experimental method is only one of them. At the point that theories direct attention to patterns of interaction—to how persons behave toward each other—the experimental method may make a special contribution. This volume is presented with that belief and in the hope that other investigators will find something of value in it that they can use in their own research.

ELLIOT G. MISHLER
NANCY E. WAXLER

Part I

A REVIEW OF CURRENT THEORIES

CHAPTER ONE

FAMILY INTERACTION PROCESSES AND SCHIZOPHRENIA: A REVIEW OF CURRENT THEORIES *

ELLIOT G. MISHLER and NANCY E. WAXLER

MANY INVESTIGATORS HAVE been concerned with whether specific features of family life are associated with the etiology and development of schizophrenia. Both personality characteristics and social attributes of parents have been objects of considerable research and speculation since the pre-World War II period; the well-known notion of the schizophrenogenic mother was one of the products of this early line of inquiry.[1] During the past decade there has been a noticeable shift in the focus of attention among students of this problem. Interest is now centered on the whole family as a unit for study and conceptualization and, in particular, on the patterns of interaction and communication among the members of the family.

* Reprinted from The Merrill-Palmer Quarterly of Behavior and Development, 11:269-315, 1965. This is a report from a project entitled, "An Experimental Study of Families with Schizophrenics," which is supported in part by NIMH Grant No. MH-06276. The authors wish to acknowledge the detailed and serious response to an earlier draft of this paper by several of the investigators whose works are reviewed here—Gregory Bateson, Jay Haley, Don D. Jackson, Theodore Lidz, Yi-chuang Lu and Lyman Wynne. The paper has benefited greatly from their suggestions and criticisms, although responsibility for the use made of those comments of course rests solely with the authors. Extended discussions with Alan Blum, Loren Mosher, and Rhona Rapoport of a number of issues raised in the paper were also most valuable in preparing the final revision.

3

This has been an exciting development accompanied by an array of new concepts and hypotheses about schizophrenia, suggestive of new techniques of treatment and productive of a growing body of research. It seemed to us both appropriate and timely to attempt a review and comparative analysis of current theories relating family processes and schizophrenia.[2] While many investigators have contributed to this development, three groups of investigators have had a major influence on the shape and direction of current thought and research; these are the research groups led by Gregory Bateson, Theodore Lidz, and Lyman Wynne. We shall place particular emphasis on their formulations.

Our intent is both expository and analytic. We wish to clarify each theory's basic concepts, and compare their respective foci and levels of conceptualization. We have a special interest in how well the theories might serve as guides for research and will therefore be concerned with the degree of precision and testability of the various hypotheses. Experimental approaches to the study of family interaction have seemed to us to have a special relevance for these new formulations, and we shall refer at a number of points to the methods and findings of experimental studies of patient families. We hope that this review of these theories and methods will permit a specification of particularly critical areas for further work.

It will be seen below that the several theories differ from each other in a number of important ways—from their descriptive terms to their assumptions about schizophrenia; in whether they focus on difficulties in communication or affective relationships; in the degree of their concern with social roles or personality dynamics. While we have tried to preserve the flavor and the essential conceptual concerns of each theory, our primary interest has been in comparing them with each other. This has been done by contrasting the answers that each gives to a minimum set of basic questions with which any serious and systematic theory of family process and schizophrenia must be concerned. Taken together, answers to these questions would permit a relatively complete account of the specific conditions under which schizophrenia develops. This paper is organized around this set of questions.*

1. What are the patterns of family interaction that are related to the development of schizophrenia?

2. What is schizophrenia, and what are the psychological mechanisms through which family patterns of interaction enter into the development of the schizophrenic process?

3. How do these interaction patterns persist over time, that is, what individual and family functions are served that help to maintain the schizogenic forms of interaction?

4. What are the preconditions for these patterns of interaction? That is, what are the social and personal attributes of family members that are associated with the development of these processes?

Only the theories associated with Bateson, Lidz, and Wynne will be examined in detail. However, other formulations will be referred to at points in the discussion where they may provide further understanding of the various issues.

Before presenting detailed analyses in terms of the outline of critical questions listed above, it may be useful to the reader unfamiliar with one or another of the theories to have brief résumés of each of them in which the major concepts and special emphases may be seen in overall view.

---

* Response to an earlier draft of the chapter has called our attention to a special problem of comparative analysis of theories that are still in process of development. In brief, the theorists felt that we did not emphasize sufficiently the fact that their formulations were presented over a period of time and that their theories are not finished statements but theories "in process." We do not believe that there is a completely satisfactory solution to this problem since any attempt at analysis involves the use of standard dimensions for comparison and requires an assumption that a theory at any point in time is to be taken seriously as it is stated at that point in time. We have tried, however, to remain sensitive to what we see as the basic thrust and direction of each theory and to give primacy to the most current statements in our interpretations of their work. The reader is asked to bear in mind this historical and developmental aspect of the theories discussed.

RESUMES OF THEORIES

Bateson Group

The general theory of the Bateson group is often identified with the idea of the *double bind*. While this one concept does not do full justice to the complexity of the theory, it nevertheless mirrors in microcosm many of the latter's important aspects. The *double bind* is defined as a special type of learning context from which the growing child cannot escape; a context where he is subjected to incongruent messages that require him to deny important aspects of his self or his experience. The necessary ingredients are: repeated experience between two or more persons where one of them, i.e., the victim, is confronted with two incongruent negative injunctions, for example, "I order you to disobey me." Negative injunctions could be expressed in the affective quality of statements or be implicit in the situation of interaction as well as being expressed directly in verbal content. Punishment is expected to follow either choice in this conflict situation; a third negative injunction is present that prohibits the child from attempting to escape from the situation. Repeated exposure to such situations results in the individual's stripping his own messages of meaning since punishment can be avoided only by preventing the other person from understanding his response. Eventually, he behaves as if he had lost the ability to discriminate the true meanings of his own and others' messages; that is, he manifests schizophrenic behavior.

It is important to note that these hypotheses about schizophrenia derive from a proposed general model about human behavior where communication is viewed as equivalent to human behavior rather than as only one aspect among others. Further, there is a special focus in this theory on the equilibrium of the family state, that is, on the ways family members maintain stability in their communication with each other by developing rules governing who says what to whom in what contexts.

Originally, the theory was arrived at deductively, that is, by considering the nature of schizophrenic communication and "deducing" a set of requirements in the family that would lead to this form of pathological communication. Since that beginning, the formulation has developed through observations and analyses of family therapy sessions and, more recently, experimental studies of family behavior.

Lidz Group

While an explicit focus on the family as the unit of theoretical and empirical interest distinguishes the Lidz group's formulation, there is, nevertheless, a close resemblance to familiar psychodynamic traditions of theorizing about personality development and psychopathology. In many ways, this theory is a direct extension and application of orthodox psychoanalytic concepts to the family triad. There is a central concern with age-sex structure of the family. A critical etiological feature for schizophrenia lies for these theorists in the blurring of age and generation boundaries; parents behave inappropriately for their sex and age with respect both to each other and to their child, and the child therefore learns inappropriate behavior. The consequence is that identity development for the child is distorted, and it is in the distortion of adequate identity development that the theory locates the psychological basis for schizophrenia. Empirically two types of schizogenic families are distinguished—one organized around a central, dominating, pathological figure, usually the mother, and referred to as "skewed"; a second pattern of "schism" where the relationship is characterized by chronic hostility and mutual withdrawal. Different processes in the development of schizophrenia for males and females are postulated and related to the different problems of identity development in each of these types of families. The entire family is seen as pathological, and patterns of irrational thinking and unrealistic views of the outside world are taught to the developing child. Finally, the dramatic quality of family relationships is described more explicitly here than in the

7

other theories; both murderous and incestuous wishes, recipro-
cated by parents, threaten to break out of control during adolescence and are seen to play an important part in the schizophrenic breakdown.

Empirical work of the Lidz group has centered on an extensive
investigation of a small sample of hospitalized schizophrenic patients and their families; information has been gathered largely
through diagnostic and therapeutic interviews.

Wynne Group

The theory of the Wynne group is closer to that tradition in
social psychological theory about socialization and personality
development that gives prominence to the concept of an individual's identity as the link between the person and his culture.
Within this general orientation, special attention is given to the
impairment of ego functioning and its associated thought disorders in schizophrenia. In Wynne's formulation, an adequate
identity and a healthy, well-functioning ego require not only a
stable and coherently meaningful environment but an opportunity
to test out and to select as part of one's own individual identity
a variety of roles during the course of development. The families
of schizophrenics do not provide such a stable environment—in
role structure they are either too rigid or too loosely and ambiguously structured, a lack of true complementarity is concealed
under a façade of "pseudo mutuality," communication and interaction are disjointed and fragmented, irrational shifts in the
focus of attention prevent real continuity of interaction. Pressures to maintain this façade and to deny or to avoid the recognition of the basic meaninglessness of the relationships force the
child to conform to the family system; the imposition of sanctions isolates him effectively from other sources of socialization.
There is a general guiding hypothesis that the thought disorder
in schizophrenia derives from the disordered patterns of interaction in the family.

Observation of families in family therapy situations were the major source of early formulations. More recently, emphasis has shifted to the systematic analysis of both psychological test protocols and family interactions within a "predictive" research strategy, that is, an attempt to predict from parental characteristics to presence and type of schizophrenia in the child.

INTERACTION PATTERNS IN SCHIZOGENIC FAMILIES

IF SOCIAL INTERACTION is defined broadly to include consistent ways in which persons act toward and respond to each other, then each theory under review gives a central place to the influence of certain types of intrafamilial interaction on the development of schizophrenia. However, the theories also differ markedly from each other, at the general level of the aspect or dimension of interaction with which each is concerned, and specifically in the particular types of distortion of normal interaction that are seen as critical and distinctive in schizophrenogenic families. Their similarities and differences in these respects will be explored in this section.

The Bateson group's felicitous phrase, *the double bind*, has gained wide currency although its precise intended meaning seems not to be as well understood as its general usage would suggest.[3] In part, its success as a term may reflect its surface relationship to the popular notion of a "bind" as a troubled and self-defeating interpersonal relationship. The difficulty is that a "bind" is a term with a vague referent rather than a precise definition of a particular type of relationship. If it is assimilated to this familiar and unclear concept, the new concept of the *double bind* loses both the formal precision that entered into its original formulation as well as its specific properties.

In their first comprehensive statement of a "communicational theory of the origin and nature of schizophrenia"—that is, a theory that centers the etiology of schizophrenia in parental communication to the child—Bateson and his co-workers specified the following necessary ingredients of a double-bind situation: "1. Two or more persons. . . . 2. Repeated experience. . . . 3. A primary negative injunction. . . . 4. A secondary injunction conflicting with the first at a more abstract level, and like the first enforced by punishments or signals which threaten survival. . . . 5. A tertiary negative injunction prohibiting the victim from escaping from the field. . . ." [4] These five elements exemplify in concrete form one of the ways in which the abstract idea of the double bind becomes manifest as a system of interaction.

In addition to this general formulation of a communication pattern consisting of conflicting injunctions, there is specification of three other features of the double bind that in this theory are necessary conditions for the development of schizophrenic reactions. In a sense, these are different types of "tertiary negative injunctions"—first, the fact of conflicting injunctions is denied; second, the child cannot escape from the situation; third, he is not permitted to "metacommunicate," that is, he can neither comment upon nor point to the contradictory nature of the communication. Of these "other features of the context" also to be mentioned, Bateson states: ". . . there is, or appears to be, an absolute prohibition upon calling attention to the parents' incongruity in any overt way. . . . Neither the parents nor the patient is able to act as if fully aware of the incongruities. There is also a prohibition upon escaping from the field and, in addition, an insistence on the part of the parents that the patient respond. There shall be no non-responding and no not-caring and all these prohibitions are linked together. After all, to leave the field or to express 'not caring' would be to point the finger at the incongruities." [5]

In the earlier paper, he and his co-workers provide a good example of a double bind in describing a situation involving a schizophrenic patient and his mother:

A young man who had fairly well recovered from an acute schizophrenic episode was visited in the hospital by his mother. He was glad to see her and impulsively put his arm around her shoulders, whereupon she stiffened. He withdrew his arm, and she asked, "Don't you love me any more?" He then blushed, and she said, "Dear, you must not be so easily embarrassed and afraid of your feelings." [6]

The mother's communication includes conflicting sets of messages, putting her son in an impossible dilemma:" If I am to keep my tie to mother I must not show her that I love her, but if I do not show her that I love her, then I will lose her."

This is a "damned if you do and damned if you don't" situation for the child, who is trapped by the incongruent demands and forbidden to call attention to his predicament. Such a patient is, to apply here a statement made elsewhere by Bateson, "faced with the dilemma either of being wrong in the primary context or of being right for the wrong reasons or in the wrong way. This is the so-called double bind. We are investigating the hypothesis that schizophrenic communication is learned and becomes habitual as a result of continued traumata of this kind." [7]

The idea of incongruity is pervasive in the writings of members of this group of investigators. It is defined by example and implication and refers essentially to the lack of consistency between different aspects, levels, or elements of a message. Incongruity in communication may take any of a variety of forms. For example, the affect conveyed by tone of voice may differ from the literal meaning of the words, as in sarcasm or in joking hostility; the message may be inappropriate to its context, as in gallows humor; or the gestures may contradict the verbal content, as in the previous example of a double-bind situation between a patient and his mother; incongruity may result from denying or negating any of the elements of a message.

Such incongruities are involved in many forms of human discourse including humor and poetic metaphor. The problem lies with those special types of incongruity, that is, double binds, where the individual is threatened with punishment whichever aspect of the incongruent message he chooses to respond to and where there is the underlying "prohibition upon comment." Bateson and his group generalize their views by referring them to

11

Russell's theory of logical types where basic paradoxes are explored that result from the proposition that a class cannot be a member of itself.* If we understand them correctly, they are suggesting that the analogue to resolving logical paradoxes, by recognizing that two different levels of abstraction are involved, is the act of metacommunicating or commenting upon the incongruity between parts of a message. Where this last is forbidden, the incongruency cannot be resolved and the person receiving the messages remains trapped.

As a formal statement of relationships among levels of meaning, the double-bind hypothesis and its associated ideas is viewed as applicable to all types of social and cultural systems.[8] However, within the narrow frame of family interaction the hypothesis as originally stated focused attention primarily on dyadic interaction, particularly between mother and child, in the etiology of schizophrenia—with the emphasis placed on the problems faced by the growing child "caught" in the double bind. More recently, there has been increased emphasis on the active role of the "victim" in maintaining this system.

While he uses the same basic paradigm of the double bind and its insoluble paradoxes, Haley, in further developing the original formulation, gives more emphasis to the whole family unit as an interacting system.[9] In so doing he suggests some of the parameters of a social system within which double binds may be adaptive responses. He points to the importance of the struggle for power and control in these families and suggests that a primary issue in all human relationships has to do with "who" is going to set the rules for the relationship. He defines the family as a self-corrective social system in which behavior is governed,

* Historically, interest in Russell's theory of logical types preceeded work on schizophrenia; the schizophrenic was seen as a person who manifested special difficulties in the classification of messages. The original article on the theory of schizophrenia was ". . . a product of deduction more than of observation, for we had hardly looked at the families of schizophrenics. It was hypothesized that given a learning organism which communicates like this then this sort of learning context [i.e., one involving conflicts in levels of communication] would have led to his communicating like this." (Jay Haley, personal communication.)

regulated, and patterned by internal processes where family members set limits to each other's behavior. Haley stresses the need for complex models of such systems, since ". . . two levels of governing processes must be included: (a) the error-activated response by a member if any member exceeds a certain range of behavior, and (b) the attempt by family members to be the meta-governor, i.e., the one who sets the limits of that range." [10]

As in all families, members of schizogenic families govern each other's behavior by imposing sanctions and other correctives when their rules and prohibitions are violated. The difference in these families, according to Haley, lies in the collective denial that anyone is setting the rules, that is, that anyone is the meta-governor. In this respect he notes:

> Typically in these families the mother tends to initiate what happens, while indicating either that she isn't, or that someone else should. The father will invite her to initiate what happens while condemning her when she does. Often they suggest the child take the lead, and then disqualify his attempts. . . . The family "just happens" to take actions in particular directions with no individual accepting the label as the one responsible for any action. . . .[11] The family of the schizophrenic would seem to be not only establishing and following a system of rules, as other families do, but also following a prohibition on any acknowledgment that a family member is setting rules. Each refuses to concede that he is circumscribing the behavior of others, and each refuses to concede that any other family member is governing him.[12]

Haley points out that the act of communicating inherently involves defining one's relationship with the other person; that is, to communicate is to set rules at some level with regard to the nature of the behavior that is to take place in the relationship. Within schizogenic families, the members attempt to avoid defining their relationships to each other by negating or disqualifying any or all elements of their messages. These elements are listed as: "(1) I (2) am saying something (3) to you (4) in this situation." [13] A person may deny that he is the person speaking, may contradict one message with another, may refuse to acknowledge whom he is addressing. For example, Haley describes the husband whose wife asks him to do the dishes, responding with: "I would like to do the dishes, but I can't. I have a headache." By this response, the husband indicates that *he* is not defining the relationship by this refusal; after all it was the headache which prevented the dishwashing, not he. In a sense, these different ways of denying elements of a message appear to be varieties of double binds. Haley seems to be suggesting that the double bind is an adaptive response in a family whose members refuse to acknowledge that they are setting rules for each other's behavior, and as a consequence interaction is oriented toward denying any responsibility for the nature of their relationships.

Among other theorists concerned with the etiological role of family interaction processes in the development of schizophrenia, both Searles and Laing have described mechanisms that emphasize types of incongruity similar to those described in the Bateson-Haley formulations. Searles outlines six "modes of driving the other person crazy," each of which tends to activate various areas of the person's personality in opposition to each other.[14] These modes are: pointing out areas of the other's personality, of which he may be unaware, that are inconsistent with his ideal or actual self-image; stimulating the person sexually in settings where attempts at gratification would be disastrous; simultaneous or rapidly alternating stimulation and frustration; relating to the other simultaneously on two unrelated levels, for example, sexual advances during an intellectual-political discussion; switching erratically from one emotional wave length to the other while discussing the same topic; switching topics while maintaining the same emotional wave length, for example, discussing life and death issues in the same manner as trivial happenings.

While each of these is a concrete example of a pair of conflicting messages and therefore stands as an instance of that one ingredient of the double bind, Searles' treatment of the "binding" nature of these interactions focuses on the mutual satisfaction of needs rather than on the formal structure of the interaction.

Laing discusses "confirmation" of the self as a process through which individuals are recognized, acknowledged, "endorsed" by others—"the crux seems to be that it is a response by the other that is *relevant* to the evocative action, . . . a direct response, in the sense at least of being 'to the point,' or 'on the same beam' or 'wave-length' as the first person's initiatory or evocatory action." [15] His discussion of the lack of true confirmation in the families of schizophrenics bears obvious similarities to the general idea of the double bind, but differs in the stress Laing places on the experiencing self as the object of the incongruous act. Thus, ". . . there is minimal genuine confirmation of the parents by each other and of the child by each parent, separately or together, but there may not be obvious disconfirmation. One finds, rather, interactions marked by pseudo-confirmation, by acts which masquerade as confirming actions but are counterfeit. . . . The schizogenic potential of the situation seems to reside largely in the fact that it is not recognized by anyone; or, . . . this knowledge is not brought out into the open." [16] This tangential failure to "endorse" the other's experience is evident in the incident reported by Laing where a little boy runs to his mother with a worm in his hand and says, "Mummy, look what a big fat worm I have got." To which the mother responds, "You are filthy. Away and clean yourself immediately." [17]

There are several problems that deserve brief mention in concluding this summary of the Bateson group's formulation of critical interaction processes in the families of schizophrenics. First, there is a lack of precision and clarity in their writings that presents serious difficulties for an accurate understanding of the types of interaction sequences that do and do not fall within the definition of the double bind. From the way the concept is used, it sometimes appears that all communication sequences may be interpretable, at some level of analysis, as double binds, and, if this be so, the concept loses all usefulness. This ambiguity regarding the generality of the concept also obscures its specific relationship to related formulations. For example, the relations

15

between the original double-bind hypothesis and Haley's later analyses of family rules have not been made explicit and remain unclear.

Two important problems do not receive attention in the writings of this group. One is that, in emphasizing the structure of communicative acts, the possibility is ignored that the critical influence of the double bind may reflect the substantive nature of the conflict presented. For example, if the conflict embodies deep and important intrapsychic conflicts (perhaps love vs. hate, or dependence vs. autonomy) or centers around significant family norms, then this may be more important than if the conflict concerns more trivial issues. Laing makes the same point: "It may be that there are some areas of a person's being for which there is a more crying need for confirmation than others. It may be that there are some forms of disconfirmation which may be more actively destructive of the person's developing sense of himself than others, and which could therefore be schizogenic." [18] However, this view is not shared by the Bateson group. Jackson writes that they "have not been impressed" by the need to include content in their analysis since they find a particular style of interaction manifesting itself irrespective of the content discussed. "The act itself alerts the participants that there is conflict and in itself constitutes a kind of psychological trauma, whatever the substantive issue." [19]

Second, there is the question of whose perspective is being used in determining the presence of incongruency or of disqualification. While the theory appears to refer to the perspectives of participants in the interaction, case materials and interpretations tend to reflect observers' viewpoints as to what are considered congruent or incongruent messages. This is a difficult problem for research and analysis, since messages an observer judges to be incongruent with reference to general external standards may carry with them implicit meanings, developed in the culture of that particular family, that make the messages congruent to the family members. While either the internal or external perspective could provide useful bases for interpretation, the differences between them are of critical importance and criteria for making the appropriate judgment require a more explicit statement than they have so far received.

There are many contrasts between the Bateson group's formulation and that of Lidz and his co-workers to whom we now turn. One of the most noticeable differences is the less formal and less abstract quality of the latter's statements; there is marked emphasis on the content of the pressures and conflicts as well as on their structure. Also, the point of reference of the theory shifts away from the level of communicative acts to the level of interpersonal role relationships.

The age and sex axes of role differentiation have a critical place in the Lidz analyses of different types of schizogenic families, and specific distortions in what they consider to be normal parent-child role relationships play a key role in their interpretations of the development of schizophrenia. The influence of Talcott Parsons' sociological formulation of family role structure is explicitly acknowledged. Thus, Lidz writes that there are certain "requisites" for a marital relationship if it is to provide for the harmonious development of its offspring: "What appears to be essential can be stated simply. . . . The spouses need to form a coalition as members of the parental generation maintaining their respective gender-linked roles, and be capable of transmitting instrumentally useful ways of adaptation suited to the society in which they live." [20]

This ideal model of a normal family, implied in the above quotation, pervades much of the work of these investigators. They find two deviant types of marital relationships in the family backgrounds of schizophrenic patients, one of which appears empirically to be associated with schizophrenia in female children and the other in male children. In the first pattern, designated as *marital schism*, there is a "state of severe chronic disequilibrium and discord . . . [and] recurrent threats of separation. . . . Communication consists primarily of coercive efforts and defiance or of efforts to mask the defiance to avoid fighting. There is little or no sharing of problems or satisfactions. . . . [There is] chronic 'undercutting' of the worth of one partner to the children by the other. The tendency to compete for the children's loyalty and affection is prominent. . . . Absence of any positive satisfaction from the marital relationship (excluding the children) is striking. . . . Mutual distrust of motivations is the rule. . . ." [21] In the second pattern, called *marital skew*, the couples achieve a state of relative equilibrium in which the continuation of the marriage is not constantly threatened. However, ". . . family life was distorted by a skew in the marital relationship. . . . The rather serious psychopathology of one marital partner dominated the home." [22]

Their emphasis on the concrete substance of underlying conflicts, and on the strength of both the hostile and seductive elements in the situation, has led this group to explore the different implications for the development of schizophrenia of these two types of pathogenic marital relationships. They find that schizophrenic girls are more likely to have had a "schismatic" background; each parent in this open conflict situation seeks the support of the daughter. The boys with schizophrenia, on the other hand, are more likely to come from "skewed" situations which tend to have dominant mothers and passive fathers.

In neither of these types of marital relationship is there true "role reciprocity" which Lidz and his group see as one of the requisites for a successful marriage. They note that ". . . role reciprocity requires common understanding and acceptance of each other's roles, goals, and motivation, and a reasonable sharing of cultural value orientations." [23] This lack of role reciprocity is associated with distortions in role-appropriate behaviors for the different age-sex groups within the family. Thus, distinctions between the generations are not observed, the normal parental coalition is not maintained, and children become involved in the parental conflicts, with each parent competing for the child's support.

A schismatic family that includes many of these elements is thus described by Lidz:

Mr. Nussbaum remained away from home as much as possible, and turned to his daughter [the patient] for the affection and admiration he could not gain from his wife. At times, he seemed to be spiting his wife by the alliance with the girl. He became very seductive toward the daughter, sleeping with her when she became anxious at night, and cuddling her to sleep until she began, during adolescence, to express fears of becoming pregnant. The child's problems became a major concern to both parents, but also a source of mutual recrimination. The mother sought to devote herself to her daughter's care when she became increasingly difficult during adolescence, but would lose patience and go into rages in which she would tell the girl that she wished she were dead. The mother, fairly typically, lacked empathy for her daughter and, because of her inconsistent behavior and the father's devaluation of her, formed an unacceptable model, while the father seductively substituted the daughter for his wife. Thus the patient was at times a scapegoat and at other times a divisive influence.[24]

Lidz attaches much significance to the notion of role reciprocity, but it is not given a more precise definition than that implied in the quotation in the preceding paragraph. While Spiegel's analysis of family equilibrium and disequilibrium in terms of complementary role expectations is referred to as an explicit source, there are some differences in Lidz's use of the concept and some special problems associated with these differences. First, his idea of role-appropriate behavior involves the use of an assumed model of normatively correct family role behavior. Spiegel's original formulation leaves room for much interfamilial as well as subcultural variation in role expectations; Lidz, on the other hand, tends to neglect these variant patterns. Spiegel also provides for the possibility that strain and tendencies toward disequilibrium may exist with complementary role expectations, whereas equilibrium and role reciprocity appear to be viewed as synonymous in Lidz's formulation.[25]

Associated with the general blurring of sex-generation roles in the families of schizophrenics is a preoccupation with and anxiety about incestuous feelings and behavior. "In our studies, we have noted the central moment of incestuous impulses, and our studies of their families revealed that these were not simply regressive symptoms of the patient, but that one or both parents was also caught in incestuous ties to the patient. . . . There is a reciprocity to these impulses of the patient that provokes panic lest loss of their own self-control might lead to actual incest." [26]

These types of interpersonal relationships are viewed as "abnormal" family environments in which it is difficult for children to learn and behave in ways appropriate to their age and sex during the course of development. As a further consequence, these relationships predispose toward irrationality and distortions in thinking. Lidz has described it as ". . . a strange family milieu filled with inconsistencies, contradictory meanings, and denial of what should be obvious. Facts are constantly being altered to suit emotionally determined needs. The children . . . learn that meanings are not primarily in the service of reality testing. . . . The acceptance of mutually contradictory experiences requires paralogical thinking. Such environments provide training in irrationality." [27] Lidz also points to a tendency for these families to be isolated from their social and cultural environments, noting, for example, ". . . that the patients were habitually exposed to conflicts and meanings deviant from the shared communicative meanings of the culture. . . ." [28] Opportunities for reality-testing that would be provided by more contact with the normal world outside the family are restricted, and internal irrational patterns in the family are further reinforced.

Generally speaking, this formulation has both the flavor and vocabulary of traditional psychoanalytic theory—but as applied to the family rather than the individual as the unit of description and analysis. For example, as we shall see below, incestuous and hostile wishes, as well as difficulties in the successful resolution of the Oedipal situation figure prominently in their analyses of why these particular family patterns appear to be conducive to schizophrenia. This psychoanalytic toning of the theory is also evident in their treatment of social roles. While there is frequent reference to the concept of social role and to the notion of the family as a social system, the real dynamic sources of interaction in this theory lie in the personality structures of the individuals. Thus, the difficulties in establishing a harmonious marital relationship with true role reciprocity are attributed to the psychological problems brought to the marriage by husband and wife. Further, while pathogenic family backgrounds are described by such system terms as schism and skew, these family types appear empirically to be related to different types of parental personalities—a cold, punitive mother with a seductive father in the former; a dominant, seductive mother and a passive father in the latter. In attempting to predict the likelihood of a schizophrenic outcome, it appears that we have to depend on an understanding of the psychodynamics of the parents; to the extent that this is necessary, the analysis of the family as a social system is superfluous.

Unfortunately, there is much vagueness and ambiguity in Lidz's use of the social role concept. Sometimes, particularly in the early papers, it refers simply to stable ways of interacting that reflect personality, such as the "dominant mother" role. At other times, roles are normatively defined modes of "appropriate" behavior, that is, differentially appropriate for specified age and sex categories. In general, the complicated relationships between personality, role, and interaction are not specified; at times they appear to be used as different names for the same thing.

In general, Lidz's formulations are weakest when considered critically from the point of view of evaluating his theory as a set of coherent and rigorously defined concepts and abstract propositions. Concepts are borrowed from sociology, psychoanalysis, and theories of language development; these concepts have not yet been welded together into a unified system. On the other hand, the strength of this group's approach lies in their emphasis on those powerful concrete parameters of family life, namely, the differentiating axes of age and sex. This has been associated with their discovery of different types of family structures in the developmental histories of male and female schizophrenics; such distinctions are not made systematically by other investigators.

The theory of schizophrenic development proposed by Bowen and Brodey deserves mention at this point, since it has marked similarity to that of Lidz as well as an important difference in the conception of family roles. The similarity is evident in such things as the description by Bowen and Brodey of their study families as having marked conflict, "emotional divorce" between the parents, an over-adequate mother with a peripherally attached father [29]—a pattern closely resembling Lidz's schismatic group. There is also an emphasis on the psychodynamic sources of the marital role relationships. The difference lies in the etiological significance attributed by Bowen and Brodey to the structure of the role relationships rather than to its content. The important factor for them is the extremity and rigidity of the role structure. The tendency in these families as they describe them is for the roles to become polarized, for example, for an omnipotent-helpless polarity to develop.[30] Behavior is then molded into conformity with these extreme and stereotyped role definitions. While a high degree of rigidity in role structure is evident in the case descriptions given by Lidz, this feature does not enter into their formulations as a significant variable. As with Lidz, there is some difficulty with the Bowen-Brodey formulations in separating personality pathology in the parents from the pattern of role polarization as etiological influences in the development of schizophrenia.

Wynne and his coinvestigators at the National Institute of Mental Health are also concerned primarily with the quality and structure of role relationships within the family, rather than with the particular content of these relationships. Their emphasis is on the family system as the unit of conceptualization rather than on dyadic or triadic relationships within the family. Thus, their objective is to develop an interpretation of schizophrenia "that takes into conceptual account the social organization of the family as a whole." [31] The rationale for this approach, stated in an early paper, is made explicit in the general hypothesis underlying their work: "The fragmentation of experience, the identity diffusion, the disturbed modes of perception and communication, and certain other characteristics of the acute reactive schizophrenic personality structure are to a significant extent derived, by processes of internalization, from characteristics of the family social organization, . . . also internalized are the ways of thinking and of deriving meaning, the points of anxiety, and the irrationality, confusion, and ambiguities that were expressed in the shared mechanism of the family social organization." [32]

The definition of schizophrenia and the psychological mechanisms involved, that are implicit in the above statement of rationale, will be examined in later sections of this paper. At this point we wish to review the specific properties of family social organization that are thought to be significant by the NIMH group.

In a number of papers dealing with the relationships between schizophrenic thinking disorders and family transactions, Wynne and Singer have described what they believe to be the main features differentiating the families of young adult schizophrenics from other families. They note that these are the features that "work" empirically in the sense that they permit predictions to whether and what type of schizophrenia is present in the offspring on the basis of information about parental patterns of behavior and cognition. A recent statement refers to the four main features of these families as follows:

> . . . first and foremost, *patterns of handling attention and meaning* [that interfere with the child's capacity for selective attention and purposive behavior]; second, styles of relating, *especially erratic and inappropriate kinds of distance and closeness*; third, *underlying feelings of pervasive meaninglessness, pointlessness and emptiness*; and fourth, an *over-all structure of the family* in which members have collusively joined together in shared maneuvers which deny or reinterpret the reality or existence of anxiety-provoking feelings and events. These shared maneuvers, including what has been called pseudo-mutuality and pseudo-hostility, tend to encompass the experience of the growing child and cut off or render anxiety-laden, experiences with peers and the broader culture. This kind of family structuring, previously described as the "rubber fence" phenomenon, reduces or negates the corrective influence which extra-familial con-

tacts could otherwise have and heightens the impact of the disturbed intra-familial environment.[33]

Major attention has been given in their recent work to the first of the four features—patterns of handling attention and meaning in the family. The "transactional thought disorders" in schizophrenic families are evident in communications that are fragmented, blurred, poorly integrated and disjunctive. The assumption here is that these "familial transactions and maneuvers would be especially likely to disrupt and impair the development of an offspring's capacity to focus attention and to think sequentially and adaptively." [34]

Transactional thought disorders, represented in the communication and the interaction of the whole family, are classified along the same amorphous-fragmented continuum as are individual thought disorders. Amorphous patterns of interaction in these families are exemplified by vague drifting of a discussion through shifts in the object of attention, blurring of meaning by using uncertain referents, and irrelevant meanings. Singer and Wynne describe an amorphous response to a TAT story given by the parent of a schizophrenic that might be considered an example of how this parent interacts with his child: "A father began a story about a young boy wanting to go out with his friends instead of practicing his violin. He was reminded of a movie about an older fellow who went joy-riding with his friends. After a lengthy, aimless story, he concluded: 'And so, into the sunset.' " [35] Fragmented patterns of interaction and communication consist of such characteristics as intrusion of primary process, using odd vantage points for communications such as peculiar spatial or temporal positions, and crypticness; each of these modes of communication results in poorly integrated messages. For example, one parent's complete response to a Rorschach card was, "If you read stories of Cossacks, that's self-explanatory."

These styles of communicating meaning are assumed to be characteristic of the family as a whole, not simply the thought patterns of one parent. Further, it is hypothesized that these ". . . styles of attending, perceiving, thinking, communicating and relating used in family transactions are likely to have promoted the cognitive development of the offspring in certain directions, either by serving as models for identification or by eliciting complementary behaviors." [36]

The second general feature of the schizophrenic family included in the summary listing given above has to do with styles of relating, especially with erratic and inappropriate kinds of distance and closeness. Here the maintenance of proper distance refers both to cognitive and affective functions, both to distance from people and distance from ideas or objects. Schizophrenic family patterns seem to be characterized by "fluctuating and variable cognitive sets and relational distances. . . . The distance taken is often inappropriately close or remote and when an alteration in 'focal distance' is made, which in normals occurs smoothly and unnoticed, it is disjunctive and awkward." [37] For example, the mother of a schizophrenic child related to the psychologist in much the same way she probably related to her child. "[She] limited herself to describing the Rorschach cards as symmetrical, and as 'reproductions,' [and] seemed remote both from the card and the tester. Suddenly she asked the tester what brand of lipstick she was wearing." [38] These shifts in affect and style of relating make for confused expectations in the child and provide odd and fragmented models for identification.

These modes for handling meaning and the styles of relating, in Wynne's theory, seem to serve as defenses against underlying feelings of pervasive meaninglessness, pointlessness, and emptiness. Feelings of meaninglessness are defined as subjective states, "in which purposes, wishes, aspirations, interpersonal relationships, work, and other activity are felt by the person himself to be without point, without direction, without leading to decisive satisfaction or dissatisfaction, to clear success or defeat, to genuine mutuality or total alienation or separation." [39] These feelings are not continuously present and manifest to family members but rather are similar to repressed or unconscious material in the sense that family members attempt to defend themselves against their recognition.

Finally, the over-all structure of the schizophrenic family is characterized by shared maneuvers that serve to deny or reinterpret the reality of anxiety-provoking feelings, and apparently, of the underlying meaninglessness of the relationships. Wynne uses the concepts of pseudomutuality and pseudohostility to describe these structural patterns. Pseudomutuality is defined by contrasting it both with mutuality or a relationship of true complementarity, and with nonmutuality or a situation without reciprocal obligations. Complementarity is lacking in pseudomutual relationship, but the façade of mutuality is maintained energetically: ". . . in describing pseudo-mutuality, we are emphasizing a predominant absorption in fitting together, at the expense of the differentiation of the identities of the persons in the relation. . . . In pseudo-mutuality emotional investment is directed more toward maintaining the *sense* of reciprocal fulfillment of expectations than toward accurately perceiving changing expectations." [40]

In illustration, Wynne quotes one mother whose desperate preoccupation with harmony at all costs is obvious. "We are all peaceful. I like peace even if I have to kill someone to get it. . . . A more normal, happy kid would be hard to find. I was pleased with my child! I was pleased with my husband! I was pleased with my life. I have *always* been pleased. We have had twenty-five years of the happiest married life and of being a father and mother." [41]

The negative counterpart of pseudomutuality is pseudohostility. It differs from the former in defining a state of chronic conflict and alienation among family members, but this difference is seen as unimportant and superficial. What is important is that both states are fixed, rigid, and "pseudo." Both are viewed as collective defenses, permitting family members to maintain some semblance of a life together without having to confront directly the essential and pervasive "meaninglessness" of their life as well as their underlying fears of separation, hostility, tenderness, or intimacy.

These qualities of family relationship are associated with family role structures that are either rigid and stereotyped or loosely and ambiguously structured. The specific type of structure, whether rigid or ambiguous, may be associated with the specific subtype of schizophrenia developed (a point to which we shall return), but either structure creates difficulties for the development of appropriate personality-role and role-role relationships. The sources of these difficulties are as follows: Deviation is not permitted from prescribed and simple "formulas" for behaving; distinctions are not made between the person and his role. This "blurring" of boundaries between individual and role results in the family's being experienced by the developing child as all-encompassing of the self; there is no identity separate from one's role within the family.

A number of mechanisms are described through which deviations from the family's rigid role structure are either excluded from recognition or reinterpreted, thus preserving the illusion of harmony and mutuality. Among these are family myths and legends that stress the catastrophic consequences of divergence from the rigidly defined roles; a bland and indiscriminate approval of each other's actions preserving a façade of harmony and peace; the denial of contradictions in one's own or others' behavior; a stress on secrecy and a concomitant concern with prying into other persons' private experiences; and a formalization or ritualization of normal family experiences. Reinforcing these processes is the lack of adequate articulation between the family and the larger social system—so that ". . . family members try to act as if the family could be a truly self-sufficient social system with a completely encircling boundary." [42] This "continuous but elastic" boundary is referred to as a "rubber fence."

In his attempt to characterize the patterns of interaction in these families, Wynne employs concepts at several different levels of analysis. Thus, the structure of role relationships is described as falling along a continuum from rigidity to amorphousness, the

27

affective quality of relationships varies from pseudomutual to pseudohostile or fluctuates from close to distant, and interpersonal communication shows degrees of fragmentation or amorphousness. Further, the structure of role relationships is seen as a collective defense against recognizing the underlying "meaninglessness" of the relationship. The strategy of research and theory formation seems to be to view each of these as independent dimensions and to determine whether and how they are empirically associated with each other. Thus, no *a priori* claim is made that pseudomutuality is theoretically required by rigid roles, or that fragmentation is a function of pseudomutuality. Rather than deriving the connections among these different levels from systematic theory, the aim is to accumulate relevant data and work toward empirical generalizations of the conditions under which these different patterns are found together.

The preceding review of how these different theories approach the problem of schizophrenia suggests some of the difficulties of comparing them to each other in a systematic way. While they share an emphasis on family interaction, the conceptual foci vary markedly as do the particular dimensions of interaction they isolate as significant. It is tempting—but we believe deceptive and not particularly useful—to consider double binds as illustrative of fragmented communication, or pseudomutuality as the affective quality of a skewed marital relationship. The formulations differ from each other in more serious and significant ways than in the labels they apply to phenomena. They point to different phenomena, and these differences merit clarification before an attempt is made to reduce them to one comprehensive theory.

Some of these differences will become more evident in the following sections, but a few may be noted here. First there is the question of conceptual focus—of how "sociological," "psychological," or "interactional" the different theories are. It seems to us that Wynne and Haley in focusing on family roles and norms are most sociological in their analysis. Lidz's use of role terms, as we have noted before, is not systematic and his primary emphasis on personality and motive places him at the psychological pole of theorizing. Bateson is concerned neither with roles nor motives but with a different unit of analysis entirely, namely, the communicative act. Both Haley and Wynne, of course, are also interested in communication but always within its context of the role structure. These varied conceptual foci permit the different theories to avoid direct confrontation at a theoretical level. Empirical comparison of the theories with each other is, for this reason, an extremely difficult and complex problem.

A further point of difference refers to the concrete relationship that the theories tend to focus upon. Bateson's use of the double bind in its specific application to schizophrenia is dyadic in emphasis; for example, one of the stated essential ingredients is two persons. One consequence is that the family tends to be viewed as consisting of a set of dyadic relationships. In Lidz, the stress is also on the dyad, in this instance the marital relationship; however, it is a dyadic relationship that has an effect on a third person, that is, the developing child. Finally, in Wynne and Haley, the concepts refer to the whole family as the unit for analysis and theory without concern for any specific role player or players.

Both of these points on the different emphasis of the several theories must be qualified by noting that over time each theory has tended to become more comprehensive and more eclectic. Wynne's view has already been referred to regarding the independence of the different levels—role, interaction, and psychological functioning. Lidz, for whom ". . . every area of interaction in these families was found to be faulty in some respect. . . ." [43] views each separate area of deficiency or failure—parental nurturance, appropriate role structure, and the transmission of culturally instrumental techniques—as related to a specific problem in development. And he suggests that the severity of the illness may be related to how extreme and generalized the deficiencies are. In Bateson's formulation, the distinctions between levels are erased through the use of the highly abstract model of communicative behavior as a general framework for describing all behavior.

Since each of the theories is concerned with the same basic

phenomena, this "strain toward comprehensiveness" gives recent statements of the Wynne, Lidz, and Bateson groups a stronger appearance of similarity than was evident in early statements. However, it has seemed to us that the differences in emphasis outlined in this section, and detailed further in the following ones, remain and are important determinants of both the research and theoretical directions still being pursued by the different groups.

THE SCHIZOPHRENIC PROCESS

THE DISTINCTIVE FEATURE of the theories we have been discussing lies in their emphasis on the critical role in the development of schizophrenia played by particular interaction patterns and family role relationships. In this section we shall be concerned with the accounts given by each of the theories about the ways in which this family environment leads to schizophrenia in the child. Several different questions are involved, and the theories vary in the degree of explicitness and detail with which they attempt to answer them. How is schizophrenia defined? What are the psychological mechanisms through which a person becomes schizophrenic? What distinguishes the prepsychotic schizophrenic personality structure from the psychotic schizophrenic? What are the precipitating events for a psychotic breakdown?

In discussing "overt" schizophrenia or the "identified" schizophrenic in the family (thus distinguishing this from the endemic "covert" schizophrenia in these families), Bateson states:

The more serious and conspicuous degree of symptomatology is what is conventionally called schizophrenic. . . . [They] behave in ways which are grossly deviant from the cultural environment . . . characterized by conspicuous or exaggerated errors and distortions regarding the nature and typing of their own messages (internal and external) and the messages which they receive from others. . . . In general, these distortions boil down to this: that the patient behaves in such a way that he shall be responsible for no metacommunicative aspects of his messages. He does this, moreover, in a manner which makes his behavior conspicuous.[44]

Elsewhere the typical schizophrenic message is described as a "stripping of all explicit or implicit metacommunicative material . . ." and the "boundary of sanity is, however, crossed when the subject uses these tricks of communication in situations which the common man—one hesitates to say the 'normal'—would not perceive as the schizophrenic seems to perceive them." [45]

For Bateson, distinguishing between "overt" and "covert" schizophrenia is an explicit problem, because the ways in which schizophrenic patients communicate appear (in terms of his theory) to be only exaggerations of forms of communication that are pervasive in their families. On the whole, while he is not clear on this matter, Bateson would appear to make the distinction between overt and covert schizophrenia a function of the severity and extent of these forms of communication. The identified schizophrenic behaves this way "conspicuously" and in "normal" situations; the other members of his family are more selective and restrained.

Bateson's views about schizophrenia as an "illness" are outlined in his introduction to an autobiographical account of a schizophrenic psychosis, *Perceval's Narrative.*[46] In a sense, he turns the whole question of illness on its head—by proposing that the symptoms of schizophrenia are adaptive responses of an individual to an underlying illness, in much the same way that fevers and other somatic symptoms are recognized in medicine today as the body's response to primary pathology. While he does not explicitly connect these observations with his other views on the role of the overt schizophrenic within the family, it appears as if the "pathology" to which the psychosis is a response refers to the distorted patterns of family relationships. In this context, the schizophrenic psychosis is conceived to have a potentially curative function and a normal course that may end with the

31

remission of symptoms, a course that may be aided or hindered by the forms of therapeutic intervention attempted. As he has stated in the introduction referred to:

[this is] . . . one of the most interesting characteristics of the strange condition known as schizophrenia: that the disease, if it be one, seems sometimes to have curative properties. . . . We are today familiar with the fact that many of the so-called symptoms of organic disease are the efforts that the body makes to correct some deeper pathology. . . . The dynamics of the curative nightmare are, however, quite obscure. It is one thing to see the symptom as a part of a defense mechanism; it is quite another to conceive that the body or the mind contains, in some form, such wisdom that it can create that *attack* upon itself that will lead to a later resolution of the pathology. . . . Once precipitated into psychosis the patient has a course to run. . . . Once begun, a schizophrenic episode would appear to have as definite a course as an initiation ceremony—a death and rebirth—into which the novice may have been precipitated by his family or by adventitious circumstances, but which in its course is largely steered by endogenous process.[47]

Haley approaches the problem of defining the nature of schizophrenia within the context of an attempt to develop an interactional description of schizophrenia, in contrast to either the classic psychiatric or psychodynamic approaches. Expanding upon a basic theme that persons cannot avoid dealing with the problems of the definition and control of their relationships with others (since all communication presupposes rules about "who" is permitted to say "what" to "whom," "when," and "where"), Haley proposes that there is, however, one way by which a person can avoid defining a relationship and that way is by negating or disqualifying his communications. It is not easy to "strip" one's messages of their metacommunicative meanings; Haley suggests that it requires various types of denial and distortion of one's responsibility for messages. He notes:

When everything a person says to another person defines the relationship with that person, he can avoid indicating what sort of relationship he is in only by denying that he is speaking, denying that

anything is said, denying that it is said to the other person, or denying that the interchange is occurring in this place at this time. . . .
It seems apparent that the list of ways to avoid defining a relationship
is a list of schizophrenic symptoms. . . . The various and seemingly
unconnected and bizarre symptoms of schizophrenia can be seen to
have a central and rather simple nucleus. If one is determined to
avoid defining his relationship, he can do so only by behaving in
those ways which are describable as symptoms of schizophrenia. . . .
The differences from the normal lie in the consistency of the schizophrenic's behavior and the extremes to which he goes.[48]

Thus, schizophrenic behavior is viewed both as purposeful, in
that the individual is attempting through his behavior to avoid
committing himself to a particular definition of his relationships
with others, and as unavoidable, since the only solution open to
someone caught in a double bind is to respond in kind. In the
end he gives up the attempt to discriminate meanings in the
messages of others and attempts only to ensure that others will
not find "meaning" in his own messages. It is not clear whether
Bateson, Haley, and others in this group view the schizophrenic
patient as having lost the capacity to discriminate or whether it
is simply that he ceases to respond in terms of normally discriminated meanings. Their descriptions focus on his behavior
rather than on his internal states. His behavior is "learned" in the
sense that all human communicative behavior is learned. The
learning context, however, is the rather special one where he is
punished by withdrawal of love, abandonment, or hostility for
alternative and more adequate responses to the double bind.

Haley considers the overt psychotic phase of schizophrenia "an
intermittent type of behavior" occurring in situations of a particular kind of stress: ". . . when the patient is staying within the
rules of his family system, he is behaving 'normally.' However,
when he is required to infringe the rules, and at the same time
remain within them, he adapts by schizophrenic behavior." [49] By
"normal," Haley means normal for the patient's family in the
sense that he is qualifying his statements in ways that are similar
to those of his parents. Faced with the possibility of having to

violate a family prohibition, "[as] when (1) two family prohibitions conflict with each other and he must respond to both, (2) when forces outside the family, or maturational forces within himself, require him to infringe them, or (3) when prohibitions special to him conflict with prohibitions applying to all family members," [50] the schizophrenic behaves in a unique and actively psychotic way; that is, he displays incongruence at all levels of communication. These conflicting prohibitions may occur when the patient is in treatment and involved with both his mother and therapist, or they may occur with greater frequency at certain times, such as in adolescence.

In the formulations of Bateson, Haley, and their co-workers, schizophrenia as an active psychosis is intermittent and specific to the "identified" patient in the family. The schizophrenic process as a form of communication, however, is continuous and generalized to all family members. Thus, any member of the family might become an "overt" schizophrenic if faced with the conflict of violating and staying within the family prohibitions. In another aspect of his analysis, which we shall discuss in the next section, Bateson also hypothesizes that these families require only one "overt" schizophrenic and that his existence serves to stabilize the family.

There are many contrasts between the views outlined above and those of Wynne and his collaborators regarding the nature of and basic processes involved in schizophrenia. In overview, the Wynne group sees schizophrenia as the result of an individual's failure to develop a clear and stable ego identity—a failure reflecting a faulty family environment that prevents the individual from developing the necessary ego capacities and strengths for normal personality development. Within this general approach, they have centered their specific research and conceptual analyses on the thought disorder aspects of schizophrenia. "We have stressed the desirability of focusing research upon those aspects of schizophrenia which have seemed central and primary, rather than peripheral and secondary, that is, upon *structural* features, particularly the formal thinking disorders, rather than the content of the disturbance." [51]

In their general formulation, the process of schizophrenic development is contrasted explicitly with a model of normal personality development. An assumed basic requisite for normal development is the establishment of an adequate ego identity. This, in turn, is viewed as dependent upon a family environment with a clear and organized role structure where the focus of attention in interaction is consistent and unambiguous. In other words, the family system must be a learning environment that permits both appropriate identification and reality testing. With explicit acknowledgement of Erikson's formulations, Wynne conceives of an adequate and healthy identity as not only consisting of the sum of different role components, but as involving the selective integration of various role components into a unique personal identity.

The learning environment constituted by the role structure and interaction processes in families of schizophrenic patients, described in the previous section of this paper, permits neither adequate reality testing nor opportunities for the flexible integration of roles into the developing self. For example, the rigid role structure combined with the norm of pseudo mutuality force the child to act out the form of a role but not to grasp its substance. The role cannot be adequately integrated as a part of his self since the required actions do not correspond to inner feelings and needs. Thus, in describing the process of internalization of the family role structure, Wynne and associates state: ". . . roles and role behavior in intense pseudomutual relations come to be largely dissociated from subjective experience. Such roles are not integrated into the functioning of an actively perceiving ego, but come to govern the person's behavior in an automatic 'reflex' fashion, having the quality of 'going through the motions.' These patterns of role behavior . . . in a general sense are internalized into the personality, although they are not under the jurisdiction of an actively discriminating ego." [52]

35

Further, because the patterns of interaction are either amorphous or fragmented, in ways described previously, a stable and coherent "focus of attention" is lacking that would permit adequate reality testing and the development of rational and ordered thought. In formulating the link between the type of thought disorder present in schizophrenia and patterns of family interaction, the concept of "focal attention" (borrowed from Schachtel) is given a prominent place. "In schizophrenia, as we are formulating it, there is an impairment or defect of those ego structures which involve the various aspects of focal attention . . . the failure of the capacity to focus and maintain a major set in the face of intrusiveness from both external and internal stimuli." [53] The family patterns of handling attention and meaning, described above as lying along the continuum from amorphous though fragmented styles of interaction, are seen as "directly related to the development of capacities for focal attention in offspring."

While these distorted modes of thinking and patterns of rigid role performance are inadequate and inappropriate from the point of view of the general culture, they nevertheless permit the individual to function adequately within his family until adolescence. At this point in his life, both his inner drives and the expectations of society require an independent and secure ego identity if the individual is to participate fully on the wider social scene. Acute schizophrenia, in this theory, occurs in the context of an identity crisis. This crisis derives from the societal requirement that the individual move out of the rigid family role structure and behave as an independent and flexible person. This is an insoluble problem for the child since he can no longer remain completely within the family but cannot meet adequately the new demands. The schizophrenic reaction is his solution.

Wynne and Singer also distinguish between types of schizophrenics—those with primarily amorphous and those with primarily fragmented thought disorders. Although mentioned occasionally, such distinctions are not used systematically by other theorists. They suggest that these differences may be rooted in different family structures: "In using this differentiation-integration formulation for classifying schizophrenia, we shall group global, predominantly undifferentiated forms of functioning under the heading of '*amorphousness.*' Failures of hierarchic integration, after some degree of clear differentiation has been achieved, we shall call '*fragmentation.*' Along a continuum these represent, in our formulation, different varieties of cognitive disorganization or thought disorder." [54] They also suggest that these types of schizophrenic thought disorders may be associated respectively with different family types whose interaction characteristics correspond to the amorphous-fragmented patterns of cognitive disorganization: ". . . One of the implications of the work is that patterns of the families of schizophrenics need to be considered as heterogeneous in order to link them successfully with the heterogeneity of schizophrenic offspring." [55]

Given the pervasiveness of thought disorder within these families, should all members be viewed as schizophrenic—perhaps covert schizophrenics as in Bateson's formulation? Wynne does not deal explicitly with this question and does not distinguish between thought disorder as part of the active psychosis and thought disorder as part of a more general schizophrenic-type process. It appears as if he starts with the schizophrenic patient as a "given" and then attempts to define and describe his characteristic ways of thinking. Thus, in a sense, the patient has been diagnosed as schizophrenic on other grounds, and features of his cognitive styles are then examined to determine if there are consistencies in this area of his behavior. In this connection we find the following view expressed:

. . . it should be clear that we do *not* regard the patterning of attentional and thinking disorders as basically transitory states which come and go in response to temporary stresses whether induced by psychological disturbance, drugs, fatigue, etc., but as underlying enduring forms or styles of functioning. To be sure, psychological or physiological stresses may facilitate the emergence into view of the disorders, but more fundamentally they are the relatively stable, built-

37

in pattern in which an individual functions in a considerable variety of circumstances, experimental and clinical.[56]

Wynne's formulations have been developed on the basis of data derived from family therapy, experimental studies, and the use of a predictive method. The latter has been particularly prominent in the recent work.[57] Essentially, in this method an attempt has been made to predict whether and what type of schizophrenic illness is present in an offspring (typed in terms of style of thinking) on the basis of an analysis of data from other members of the patient's family; this data has usually been projective test material, but excerpts of parental interaction have also been used. They believe that the systematic use of this method has moved them toward ". . . greater precision in differentiating and defining concepts and greater attention to the processes and methods by which data are assessed." [58] Associated with the increased use of this method in their work has been increased attention to psychological processes in the development of schizophrenia, and less emphasis than there was in the early papers on the patterning of roles within these families.

The view of schizophrenia presented by Lidz and his coinvestigators is similar in many respects to that of Wynne and his NIMH group. Thought disorder is paramount in the definition of the illness: ". . . the critical characteristics that distinguish this category of mental illness concern the disturbed symbolic processes without degradation of the intelligence potential. The core problem . . . : disordered concept formation, concretistic thinking, mislabelled metaphor, impaired categorical thinking, intrusions of primary process material, derailment of association, etc." [59] Further similarities with Wynne lie in Lidz's view of schizophrenia as primarily a disease of adolescence and in the emphasis placed both on the lack of an adequate identity and on the learning of paralogic and distorted ways of thinking as major components of the schizophrenic developmental process.

However, the problems of identity formation in adolescence and the consequences for the child are specified very differently.

Rather than locating the source of identity problems in either a poorly or rigidly articulated role structure, as Wynne does, Lidz sees the basic problem as consisting in a lack of adequate identity models within the family. He distinguishes between concrete problems in development for boys and girls. However, he notes that in both cases the essential difficulty is the same, that is, how to form a sex-appropriate identity in the presence of the faulty identity model provided by the parent of the same sex. For the girl, the mother is cold, aloof, and hostile; for the boy, the father is passive and inadequate. In both cases the opposite sex parent is engaged in undercutting his or her spouse and in making seductive overtures to the child. This blurring of generation boundaries and the lack of proper adult models results in an inadequate, weak ego identity: ". . . these parents fail to provide a satisfactory family milieu because they cannot form a coalition as members of the parental generation maintaining their appropriate sex-linked roles, or transmit instrumentally valid ways of thinking, feeling, and communicating suited to the society into which the child must emerge. The child who grows up in a family lacking in these fundamentals has confused and confusing models for identification, has difficulty in achieving a sex-linked identity, in overcoming his incestuous attachments, and in finding meaningful and consistent guides for relating to others. . . ." [60]

At adolescence, rather than an identity crisis of the kind described by Wynne, the acute onset of a schizophrenic psychosis is precipitated by the fear of loss of control over either incestuous or hostile impulses. The threat of being overwhelmed by these drives, of being unable to control them, forces the child to adopt a schizophrenic response where either the perception of his own needs is altered radically or he abandons rational ways of behaving. Or as outlined by Lidz:

[The] progression of the erotically toned child-parent attraction to an incestuous bond threatens the existence of the nuclear family, prevents the child from investing energy into extra-familial socializing channels, and blocks his emergence as an adult. . . . His conscious avoidance of incest becomes necessary because of defective family structure and role confusion, the personalities of family members become further distorted because spontaneous interaction becomes impossible, role conflict inevitable, and crippling defenses necessary. . . . Confronted by an untenable conflict and unable to find a path into the future, the schizophrenic patient withdraws from the demands of society and reality by breaking the confines imposed by the meanings and logic of his culture which, in turn further isolates the patient. The condition tends to become self-perpetuating, because the patient ceases to test the instrumental utility of his concepts and no longer seeks the consensus of meanings required for living cooperatively with others.[61]

Essentially this is a description of a psychosis that develops when a weak ego can no longer manage its inner drives. Contributing to the choice of a schizophrenic pattern in this conflict is the fact that the child's background has been deficient in rational problem-solving. His learning environment was one where irrationality and denial were pervasive. He thus has little in the way of either internal or external resources that can be drawn upon at the time of acute crisis.

The problems of development outlined above are linked by Lidz to general deficiencies in parental nurturance patterns and the failure of the familial environment to provide an adequate socialization context for normal personality development. In recent papers, equal attention has been directed to "defects in transmitting the communicative and other basic instrumental techniques of the culture to the child." [62] The acquisition of language is seen as primary to the acquisition of other adaptive skills for participation in the culture:

The foundations of language are established within the family. Whether the child gains trust in the utility and validity of verbal communication as a means of understanding and collaborating with others, or learns that words are in the service of fantasy rather than of problem solving, or are a means of avoiding recognition of the obvious, or are used to blur or obfuscate, depends upon the nature of the intrafamilial communications. The topic is crucial to the study of schizophrenia and extremely complex. Here, we can only assert that these families in which schizophrenic patients grew up fail to inculcate consistent or instrumentally valid meanings.[63]

The critical role in the onset of schizophrenia assigned by Bateson, Wynne, and Lidz to the stressful period of adolescence is in agreement both with epidemiological findings on age differentials in rates of schizophrenia [64] and with the views of many other investigators of family relationships in schizophrenia. There are some differences, however, in the nature of the particular stresses that are judged to be important. For example, the conflict between dependence and independence is stressed by such workers as Lu, Bowen, and Brodey.[65] They suggest that the groundwork for the particularly intense conflict experienced by the individual who becomes schizophrenic is prepared by parents who overtly stress independence and achievement in one context, but foster dependence in another context sometimes at a covert and sometimes at an overt level. At adolescence there is either a sudden demand for adult responsible behavior, failure to meet this demand, and consequent schizophrenic withdrawal; or the individual is faced with insoluble and conflicting demands to be both dependent and independent and resolves his dilemma by a schizophrenic breakdown.

From this discussion, certain contrasting emphases are evident among these theorists in how they define schizophrenia and see its development. Wynne sees schizophrenia as essentially a problem in identity development with associated cognitive difficulty; the psychosis is an exaggerated form of a relatively enduring cognitive style. Bateson, on the other hand, views schizophrenia as an inability to label and respond accurately to messages, which inability has developed from particular types of learning situations. While the manifestations of the psychosis in distorted patterns of communication are exaggerations of previous patterns, the psychosis is for Bateson a symptom of the individual's struggle for psychological health. Lidz seems to combine problems of

41

sex-role identification with the learning of distorted and maladaptive ways of thinking in his characterization of the nature of the illness; schizophrenia is seen as a "deficiency" disease, that is, the end result of a long family history of failures in adequate enculturation.

These different formulations of the schizophrenic process correspond in many ways to the theorists' different descriptions of patterns of family structure and interaction that were presented in an earlier section. Thus, in seeing schizophrenia as a problem in identity development, Wynne tends to describe the socializing environment in terms of inadequate role relationships, that is, a rigid or ambiguous family role structure. These relationships prevent healthy role identifications and at the same time provide a confusing learning environment that interferes with the development of a stable identity. If, on the other hand, schizophrenia is seen as a problem of distortions in communication, as Bateson sees it, then the developmental context tends to be described in terms of situations where one is punished for responding to messages as if they contained clear and definite meaning. There are both gains and losses from a degree of internal consistency of point of view within each theory. Obviously, there must be some form of correspondence between the descriptions of interaction patterns and the schizophrenic process if the former are to be etiologically related to the latter. However, it is also obvious that if the theories are to provide comprehensive accounts of the etiology of schizophrenia, then additional concepts must be introduced which may stretch this fabric of consistency. Lidz and Wynne have been moving toward more comprehensive statements. For example, both are concerned with cognitive and affective aspects of personality, and with developmental sequences and processes, as well as with family interaction processes. The relationships between the different types and levels of concepts is not always clear in their work and the gaps between levels tend to be bridged by implicit assumptions rather than by empirical findings. We shall return to this general problem in the concluding section of this paper.

THE PERSISTENCE OF INTERACTION PATTERNS

THE PREVIOUS TWO sections were devoted to the central questions with which these theories are concerned, namely, what are the special characteristics of interaction in the families of schizophrenics, and how do they lead to schizophrenia. While answers to these two questions constitute the core of each of the theories with respect to the etiology of schizophrenia, there are two other questions that are of interest in their own right and also throw additional light on the similarities and differences among the several approaches that we have been comparing. These are: first, what accounts for the persistence in these family patterns? Second, what are the predisposing background factors for the development of these interaction patterns and the schizophrenic solution? We will discuss the first question in this section and the second in the following one.

While the level and focus of description vary among the several theories under review, there appears to be general consensus about characterizing these families as in states of chronic distress. This does not imply that there is continual and manifest dissatisfaction and unhappiness. In Wynne's analysis, as one example, a family may avoid the overt expression of underlying and pervasive tension by a retreat behind a façade of harmony. However, if such a solution were adopted it would be considered in all of these formulations as inherently unstable and unsatisfying in the same sense that neurotic defenses are considered unsatisfying in analyses of personality dynamics. That is, the defenses may be necessary to avoid overwhelming anxiety and further disintegration, but serious costs are involved. Thus, the presumed cost for the family of a retreat behind a harmonious façade to the posture of Wynne's pseudo mutuality in role relationships is the denial of reality and the loss of personal identities for all family members.

Nevertheless, despite the distress and lack of mutual satisfaction, it appears that these families persist and their members persist in dealing with each other over and over again in the same

43

ways. Bateson points explicitly to the stability of the system despite its pathogenicity, in that "these families, in a gross sense, continue as families. The statement, 'this is a closely intercommunicating system,' continues to be true in spite of the very considerable unhappiness of the members. . . ." [66]

Given this paradox—of relationships that persist despite the distress they occasion—it is important to ask how the system maintains itself. Or, more precisely, it is important to ask how each of the theories attempts to answer this question. What functions are presumed to be served by these patterns of interaction, at both an individual and group level, that might account for their persistence?

In the approach of Bateson and his co-workers, functions served for the family as a social unit receive attention. In his analysis of the "steady state" of these families, Bateson writes that, "first and foremost that which is characteristic is a very tough stability . . . homeostasis. . . . When the identified patient begins to get well, we observe all sorts of subtle pressure being exerted to perpetuate his illness. . . . It is not that at all costs the identified patient must be kept confused; rather it seems as if the patient himself is an accessory—even a willing sacrifice—to the family homeostasis." [67]

How does the theory attempt to account for this "tough stability"? We could not find an explicit attempt to provide an explanation. However, in general discussions of this problem of homeostasis, two broad hypotheses are proposed that would seem to be relevant to this question of why the patterns persist—one at the level of group and the other of individual dynamics. At the level of group dynamics, Bateson suggests that these are families that do not permit stable coalitions. He views coalitions as requisites for viable solutions to the recurrent problems faced by such social units as families. In the absence of viable solutions, family members cannot achieve stable and adequate self-identities; they are "continually undergoing the experience of negation of self." This hypothesis at the level of the family as a social group is connected with a hypothesis at the individual level to account for the persistence of unsatisfactory interaction patterns.

This is the belief on the part of family members, presumably derived from the self-negating experience, that the self can actually be destroyed: "In fact, the double-binding interaction is a sort of battle around the question of whose self shall be destroyed and the basic characteristic of the family, which is shared by all the relevant members, is the premise that the self is destroyed or can be destroyed in this battle—and *therefore* the fight must go on." [68] In outline, this proposes that in families, stable coalitions are necessary for successful problem-solving and successful problem-solving is necessary for the development of adequate self-identities. In the absence of this pattern, the double bind becomes persistent and pervasive as a mode of communication, apparently because it permits individuals to avoid the complete destruction of the self that they believe would follow an unambiguous expression of real feelings and beliefs.

Haley attempts to account for these persistent patterns of mutually destructive activity by proposing a conceptual model that he believes has particular appropriateness for the analysis of interaction processes. His point of departure is the ". . . peculiar sensitivity of people to the fact that their behavior is governed by others." [69] Central to his approach are the two ideas that human communication can be classified into several message levels and that social groups are self-corrective, governed systems. "If a family confines itself to repetitive patterns within a certain range of possible behavior then they are confined to that range by some sort of governing process. No outside governor requires the family members to behave in their habitual patterns, so this governing process must exist within the family. . . . When people respond to one another they govern, or establish rules, for each other's behavior. . . . Such a system tends to be error-activated. Should one family member break a family rule, the others become activated until he either conforms to the rule again or successfully establishes a new one." [70] This analogy of an error-activated system is proposed as a model for describing all families. The special characteristic of the family of the schizophrenic is that it is "not only establishing and following a system of rules, as other families do, but also following a prohibition on any acknowledgement that a family member is setting rules. Each refuses to concede that any other family member is governing him." [71] Haley's model has obvious similarities to traditional sociological conceptualizations of social systems where behavior is mutually regulated by shared norms (i.e., rules) and where social control is exercised through the imposition of sanctions when deviant behavior occurs (i.e., error-activated responses to rule breaking).

The view that the double-bind interaction pattern may persist because it serves a defensive psychological function is noted though not stressed by Bateson. For example, a child may have a special significance for the mother such that her anxiety and hostility are aroused when she is in danger of intimate contact with the child. In order to control her anxiety, she tries to control her distance from the child by giving incongruent messages, that is, messages that reject but simultaneously deny the rejection. Haley also points to the potential psychological function of the double bind but formulates its general aim as the maintenance of a fluid and undefined relationship; the basic anxiety in this instance would seem to be that in entering into a defined relationship one must acknowledge that one is setting rules for governing the relationship.

Whether the specific defensive function is to allay anxiety about intimacy or the fact of a relationship itself, the Bateson-Haley formulation gives the child an active role in the maintenance of the pathological interaction. This results from the specific reward-punishment schedule in this type of learning context. The child is led to respond to incongruent messages with incongruencies of his own; only this type of response is rewarded since it serves to maintain the mother's denial, while other behaviors of the child are met by punishment and the threat of abandonment or the withdrawal of love.

The views set forth by Searles [72] are relevant here, since he also sees the child as actively involved in the maintenance of the special forms of interaction in these families and relates this to the child's perception of the mother's intrapsychic conflicts and needs. However, he ascribes this involvement to different sources than Bateson. Starting from the perspective that there are "positive feelings in the relationship between the schizophrenic and his mother," he suggests that the child stays within the relationship out of compassion and love for the mother, with the related concern that were he to leave her or to change the mother would be "annihilated" or "go crazy." Thus, he argues that the child is not kept in the relationship by "hateful" double binds, but remains in it so that he will not hurt the mother.

The problem of why these unsatisfying interaction patterns persist receives less explicit stress in the work of Lidz and his co-workers, although at the same time they seem to give more attention in their descriptive accounts to states of disturbance and conflict in these families. In their model of family social organization the marital role relationship serves the function of maintaining each partner's emotional equilibrium; different types of marital roles are seen as deriving from individual differences in intrapsychic needs and conflicts. As we understand the implications of this view, however distorted or abnormal the role relationship in a schizogenic family may appear to an observer, it persists because it serves tension-reducing functions for both partners. There is an obvious relationship between this formulation and their general psychodynamic approach noted earlier.

The child appears to be "recruited" into the system, that is, taught appropriate but pathological behavior, in order to help stabilize the system. In other words, he is not permitted to work out a role for himself that would threaten the existing parental role pattern, whether it be a relationship of marital schism or marital skew, since that would threaten the emotional equilibrium of one or both parents. He is permitted to take any of a number of positions within the structure—as a mediator, as a scapegoat, as an ally of one or the other parent—but any role must be consistent with the on-going relationship and in this way his actions serve to maintain the system.

We have noted previously two other characteristics of these families that are reported by Lidz which would seem to be of further help in maintaining their basic relationship patterns. These are the pervasive atmosphere of irrationality within the family and the associated isolation of family members from the common culture. The effects of this atmosphere on the child are to restrict drastically his ability to perceive and communicate appropriately in the world outside the family. The distortions of perception and communication on the part of the parents, in the service of their own rigid defense systems, are transmitted to the child who finds these forms of perceiving and behaving necessary if he is to maintain his position within the family. He is forced into a more complete dependence on the family and into patterns of behavior that are consistent with the emotional requirements of the parents.

One problem in interpreting Lidz's position on this general question is that he sometimes discusses the social organization of the family as if only the normal family had a stable organized form, defined by a condition of effective role reciprocity, while the pathology of the schizogenic family is treated as if in itself it constituted a state of disorganization.[73] However, at other times the characteristic patterns found in the schizogenic family, such as schism and skew, are clearly recognized as stable and persistent; they are simply less harmonious and more conflictful forms of family organization than that of full role reciprocity. This lack of consistency in his conceptual analysis of the idea of the family as a social organization has resulted in a lack of attention to the problem of the persistence of pathological patterns. In particular, the functional analysis has been restricted to the individual level and there has been no analysis of the functions served for the family as a social unit.

As we noted in an earlier section, Wynne and his team of NIMH investigators view pseudomutuality as a collective defense against a recognition of the underlying and pervasive meaninglessness of family members' experience and of their relationships with each other. The interaction patterns associated with the pseudo relationships appear to persist for the same reason that personality defenses persist, namely, they are effective in reducing overwhelming anxiety. As a result, considerable energy and affect is invested in the defensive pattern, and other alternatives are excluded.

In this theory, there seems to be a general but implicit assumption that social systems like families maintain themselves through complementary role expectations. Sanctions are imposed if behavior is not consistent with the normative definitions of the group; the imposition of the sanctions serves to perpetuate accepted behaviors. The pseudo relationships in the schizogenic family are like this, only more so. The respective roles are stereotyped and rigid; deviations or failures in role performance are either denied or reinterpreted. The similarity between this and Haley's formulation of the family as an error-activated system is evident. However, while Haley separates rule-setting activity from the rules themselves and proposes that it is the rule-setting activity that is denied, Wynne has emphasized the denial of violations of the rules.

In addition to this mutually regulative process of complementary role expectations, Wynne suggests that one consequence of the rigid role structure is that each family member develops a strong personal investment in maintaining things as they are. This comes about because the system does not permit a separation of their personal identities from their family roles. This is clearest in the case of the child. Wynne argues that the development of an adequate ego identity requires a socializing environment where the individual is free to step back from and reflect upon his role, to try out different ways of carrying out his role, to select and reintegrate aspects of his several different roles into his own distinctive identity. Where there is little tolerance for not fitting completely into a role and where emphasis is placed on the rigid maintenance of a façade of relationships, there is neither the proper atmosphere nor appropriate opportunities to engage in the type of role-playing experience through which the identity can be separated from the family role system. Since there is no self as distinct from the role, the role must be carried out in an exact way, or there would be no self. The same general function is served for the parents, whose identity problems derive from their own backgrounds. In order to retain any sense of self, each parent must invest great energy in maintaining the set of rigid family roles since underneath these "identities" there is only a frightening "meaninglessness."

Among these theorists, Wynne is closest to the tradition of social psychology that is equally concerned with group and personality dynamics. His formulations, therefore, share with Lidz an interest in the personality dynamics underlying an individual's behavior in his social roles and with Haley a sociological emphasis on norms and sanctions as group regulatory mechanisms. The inclusion of both levels of analysis leads, we believe, to a somewhat different orientation to the problem of persistence. Whereas for both Lidz and Haley the fact of persistence has a passive or responsive quality—the patterns serve personality needs or continue through the operation of an error-activation mechanism—for Wynne persistence is an active state. Family members struggle to maintain their existing relationship patterns and resist pressures to change. It should be noted that Bateson's views are also "dynamic" with reference to this problem and this may be related to his focus here on issues of personality development similar to Wynne's focus on identity, namely, the issue of the self and the possibilities of its destruction.

The general answer given by the several theories to the question of why particular patterns of social relationships and interaction persist is that they serve defensive functions at both an individual and group level. In attributing persistence to the functional significance of the behaviors and relationships, the theories are consistent with traditional conceptual models in the social and behavioral sciences that attempt to account for the repetitive "ongoingness" of both social and personality systems. One of the problems with such functional explanations, however, is that they lead us to infer the motives or needs in whose service the resultant behaviors are presumed to function. In Bateson, Lidz, and Searles the line of inference leads to the personality structures of the parents and, in particular, to a pathological level of anxiety when faced with problems of intimacy and control in normal parent-child relationships. In Haley and Wynne, emphasis is given to inferred group processes for maintaining or restoring stable relationships. It is important to point out that these individual and group processes are inferred from the observed patterns of interaction, and, while they are used as hypothetical explanations, as presently stated they are not useful for purposes of prediction.

PREDISPOSING FACTORS IN THE DEVELOPMENT OF SCHIZOPHRENIA

WHAT PERSONAL AND social characteristics of the parents are associated with the types of interaction patterns that are postulated as schizogenic? Are there specific attributes that make involvement in these interaction patterns more likely for one child rather than another in the family? Do certain combinations of parent-child traits increase the likelihood that these patterns will develop around a particular child? Each of the theories proposes answers to these questions by specifying predisposing factors, or "sorting" variables, that serve to make certain families and children more vulnerable than others to the postulated schizogenic processes.

There is general reference in each of the theories to the pre-existing personality pathology of one or both parents or the existence of a "difficult" interpersonal relationship between them (or a combination of these). For example, Lidz notes that a distorted marital role pattern, either "schismatic" or "skewed," is the family environment into which the child is born. He also points to their findings that half of the fathers and half of the mothers have serious personality disturbances: "All of the families were seriously disturbed. The difficulties pervaded the entire family interaction. . . . We have noted the severe psychopathology of the fathers as well as the mothers, and we have found that these families were either schismatic . . . or were 'skewed' in that the serious personality disturbance of one parent set the pattern of family interaction." [74] The emphasis in this theory is on the distortion of the "normal" role patterns resulting from and associated with personality pathology in one or both parents—"the fatners, as are so many of the mothers, are so caught up in their own problems that they can rarely satisfactorily fill the essentials of a parental role." [75]

Wynne gives little attention to the problem of predisposing background factors. While in general he seems to locate the determinants of interaction patterns in the parental role relationship, he also views the personality characteristics of the parents as among the determinants of role patterns. Bateson's discussion of these factors is also sketchy. Nevertheless, he appears to give more weight to the personality of the mother than to the parental role relationship in the initiation of the double bind; once it begins, however, other factors maintain it. For example, the mother's anxiety may be aroused when she is threatened by the possibility of a close interpersonal relationship. She tries, therefore, to develop a particular style of interaction—that is, the double bind—that will protect her from a "close" relationship with the child. The specific role of the father and his relationship to the mother in the development of the family's interaction pattern is left unstated. It is further suggested by Bateson that the pathological interaction patterns develop over time through a process of mutual reinforcement among family members: ". . . It seems that in schizophrenia the environmental factors themselves are likely to be modified by the subject's behavior whenever behavior related to schizophrenia starts to appear. . . . The symptomatic behavior of the identified patient fits with this environment and, indeed, promotes in the other members those characteristics which evoke the schizophrenic behavior." [76] In other words, while the process may start with the mother's attempts through double binds to defend herself against anxiety, the factors involved in its origin are considered less important than the process through which in time the child and other family members come to behave toward each other in similar ways.

The question of the increased or special vulnerability of a particular child comes down in large part to the question of why not all of the children in these families are schizophrenic. One solution to this problem is to propose that all the children "really" are schizophrenic but only one of them shows manifest symptomatology, usually because of the particular patterning of stressful circumstances in some situation or at some point in time. As we pointed out earlier in discussing Bateson's distinction between covert and overt schizophrenia, he tends to adopt this position. "If the family is schizophrenogenic, how does it happen that all of the siblings are not diagnosable as schizophrenic patients? . . . In the schizophrenic family there may be room for only one schizophrenic." [77] This last point is related to the more general equilibrium theme we have found in this theory; the particular type of homeostasis in these families is achieved by one and only one of its members being overtly schizophrenic. In other contexts, it is suggested that while genetics may play a role in deciding which of several siblings shall be the schizophrenic, the particular attributes of the child "selected" to be the overt schizophrenic may be less important determinants than the nature of the mother's emotional conflicts; the latter determine which child will be focused upon as "special" and threatening to her defenses. For example, in some instances male children may be special in this sense and thus be more vulnerable; in other instances it may be female children.

While Wynne is more specific in mentioning the types of biological characteristics that may be important—such as the sex of the child, place in the birth order, activity pattern at birth, or physical features—his general view is that the significance of the characteristic depends upon the psychological situation of the parents rather than upon what the concrete characteristic may be. Variations in significance reflect some "fit" between the parents' intrapsychic makeups and the attributes of the child. In their discussion of etiology, Wynne and Singer propose a "transactional and epigenetic view of development" where interactions between parents and offspring depend at each phase on the outcome of previous phases. In this context, they stress the necessity of considering the kinds of transactions the parents will make together as a team and the ways in which their "role fit and emotional meshing" give different meaning to such concrete characteristics of the child as sex, or place in the sibling order.[78]

Lidz and his co-workers have focused more directly than other theorists on the problem of specific predisposing factors. In their work the most significant attribute for the selection of one rather than another sibling for schizophrenia appears to be the sex of the child. This follows from two general assumptions in the theory: (1) the developmental tasks of male and female children differ from each other, and (2) schizophrenia occurs in a context of familial role relationships that do not permit the child to complete his or her normal cycle of development. Specifically, the male child is particularly vulnerable in the "skewed" type of family where there tends to be a passive, weak father and a seductive, engulfing mother. Thus, the male child's opportunity for normal identity development will be markedly impaired. In "schismatic" families on the other hand, it is the female child who is most vulnerable. Here, the marital role relationship typically reflects an aloof and devalued mother with a grandiose and narcissistic father. In these families, the developmental tasks for the female child are most difficult and the chances of developing a normal and adequate identity are reduced. (It should be noted that the association described between marital role type and the pathology of the particular parents is reported as a trend; there are instances where mothers are dominant and grandiose in the schismatic families and fathers are dominant in the skewed types.)

Among other theorists, Lu has been specifically concerned with differences between schizophrenics and their nonschizophrenic siblings in the relative intensity both of the contradictory demands made by the parents and the attempts by the child to fulfill the demands. She notes that the ". . . process of such parents—preschizophrenic interaction and emotional entanglement seems to begin as early as the patient's birth and infancy." [79] Two sets of unusual circumstances are described which may lead mothers to pay more attention to or give more protection to the preschizophrenic child; the child has special characteristics or the birth occurs at a time of particular frustration and tension within the family. Bowen and Brodey's formulation is similar to Wynne's in stressing that the preschizophrenic child in some sense "matches" an area of personality conflict. For example, a sickly child or one who may need extra help and nurturance has a mother with strong unresolved conflicts around dependency needs; the nonschizophrenic child does not "match" these needs and therefore can remain somewhat outside of the entangling involvement.[80]

In focusing on the differences among the theories in the predisposing factors they specify, we have given insufficient stress to certain general themes that are common to all of them. For example, in each of the theories the parents of schizophrenics are seen as immature people, anxious and conflicted, and tending to use primitive mechanisms of defense. The marital relationship is unsatisfying and distorted; role relationships are rigid; ways of meeting each other's needs are disturbed and pathological; there is a state of chronic disequilibrium in the family. The child who becomes schizophrenic is "weak" to begin with; he may have a physical handicap, be ill in infancy, have severe eating problems, or in some way be defined quite early as needing special attention. There is also reference to, although not systematic examination of, the possibility of exceptional stress at the time of the child's birth or early infancy such as extreme financial pressure, illness in the family, or sudden shifts in place of residence.

Both Bateson and Wynne are explicit about the transactional nature of the process and point out that the selected child comes to act as required and in turn elicits special types of response from others. Wynne and Singer point out how this approach differs from certain traditional points of view: "Each offspring clearly has an impact upon the rest of the family, including the parents, so that the offspring alter and help shape the family system from which they in turn derive some of the personality characteristics and forms of functioning. Our viewpoint thus differs from those psychodynamic theories which have sometimes implied that particular kinds of psychological trauma have a unidirectional effect upon a passively receptive child or that 'schizophrenogenic' mothers or parents have one-way victimizing effects upon their offspring." [81]

Associated with this transactional approach is a general recognition that none of the specific or general predisposing factors is *the* cause of schizophrenia. Rather, the several factors are viewed as setting the stage for schizophrenia by increasing the vulnerability both of the family and of the selected child to the development of the schizogenic process.

DISCUSSION

It would be relatively easy, as anyone could confirm who has read papers by Bateson, Lidz, Wynne, and their coinvestigators, to detail a long list of criticisms of these theories. Some specific criticisms have been noted explicitly at appropriate points in preceding sections. Other criticsms have been implicit but presumably evident; for example, our persistent concern with whether we had fully understood the meaning of one or another concept is obviously related to what we feel to be an unnecessarily high level of ambiguity and imprecision in their writings. The basic aim of this review, however, is not to score points but to clarify as best we can the meanings of these theories so as to achieve a fuller understanding of the implications of their work for research and theory on the role of family interaction processes in personality development. In this last section, therefore, rather than reviewing previous criticisms or listing new ones, we wish to draw attention to some of the important new directions in theory and research that are suggested by the body of work summarized in this paper. Our emphasis will be on shared characteristics of the different theories, rather than upon the differences stressed in previous sections. Thus, we shall be treating the theories as different expressions of a general approach to the study of family interaction.

Taken collectively, there are two major contributions that these theories may make to our general understanding of personality and social processes. First, their serious and sustained effort to focus on the family group as the unit of observation and conceptualization marks an important advance over traditional approaches to both normal and pathological personality development. Second, through specific concepts like the *double bind, fragmentation,* and *pseudomutuality* they have alerted us to important phenomena in family life and other interpersonal relationships that have heretofore been neglected by other investigators.

The potential significance of this focus on the total family unit cannot be overstressed. It would be inaccurate to draw the implication that information should now be collected about the husband of the schizophrenogenic mother; this would miss the point. The more accurate implication is that information must now be collected about relationships and transactions among family members; the latter, as we know from a long history of work in small group studies, cannot simply be reconstructed on the basis of knowledge of the personal attributes of the several family members. The introduction of this new level of conceptualization leads toward more complex models of causation, as, for example, in Wynne's "epigenetic transactional" approach. At the same time, it points to simple mechanisms at a concrete behavioral level through which personality is shaped by intrafamilial social processes. Because these mechanisms are specified in terms of observable behavior, they are more open to empirical study than the abstract propositions that have heretofore constituted much of social interaction theory as it has been applied to problems of socialization.

The implications of these theories are not restricted to the area of personality development but extend to our understanding of processes at work in other types of groups. Analyses of problem-solving, training, therapy, and work groups could benefit from attention to the forms of interaction isolated in these family studies. At the level of individual behavior, some of the persistent styles of interaction might transfer from the family to other group settings and the conditions under which such transfer did or did not take place would be an interesting area of investigation. At the level of group dynamics, since all groups face the same types of problems that are described as facing families—the development and reinforcement of norms, the control of affect, the differentiation of roles—the mechanisms observed in these family studies can serve as hypotheses in studies of other groups.

There is no need to multiply examples of how these theories alert and sensitize us to important aspects of interpersonal relationships. We have implied throughout that these phenomena are open to systematic investigation because they have been formulated in behavioral terms. This will permit the introduction of rigorous methods of study that have been developed in experimental studies of *ad hoc* groups. This latter complex of methods—including experimental procedures and techniques of quantitative coding of interaction—would seem to be particularly appropriate to the further study of the processes reported by clinical observers of these families. Several investigators have already recognized the potential value of linking these two traditions of experimental social psychology and the clinical study of the schizogenic family. An overview of these recent developments will help to underscore our general point that we may be approaching a confluence of these two traditions and that such an event would be of value for both of them.

We have selected five studies for brief comment to serve as examples of this direction in research. In these studies, the focus of analysis is the difference between families with diagnosed schizophrenic members and other types of families. This is clearly only a first step in assessing the hypothesized etiological function of these patterns of interaction.* Farina's experiment is the first

---

* It is recognized by many observers of the characteristics of schizogenic families that they bear a close resemblance to characteristics reported of other "disturbed" families, such as families of homosexuals, autistic children, children with school phobias, etc. Clearly one of the tasks of future research is to specify in detail the relationship between family structure and particular disturbances in the child. Meissner's review (1964; see footnote 2) includes references to studies of these varied types of families.

reported of this type. He compared interaction between parents of male schizophrenics and parents of male tuberculosis patients in order to investigate patterns of dominance and conflict.[82] Using the "revealed difference" technique to generate parental interaction,[83] he scored tape recordings on certain aspects of the structure of interaction (who speaks first, number of interruptions, etc.). He found a higher degree of conflict between the parents of schizophrenics than between parents in his tuberculosis control group. He also found systematic differences between parents of patients with good premorbid histories ("reactive" schizophrenics) and those with poor premorbid histories ("process" schizophrenics). For example, mothers of poor premorbid patients showed high dominance, but in good premorbid families fathers tended to be dominant. Caputo's study of interaction between parents of chronic schizophrenics was concerned with similar questions. He used parents of "normal" sons as a control group, and tested the hypothesis of role reversal in schizogenic families, that is, that mothers would play a dominant role and fathers an expressive role. He also predicted unilateral patterns of hostility, from wife to husband, in these families.[84] Using the "revealed difference" procedure and a modified Interaction Process Analysis category system [85] to code tape recordings, he found that none of these hypotheses was supported by the data.

It is less important at this stage of research and knowledge that the results of these two studies are somewhat inconsistent with each other than that together they suggest modifications in theory and method regarding interaction in these families. For example, Farina's findings point to the need for careful discrimination in theory and research between types of schizophrenia. Findings from both studies indicate the need for several coding systems at different levels to measure important concepts such as power and conflict that appear repeatedly in the clinical and theoretical literature. Perhaps consistent conflict patterns in these families are manifested in their styles of interaction and would be evident in an "interruptions" code such as Farina's, but not manifested in verbal content and would not be found in a verbal content code such as that used by Caputo.

Frances Cheek's experiment takes into account some of the previously mentioned design problems and her results raise the question of consistency between parental values and parental behavior. This is the first reported experimental study of schizophrenic family interaction in which the patient was actually present in the discussion and the first to compare families of male and female patients. Cheek's hypotheses center on the distribution of affect and power; she used a modified Bales system to code tape recordings. Examples of her findings are: in interaction with husband and child, mothers of male schizophrenic children show greater hostility and greater tension than mothers of females; in contrast with mothers of normal children, schizogenic mothers are more withdrawn and cold. A comparison of expressed values with observed behavior showed that mothers of schizophrenics who report high values on support and permissiveness in child training do not show this behavior in their interaction; in contrast mothers of normals report that they value giving support and being permissive to children and actually behave this way in family discussions.[86]

In these experiments indices of types of interaction are based on an average rate of participation over some period of time. However, the theories previously discussed, particularly Bateson's and Wynne's, stress the transactional nature of relationships and thus are more concerned with sequences of interaction. Haley's experiment is focused on the kind of ordered pattern of communication that may be characteristic of schizophrenic families. Comparing interaction in a set of "disturbed" families with normal families, Haley showed that when "who follows whom" patterns are compared with random sequences, the "disturbed" families tended to show a more rigid sequential pattern than the normal families. He interprets this difference as reflecting the normal family's ability to be more flexible and to change patterns in accord with the requirements of the situation.[87]

In an experimental study now in process, the present authors have attempted to take into account some of the design and measurement problems present in earlier investigations.[88] The design includes families of male and female patients with good and poor premorbid histories as well as comparable normal control families. As an important additional control, parents are observed in interaction with a well sibling of the patient as well as with the patient himself. Family discussions are generated through the "revealed difference" procedure and typescripts of the discussions are multiple-coded with the use of a number of independent coding systems. This study will permit the analysis of sequences as well as average scores and will allow for a determination of whether parental interaction patterns are child- or family-specific.

We believe that the general approach illustrated by the several studies reviewed above holds great promise. It opens up to systematic investigation the range of interpersonal relationships in natural groups which has until now been studied almost exclusively either through self-report questionnaires or qualitative case study procedures. Of equal importance, in constructing general theories about personality and group process, we will no longer be limited to findings from studies of artificial *ad hoc* groups but will be able to draw upon well-controlled studies of natural groups.

One aim of this review when we began was to derive crucial hypotheses through comparison of the several theories that would permit an empirical assessment of their relative validity. As we learned more about the theories, our conviction was reinforced that they each contained hypotheses and concepts that led easily into empirical study. We have emphasized particularly the appropriateness of experimental methods for this. However, it also became clear, as we have suggested at a number of points in the body of the paper, that the theories cannot be compared directly with each other in ways that would permit a critical empirical test of differential hypotheses. It is always evident that the theories refer to the same general phenomena, viz., schizophrenic patients and their parents. However, this is a level of similarity equivalent to asserting the similarity of Van Gogh, Monet, and Andrew Wyeth because they have all painted landscapes.

The analogy to artists is helpful in understanding a major source of the difficulty in achieving a systematic comparison of the different theories. They are less like scientific theories than artful constructions or coherent accounts arrived at independently through different perspectives and methods of conceptualization. Their value for other investigators, like that of art, lies in giving us a new way of looking at the world. Techniques and methods are available for systematic empirical study of the processes they have observed and reported. There is some likelihood that guided by this new view of the phenomenon, such studies will result in an increased understanding not only of schizophrenia but of normal human behavior as well.

Part II

EXPERIMENTAL STUDIES

THE PARENTS OF THE SCHIZOPHRENIC:
DYADIC INTERACTION

INTRODUCTION

THE THREE STUDIES in this section are similar in one critical respect—each focuses on the parental dyad. Each takes seriously the idea that the quality of the relationship between parents is of pathogenic significance. Further, these investigators assume, as do the other investigators represented in this volume, that important features of this relationship will be revealed in observing how parents interact with each other. The underlying logic of this approach is as follows: direct observation and measurement of interaction between parents will provide data about the quality of and primary characteristics of the mother-father relationship; inferences may then be made about the effects of this relationship on the personality development of children in the family.

These inferences about the linkage between the mother-father relationship and the development of schizophrenia are presented with varying degrees of explicitness in the three papers; the theories reviewed in Part I are used generally as the basis for these inferences. Lerner, who is most explicit about the source of his hypotheses, argues that parental modes of resolving role conflicts are a significant part of the learning environment. He draws particularly on the Lidz group's formulation in hypothesizing that unclear decisions and conflict resolutions involving distortion and denial serve to train the child in irrationality. This leads him to the specific hypothesis that the severity of the thought disorder in the patient would be related to the degree of inadequacy in the mode of conflict resolution found for the parents. Caputo and Farina are less explicit in stating the mechanisms through which the relationship between the parents enters into the development of schizophrenia. Both relate their studies to the more general tradition of clinical observations, in which the relationship between the parents of schizophrenic patients has been found to be deviant with respect to culturally prescribed norms for proper husband-wife and father-mother behavior. In particular, the father has often been described as passive and weak while the mother plays the dominant role, and the marital relationship has appeared to be conflictful and unsatisfying. The tacit assumption in this literature and in the work of Caputo and Farina is that this type of role-reversal between parents and the persistance of unresolved conflicts leads to an unhealthy environment for growth and development and therefore to increased vulnerability to schizophrenia. We have noted in our review that this relationship is often seen as mediated by processes of identity formation, but this specification of a mechanism is not relied upon in the hypotheses and interpretations of these studies.

The design of an experimental investigation requires a degree of explicitness usually not found in clinical investigations with regard to the variables that are to be controlled and studied. A variety of decisions must be made about sample size and composition, independent and control variables as well as about the experimental procedures to be used; in order to minimize the intrusion into the data of unknown sources of error and variance, standard guidelines and criteria must be stated for each of these decisions. These features of experimental work are present in each of the studies in this volume. The three studies in this section build their designs with explicit attention to the types of experimental and control groups included. Farina, for example, samples two types of schizophrenia—those with either good or poor premorbid illness histories. His control group suffers from tuberculosis, a chronic nonpsychiatric illness. Comparisons between such psychiatric and nonpsychiatric patient samples will permit him to argue that his findings are not a function of hospitalization for an illness. Lerner's design is similar to Farina's in its formal characteristics in that he includes two types of schizophrenics and a control group of hospitalized nonpsychiatric patients. However, his theoretical focus leads to a specification of his patient samples in terms of severity of thought disorder rather than premorbid history. Caputo's normal control group is not matched for hospitalization and his design contains only one schizophrenic sample. However, he shares the concern about the heterogeneity of patients labeled as schizophrenic and his sample is defined specifically as a chronic group. In all instances attempts are made to match the control and patient samples on a variety of demographic characteristics such as age, social class of parents, and duration of hospitalization where this is relevant.

In evaluating the generality of the findings, two important common elements in the designs of the three studies must be kept in mind. First, the samples are restricted to male patients. There is reason to believe, and some evidence will be found in studies reported in later sections, that there are differences in family relationships in the families of male and female patients. For this reason interpretations of the findings of these studies must always be qualified by noting their restriction to male schizophrenic patients. Second, because of the interest in parental interaction, the samples are restricted to patients with intact families; this restriction applies to other studies included in this volume. Broken homes are hardly infrequent in the family histories of schizophrenic patients. In addition, many patients have drifted away from their families by the time they are admitted to a hospital and have been living in isolated situations. For many others, as their time in the hospital has lengthened, there is likely to be a corresponding decrease in the intactness and availability of their parents. For these reasons, one must be cautious in extrapolating these findings on parental interaction to all schizophrenics.

The aim of studying interaction requires a standard procedure for producing discussion between the parents. Each study uses a task that allows a mother and father to talk together about an issue or problem. While the content of these problems is of general relevance to parents—for example, parent-child relationships—they are standard situations and are not designed with reference to the particular concrete problems of each family. In each study an opportunity is provided for the mother and father to express separately their individual opinions and then to talk together to arrive at a joint solution to the problem. Caputo and Lerner use the revealed-difference procedure in which the parents are asked to reach agreement on items on which they showed differences of opinion in their individual responses. Farina asks parents to discuss together a set of hypothetical problem situations to which each of them has previously responded.

Tape recordings of these joint discussions provide the basic data—the samples of interaction to which different scoring and coding schemes are applied. There are both substantive and methodological differences among the several coding systems employed. From our earlier description of the conceptual foci in these studies, we would expect that Lerner would be interested in measuring modes of conflict resolution. His categories distinguish solutions that are mutually acceptable compromises from those where one partner yields to the other. In addition, he takes into account whether or not the couple is aware of or distorts the process of arriving at a joint decision. Both Caputo and Farina are concerned with levels and patterns of conflict and dominance.

These differences in conceptual foci are related to the type and amount of information used in coding. In comparing their approaches, it is useful to distinguish between semantic and structural codes, with the former based on the meaning of the discussion and the latter on other features of the interaction. Lerner's code is semantic in that the actual content of the decisions and the ways in which they are stated provide the basis for coding the mode of conflict resolution. Further, the entire discussion must be taken into account in order to determine how to classify or rate the mode of resolution followed. Farina's codes are structural and refer to such features of the interaction as who speaks first and last, amount of time taken to reach a decision, interruptions, and so forth. His measure of change in the position of either partner does not depend on an analysis of the content of the discussion but is based on the difference between a rating of the decision each makes when alone and their common decision after joint discussion. Caputo applies the standard Bales IPA system to tape recordings. This is a mixed code that uses both content and noncontent aspects of statements to classify them as positive or negative in quality and as expressive or instrumental in their function.

It is clear from the above that different amounts, as well as different types, of information enter into the codes. Lerner uses the entire discussion in order to assign a single score; Caputo sorts each statement into one of twelve categories and then sums to produce a total frequency distribution for each individual; Farina counts up the instances of certain specific occurrences. From their reports, each of these approaches may be used reliably.

We noted above that these studies are directed to three general questions: patterns of mother-father dominance with particular interest in the possibility of role-reversal for parents of schizophrenic patients, levels of conflict, and strategies for decision making and conflict resolution. Although experimental and scoring procedures vary among the studies, the explicitness of the research design and of the rules for measurement allow us to compare their findings with each other. This will be done separately for each of these basic questions.

Both Farina and Caputo report findings relevant to the hypothesis on role reversal between parents of schizophrenics. Their findings seem to be inconsistent with each other. Caputo finds no differences in the dominance relationships of parents of chronic schizophrenic patients and the matched normal control parents included in his study. Farina reports that the parents of the poor premorbid patients (who would resemble Caputo's chronic group) do show role-reversal in which the father is less dominating than the mother in comparison across his three groups of families. The good premorbid group is most different from the poor premorbids when the father is highest and the mother lowest on the dominance indices.

This difference between Caputo and Farina is more apparent than real. An examination of Farina's tables will show that the normal control and poor premorbid families are not significantly different from each other on any of the dominance indices; all significant differences are a function of the extreme position of the good premorbid parental pairs. Thus, if Farina had included only poor premorbid patients in his design, he would have found no differences between their parents and the normal control parents—a finding that is identical with Caputo's. Farina's findings also suggest that the original hypothesis requires modification. On most of his indices of dominance, the mothers show a dominant and the fathers a nondominant pattern within the normal families. Where the good premorbid parents differ from the normals is in showing a father-dominant pattern. This set of findings differs from the usual assumption about normal parental role relationships. Thus the original hypothesis was based on an assumption about normal parental roles that was not confirmed in this study and may be generally invalid.

Caputo and Farina begin with somewhat different hypotheses about levels of conflict between parents of schizophrenic patients, but their findings fit together neatly. Both find that there is more conflict between the parents of the chronic, or poor premorbid, patient than is present in their normal control group. Caputo, however, does not find the differentials he expected between mothers and fathers, and Farina finds that his good premorbid group does not differ from the normal control group.

On both of these questions—role-reversal and conflict—the findings of two experimental studies are found to be consistent with each other, despite differences in experimental and scoring procedures, when we make the proper comparisons. However, the findings are not consistent with frequently-asserted hypotheses about the "Schizogenic" family. On role-reversal, the evidence disconfirms the maternal dominance hypothesis; on parental conflict, the findings suggest that more than the normal amounts may be found in one but not other types of schizophrenic patient families.

Decision-making and conflict-resolution patterns are more difficult to compare across studies. Lerner's code is most elaborate and takes into account the whole course of the discussion. He finds that his normal control parents are more able to reach mutually acceptable compromise decisions, because they are not able to agree, and distort or make disagreement, and his schizophrenic parents arrive at less adequate solutions. Most relevant to this is Caputo's finding that his schizophrenic patients' parents were markedly unable to reach agreement on the revealed difference items. There is consistent evidence in these studies that normal parents are able not only to change their positions but also to recognize explicitly that they are changing, while the parents of schizophrenic patients find it more difficult both to change and to recognize that they have not changed.

While these studies are good examples of what may be gained from the application of experimental methods to this problem area, they are not without their limitations. Three complex questions about the quality of the mother-father relationship have been examined by systematically collecting and scoring samples of parental interaction. Given the variability in methods, consistent findings must be taken seriously. Generalizations about the relative dominance of mothers and fathers, levels of mutual hostility and conflict, and modes of conflict resolution will have to be qualified and specified since there are different findings dependent upon the chronicity of the patient's illness. The studies tell us nothing about the parents of female patients, and the experimental study of such samples is clearly a task of high priority. Further, the linkage between these parental interaction patterns and the development of schizophrenia remains unclear both empirically and theoretically. Through the study of the interaction of parents with their schizophrenic child some progress in establishing such linkages may result. Such studies are reported in the succeeding sections of this volume.

CHAPTER TWO

PATTERNS OF ROLE DOMINANCE AND CONFLICT IN PARENTS OF SCHIZOPHRENIC PATIENTS *

AMERIGO FARINA

A GREAT DEAL of effort has been directed toward determining the possible role played by familial factors in the development of schizophrenia. In past years the role of the mother of the schizophrenic patient has frequently been given primacy.[1] However, the nature of the total family structure and the pattern of parental relationships have also received attention, especially in more recent reports. According to these studies, a characteristic interaction pattern of parents of schizophrenic patients is that of greater dominance of one over the other than would be expected in a population of parents of nonschizophrenic offspring.[2] Also some preliminary studies have indicated a systematic relationship between the sex of the dominant parent and important patterns of adjustment on the part of the son. In several instances, it has

* Reprinted from Journal of Abnormal and Social Psychology, 61:31-38, 1960. This report is based on a PhD thesis submitted to the Graduate School of Arts and Sciences at Duke University. The research was in part financed by a research grant (M-629) from the National Institute of Mental Health. Grateful appreciation is expressed to Norman Garmezy, Eliot H. Rodnick and Edward E. Jones for their help and suggestions. Thanks are due to the staffs of the State Hospital of Butner, North Carolina and Oteen VA Hospital, Oteen, North Carolina for their help in obtaining Ss.

been found that patients from father-dominated families tend to be married, have numerous friends of both sexes, and generally have made a good premorbid adjustment.[3] Patients from mother-dominated families, on the other hand, tend to be single, social isolates, and to have made a marginal social-sexual adjustment prior to psychosis. These trends are supported by Opler's finding that patients from mother-dominated subcultural groups tend to be pallidly asexual, whereas those from father-dominated sub-cultures tend to be more active sexually.[4] Parents of schizophrenic patients, in addition, are reported to relate to each other in a manner characterized by heightened conflict and hostility.[5]

This study was primarily designed to investigate the reported association between the sex of the dominant parent and the pre-morbid adjustment of the schizophrenic son. In addition, the reported conflict in the interaction of these parents as well as the inequality of the dominance relationship seemed to merit investigation. Considerable difficulty is encountered, however, in determining what is usually meant by dominance and conflict in this area of investigation. Many of the studies cited are primarily clinical-qualitative, reports and little or no attempt has been made to define these two variables. None of these studies had attempted to measure systematically any aspect of actual parental interaction. In spite of this difficulty, the hope in the present study was to establish operationally defined indices of dominance and conflict which would do minimal violence to commonly held connotations of these terms. Thus, in a standardized situation where the parents are interacting, the more dominant partner can be defined as the one who speaks the most, whose decisions are accepted by the other, etc. In the same situation, extent of conflict can be measured by number of interruptions by each parent, failure to reach agreement, etc. Observing the actual interactions between the parents should have a decided advantage over drawing inferences from paper-and-pencil scales completed by each. If, in addition, the standardized situation were so structured that the parents were unaware of what was being measured, their understandable defensiveness about revealing patterns of conflict and dominance in their relationship could be minimized.

Other studies which have used comparable measures of dominance and conflict give some indication of their usefulness. Matarazzo, Saslow, and Guze have demonstrated that somewhat similar indices have excellent inter-rater reliability and have considerable stability over time for a given individual.[6] Strodtbeck and Cervin have employed similar measures for identifying the dominant member of a dyad, and their results indicate considerable usefulness for interaction situation techniques.[7]

METHOD

Subjects

The Ss were 36 pairs of white parents who were divided into three groups of 12 couples each. The grouping of these parents was determined by the premorbid adjustment and type of illness of their biological sons. Parents in the control group had sons hospitalized for pulmonary tuberculosis with a medical history free from psychiatric illness or disturbance. These parents were selected as control Ss because tuberculosis shares a number of important features with mental disorder. Society is antipathetic to both illnesses, and both result in prolonged hospitalization and social isolation of the patient. Moreover, it was possible to employ an identical procedure with these parents and the parents of schizophrenic patients. Parents in the Good Premorbid group (Goods) had sons hospitalized for schizophrenia with the symptom picture uncomplicated by organic factors or mental retardation. In addition, these sons had made a good adjustment prior to psychosis as indicated by a Phillips Premorbid Scale of 15 or less.[8] Parents in the Poor Premorbid group (Poors) were selected by the same criteria as the Goods with the difference that their sons had made a poor adjustment prior to psychosis as indicated by a Phillips Premorbid Scale score of

16 or more. The validity of this dichotomy has been reported in detail elsewhere.[9] The Good sons were mostly married and all had numerous friends, whereas, the Poors were all single and, typically, had been social isolates. For all groups, both parents and the hospitalized son had lived together as a family unit during the son's childhood and adolescence, and the parents were living together at the time of the study. The mean age of all sons was 28.7 with a range extending from 19.5 to 36 years. None had been hospitalized for his present illness prior to the age of 17. The groups of sons were quite comparable with respect to age and education. In addition, the Tuberculous and Good groups were nearly identical with respect to total years spent in the hospital and number of years since first hospitalization. However, the Poors tended to have been hospitalized at a younger age and had spent significantly more time in the hospital in comparison with the other two groups.

Pertinent data on the group of Ss (couples) are presented in Table 1. The only statistically significant differences among these

Table 1

Characteristics of Parent Groups

	Controls	Goods	Poors
Age of father:			
Mean	59.7	55.8	60.5
SD	6.9	9.1	10.2
Age of mother:			
Mean	56.6	52.3	56.7
SD	8.1	8.2	9.7
Years married:			
Mean	37.4	32.0	34.8
SD	7.2	7.0	9.5
Grades completed by mother:			
Mean	6.4	8.1	8.6
SD	2.8	2.6	3.9
Grades completed by father:			
Mean	7.3	7.2	9.5
SD	3.0	3.3	3.7
Number of children:			
Mean	5.2	4.2	4.3
SD	2.6	1.8	2.5
Number of male children:			
Mean	3.4	2.6	2.2
SD	1.4	1.2	1.1

groups for the characteristics appearing in Table 1 occur for number of male children. The control parents had significantly more male children than the other two groups. Although it is difficult to classify many of these parents into usual socioeconomic class categories because many were engaged primarily in farming, the total sample might best be described as lower middle class, and the groups appear comparable in this respect. With the exception of one mother, all Ss are native Southerners.

Procedure

When a set of parents satisfied the criteria listed above, they were sent a letter from the Clinical Director or Director of Professional Services of the hospital in which their son was a patient. This was the standard method of communicating with relatives of patients, and most parents had previously been contacted in this manner by the hospital. The letter stated that E, a clinical psychologist, was collecting information about patients hospitalized there and that the information was considered of importance in understanding and treating the son. The recipients of the letter were asked to make an appointment with E at their son's hospital.

When the parents arrived, they were told that information about their son and family was desirable and might help their offspring.* They were then interviewed about family composition and the psychotic son's premorbid history. After this interview, the father was taken to another office and asked to complete a modified form of the Parental Attitude Research Inventory (PARI).[10] E then returned to the office in which the mother was waiting and explained that the subsequent part of the interview would be recorded to insure E's recall of what was said. S was then given the following instructions:

Mrs.—, here's what I'd like us to do now. We are interested

---

* The data collected actually served a clinical purpose. Such data were made available to professional personnel who were working with sons of these parents.

in knowing how a mother handles problems that come up with children when her husband is not around. I'm going to describe some problems that come up more or less often, and I'd like you to tell me what you would do. Remember, imagine that your husband is not around to help you so that you have to handle these problems yourself.

Twelve hypothetical problem situations, adapted from a study by Jackson,[11] were then read, and S was given unlimited time to respond to each one. Three examples of these problem situations are given below:

1. Your twelve-year-old son gets home from school. He throws his books down, telling you what you have been teaching him is wrong and that he is not going to listen to you any more.

2. A gang of boys calls to your eight-year-old son to come out and play. You don't think it's good for your son to play with these boys, but now he starts to leave the house to go with them.

3. Your seventeen-year-old son has a chance to take a job which you are sure would be good for him. He knows you would like him to take it, but he doesn't want it. Instead, he wants to take a job which you think would not be good for him.

When the task was completed, the roles were reversed. The mother was taken to the other office to complete the PARI, and the father was given the same instructions and the same hypothetical situations. Finally, both parents were once more brought together in the office containing the tape recorder and given the following instructions:

Both of you have told me how you would handle problems that come up with children when you are by yourselves. We are also interested in knowing how parents would handle these problems together. Imagine that these same problems came up when both of you are there. I would like both of you to agree about what you would do and tell me what that is. Be sure both of you say "agreed" when you are finished.

The tape recorder was started once more and the problem situations were again read by E. For all Ss, these hypothetical problems were read in the same order.

Throughout the interaction between the parents, great care was exercised to insure that E did not influence their behavior. Verbal reinforcement was given only once—and this came in all instances —at the end of the parent's first response during the initial interview in which each was seen individually. Furthermore, the extent and quality of E's participation in the interaction was guided by the Jackson content scoring categories.[12] All questions by E were designed to elicit scorable responses from the parents or to determine whether or not agreement had been reached between them.

Indices of Dominance

The dominance and conflict measures employed in the analyses were taken exclusively from the interview with both parents with the exception of the "Yielding" indices, which were derived from both the individual and joint sessions. The several indices of dominance were operationally defined as follows:

1. Speaks First—The number of times one parent spoke first in 12 situations minus the number of times the other spoke first.

2. Speaks Last—The number of times one parent spoke last in 12 situations minus the number of times the other spoke last.

3. Total—First and Last—Sum of 1 and 2 above.

4. Passive Acceptance of Solution—The number of times in 12 situations one parent passively accepted the other's solution minus the number of times the other behaved similarly. A simple unelaborated agreement in response to the spouse's solution constituted passive acceptance.

5. Total Time Spoken—One parent's total speaking time for 12 situations relative to the other's total speaking time.

6. Yielding Maximum—The content of the responses to the problem situations was scored along the dimension of amount of pressure to conform which the parent, by his or her action, would bring to bear on the child. An ordinal scale developed by Jackson [13] was employed for this purpose, and yielding scores were defined in terms of scale points yielded by one parent in moving toward an acceptance of the spouse's solution. For example, if the mother was very lenient, whereas, the father applied great pressure to the child in the individual interviews, and together they arrived at a lenient solution, then the father was considered to have yielded to the mother. When more than one solution was offered to one problem situation, Yielding-Maximum was always based on the most severe solution offered by the parents, both in the individual and joint interviews.

7. Yielding-Minimum is identical to Yielding-Maximum except that it was always derived from the least severe solution offered.

Indices of Conflict*

These indices were chosen on the assumption that they would reflect the degree of respect and tolerance the Ss had for each other and would indicate the degree to which they could compromise and cooperate. They were operationally defined as follows:

1. Frequency of Simultaneous Speech—The number of occasions in the interview during which both parents spoke concurrently.

2. Duration of Simultaneous Speech—The total time in seconds during which both parents spoke concurrently.

3. Interruptions-Mother—The number of times the mother interrupted the father during the interview.

4. Interruptions-Father—The number of times the father interrupted the mother.

5. Interruptions-Total—Sum of 3 and 4 above.

* For further information see Farina.[14]

6. Disagreements and Aggressions-Mother—The number of times the mother disagreed with or aggressed against the father during the interview.

7. Disagreements and Aggressions-Father—The number of times the father disagreed with or aggressed against the mother during the interview.

8. Disagreements and Aggressions-Total—The sum of 6 and 7 above.

9. Failure to Agree—The number of situations for which the parents failed to arrive at a mutually acceptable solution.

10. Verbal Activity—the total amount of time during which the mother and father talked.

While most of the indices comprising the conflict variable appear to have considerable face validity, it may not be apparent why the index Verbal Activity was also used as a measure of conflict. Since the instructional set given to the parents in the interaction interview stressed that they arrive at a joint solution, Ss continued to speak as long as they remained in disagreement. To test the assumption that Verbal Activity could serve to reflect the difficulty experienced by the parents in reaching agreement or the extent of the disagreement between them, total time talked by both parents in situations where agreement was reached was compared to total time talked in those situations in which they failed to achieve a common solution. Since the difference was in the expected direction and highly significant ($t = 4.76$, $df = 22$, $p < 0.001$) it may be concluded that Ss do tend to talk longer in situations where they do not agree.

Reliability of Indices

Four cases were chosen for independent rating by an advanced graduate student in psychology* and two of these four cases were rerated by E without reference to his previous ratings. The resulting inter- and intrarater correlation coefficients were very similar. For four indices, Speaks First, Speaks Last, Failure to

* Appreciation is expressed to Richard Dunham for this work.

Agree, and Passive Acceptance of Solution, there was virtually perfect agreement. For these, one disagreement occurred in 360 possibilities. For the balance of the indices, the average Spearman *rho* value for inter- and intrarater reliabilities combined was +.89 with a range from +.74 to +.96. Although there are variations from index to index, each of these indices appeared sufficiently reliable to warrant its retention.

RESULTS

The main purpose of this study was to test the hypothesis that there is an association between the sex of the dominant parent and the premorbid adjustment of the schizophrenic son. The analysis of the relevant data was done by deriving indices from the mother and father scores in such a way that negative scores indicated mother dominance and positive scores father dom-

Table 2
Means and Standard Deviations of Groups on Dominance Indices *

	Controls	Goods	Poors
Speaks first:			
Mean	—0.5	+5.7	—2.2
SD	9.1	6.3	7.0
Speaks last:			
Mean	—1.0	+3.4	—2.7
SD	5.0	4.0	5.7
Total first and last:			
Mean	—1.5	+9.2	—4.8
SD	10.6	7.1	9.7
Passive acceptance of solution:			
Mean	—0.5	+3.1	—1.2
SD	4.4	3.2	1.9
Total time spoken: †			
Mean	0.72	2.0	0.72
SD	1.9	3.2	1.3
Yielding-maximum:			
Mean	+0.12	+1.3	—0.8
SD	2.4	1.1	1.7
Yielding-minimum:			
Mean	—0.13	+0.8	—1.0
SD	1.9	1.6	1.6

* + indicates father dominance; — indicates mother dominance.
† A score greater than 1 indicates father dominance; a score below 1 indicates mother dominance.

inance. For example, for Speaks First, the number of times the mother spoke first in 12 problem situations was subtracted from the number of times the father spoke first. Table 2 presents the means and standard deviations for each group on each index. Increasingly high positive numbers indicate increasing degrees of father dominance, whereas mother dominance is similarly represented by negative numbers. In the case of Total Time Spoken the mother's score was divided into the father's score so that an index greater than unity indicates father dominance and one less than unity indicates mother dominance. In brief, Table 2 shows that mother dominance was most marked for the Poor group, that the controls were intermediate, and that the Good group was characterized by father dominance.

Table 3
Levels of Significance of Difference among and between Groups for
Dominance Indices

		Between groups		
Index	Among groups	Controls vs. goods	Controls vs. poors	Goods vs. poors
Speaks first	0.06	NS	NS	0.01
Speaks last	0.019	0.025	NS	0.01
Total first and last	0.004	0.025	NS	0.001
Passive acceptance of solution	0.005	0.025	NS	0.001
Total time spoken	0.0002	0.01	NS	0.001
Yielding-maximum	0.005	NS	NS	0.001
Yielding-minimum	0.004	NS	NS	0.01

The significance of the difference among these three sets of means was evaluated by a nonparametric test suggested by Jonckheere.[15] The p values yielded by this test are shown in the first column of Table 3. All differences are significant at at least the 0.06 level of probability. A further analysis to determine the probability that any two groups were selected from the same population was made by means of the Mann-Whitney U test.[16] The p values yielded by this series of tests are presented in the last three columns of Table A. On this table, p values greater than 0.05 are listed as nonsignificant (NS). For all indices, the Good and Poor groups differed from each other at better than the

0.01 level of significance in the expected direction. All of the indices in the Good-Control group comparison reveal that the Good group was characterized by more father dominance, and four of the seven indices employed reached a statistically sig-

Table 4

Means, Standard Deviations, and Levels of Significance for Groups on Conflict Indices

	Means and SDs			Levels of significance			
	Control	Good	Poor	Control vs. total schiz- ophrenia	Control vs. good	Control vs. poor	Good vs. poor
Frequency of simultane- ous speech:							
Mean	5.4	7.5	11.4	NS	NS	NS	NS
SD	4.3	7.5	10.2				
Duration of simultane- ous speech:							
Mean	4.8	9.0	13.8	NS	NS	NS	NS
SD	3.6	12.2	16.5				
Interruptions—mother:							
Mean	1.3	3.0	5.6	*	NS	*	NS
SD	1.5	3.2	4.1				
Interruptions—father:							
Mean	1.2	2.8	4.7	†	NS	†	NS
SD	1.9	3.3	5.3				
Interruptions—total:							
Mean	2.6	5.8	10.3	*	NS	*	†
SD	2.4	6.3	9.1				
Disagreements and aggressions— mother:							
Mean	1.7	1.5	4.2	NS	NS	NS	†
SD	1.5	2.3	5.1				
Disagreements and aggressions— father:							
Mean	.8	1.2	2.4	NS	NS	†	NS
SD	1.0	1.6	2.6				
Disagreements and aggressions— total:							
Mean	2.5	2.8	6.7	NS	NS	†	†
SD	2.3	3.3	8.0				
Failure to agree:							
Mean	.9	1.0	1.9	NS	NS	†	NS
SD	1.3	1.2	1.4				
Verbal activity:							
Mean	337	424	556	†	NS	†	NS
SD	106	236	295				

† $p < 0.05$.
* $p < 0.01$.

nificant difference. Six of the seven dominance indices indicate that the Poor group was more mother-dominated than the Control group, while the seventh index was identical in the two groups. In this last comparison, none of the indices reach the 0.05 level of significance, however.

The first three columns of Table 4 present the means and standard deviations obtained by the three groups on the ten conflict indices. For nine of these ten indices, extent of conflict was least in Controls, greatest in Poors, and intermediate in the Goods. Only for the 10th index, Disagreements and Aggressions —Mother, did the Control group obtain a somewhat higher score (indicative of greater conflict) than the Goods, although for this index, too, the Poors' score was the highest. In the analysis of these data, each group was compared with every other group, and the Total Schizophrenic group, the Goods and Poors combined, was compared to the Control group. The Mann-Whitney U test was employed for these analyses. The resulting p levels are indicated in the last four columns of Table 4. The tests employed are one-tailed with the exception of the Good-Poor comparison, where the tests are two-tailed because no prediction of differences in conflict behavior had been made.

The comparisons most relevant to the hypothesis that parents of schizophrenic patients experience more conflict in their interactions than controls are those between the Control and Total Schizophrenic groups. Since all 10 indices were in the expected direction, and 4 of these reached a p level of less than 0.05, the hypothesis appears to be supported. The other comparisons reveal that the Poor group parents experienced more conflict in their interaction than either the Control or Good groups. All 10 indices were greater for the Poors than for the Controls, and 7 reached a statistically significant level. Similarly, all 10 indices were higher for the Poor than for the Good groups, and 3 reached statistical significance. The Good-Control groups comparisons failed to reveal any statistically significant differences for any index, although 9 of the 10 were higher for the Goods than for the Controls.

A test was made of the hypothesis that the interactions of parents of schizophrenic patients are characterized by dominance of one relative to the other. The dominance indices for these analyses were derived from the mother and father scores so that increasing magnitude of the score indicated an increasingly unequal dominance relationship between the parents. For example, for Speaks First, the submissive member's score, regardless of sex, was always subtracted from the dominant member's score. The index scores were very similar for the two groups and there was no observable directional trend. Four of the seven indices were higher for the Control group, and three were higher for the Total Schizophrenic group.

The PARI scores were very similar for all groups. Neither for mothers nor for fathers could any directional trends be observed on any of the nine scales administered.

DISCUSSION

The results of this investigation revealed a marked relationship between sex of the dominant parent and level of premorbid adjustment achieved by the schizophrenic son. The interactions of parents of good premorbid patients were characterized by father dominance whereas the mother was dominant in the case of parents of poor premorbid patients. However, this correlation does not permit one to assume that such parental behaviors were the cause of the offspring's behavior since this study shares the problems inherent in any retrospective study.* Clearly, one can posit alternative explanations for the relations between parental and patient behaviors. For example, it is conceivable that the son's role in the family in the past may have given rise to current parental interactions patterns or that parental awareness of the son's status and their own relationships to the hospital may have served to modify their situational test behavior. Nevertheless,

---

* These and related problems of retrospective studies will be discussed at length in a forthcoming publication.[17]

the traits displayed in a situational test such as the one employed in this study may have considerable stability over time and therefore may be representative of earlier behaviors in the family setting. For example, Naka has demonstrated that certain personality traits are persistent in most individuals over a 15-year time span.[18] Her Ss were children of 2 and 17 years of age, however.

If it is assumed that the parental behaviors as measured in this study were characteristic of the parents from the time the patient was an infant, how might these have been significant in shaping the offspring's personality? The good premorbid schizophrenic patients displayed more customary adult male behaviors prior to psychosis than was true of the poor premorbid patients. The family environment in which the good premorbid schizophrenic develops may make it easier for him to achieve a somewhat higher level of maturity and to manifest more adequate male behavioral patterns relative to the poor premorbid schizophrenic patient. Although the good premorbid may still be exposed to such pathogenic family influences as are generated by a tyrannical father and a weak, vacillating mother, the father does appear to assume dominance in the family. Consequently, he is in a position to reward the son for imitating his behavior and to serve as a model, even if a faulty one, for male identification. The poor premorbid schizophrenic, on the other hand, appears to have grown up in a family where the mother exercises control and where the father does not serve as a reasonably adequate male figure with whom the patient can identify. Even in instances where the son makes tentative efforts to identify with the father, the antagonism between the parents may inhibit an effective identification as Mowrer, has pointed out.[19] These findings appear to have implications for theories of identification and sex typing, since the behavioral differences between the good and poor premorbid schizophrenic patients are relevant to these concepts.

The findings concerning conflict appear to support the reports by many writers that relationships between parents of schizophrenic patients are characterized by hostility and contentiousness. If their behavior in the situational test can be used to infer their more general behavior, these parents do not appear to be able to cooperate with one another. Impatience with each other and a mutual lack of respect and regard are indicated by frequent interruptions and unwillingness to compromise in the task. This discord may involve the schizophrenic offspring according to Lidz, Cornelison, Fleck, and Terry, who report that he is often the focus and battleground of parental conflict.[20] Since the stimulus situations employed in this study dealt with problems of disobedience and misbehaviors of children, they may have served as effective cues for eliciting the conflictful parental interactions.

Excessive dominance by one parent, particularly dominance by the wife over the husband, has often been described as the modal parental pattern in families of schizophrenic patients. The results of the present investigation, however, suggest that the premorbid adjustment of the schizophrenic son should be considered in describing the parental dominance relationship. In fact, when the sex of the parent and the premorbid adjustment of the son are disregarded and the Goods and Poors combined are compared to the Control group, no differences in extent of dominance of one parent over the other can be discerned in these samples. Furthermore, since the role the parents play in the child's acquisition of sex-appropriate behaviors appears to vary with the sex of the child,[21] and since the process of identification may be different for females, the sex of the schizophrenic offspring should also be considered in studying the role of possible family influences in the development of a schizophrenic disorder.

SUMMARY

The major purpose of the present study was to investigate a reported association between sex of the dominant parent and the adequacy of premorbid adjustment of the schizophrenic son. The investigation was carried out by means of a situational test so designed and structured that indices of dominance could be obtained. Such indices were length of time speaking, relinquishing one's position in favor of the spouse, etc. Paternal dominance was found to be associated with good premorbid adjustment of the schizophrenic son whereas in the case of those patients whose premorbid adjustment was poor, the mothers were dominant. Because of these differences in parental behaviors, it may have been somewhat easier for the good as compared to the poor premorbid son to learn the more usual adult male behaviors and to achieve a somewhat higher level of maturity.

Extent of conflict present in the parental interactions was inferred from such measures as number of interruptions, number of disagreements, etc. The parents of the schizophrenic patients displayed more conflict than the Control parents, and this conflict was particularly marked in the parents of the poor premorbid schizophrenic sons. The results of the present investigation suggest that the premorbid adjustment and sex of the schizophrenic offspring need to be considered when investigations of the familial role in schizophrenia are undertaken.

CHAPTER THREE

THE PARENTS OF
THE SCHIZOPHRENIC *

DANIEL V. CAPUTO

THE PRESENT STUDY is concerned with the interaction between the parents of male chronic schizophrenics and the role these parents may play in the development of such psychotic reactions. Specifically, the dominant-mother passive-father notion, frequently reported to be present in the backgrounds of chronic schizophrenics, is empirically evaluated.

Descriptions of the interaction between parents of schizophrenics which supply the empirical foundation for the dominant-mother, passive-father notion have been derived largely from more or less unstructured interviews, objectivity probably suffering from the interviewer's being aware that he is dealing with the parents of schizophrenics.[1] Many of these earlier investigators have so concentrated on the mothers of schizophrenics that they have neglected the role of the father of the schizophrenic, stressing, by this exclusion, the presumed pathogenic ("schizophrenogenic") talents of the mother.[2]

* Reprinted from Family Process, 2:339-356, 1963. This paper is based upon a dissertation presented to the Department of the University of Illinois in partial fulfillment of the requirements for the degree of the Doctor of Philosophy. The author wishes to express his gratitude to the chairman of his committee, Leo A. Hellmer, and to J. McV. Hunt for their aid and encouragement.

Historically, the male pre-schizophrenic has been characterized as inadequate and anxious in many aspects of life, e.g., Boisen.[3] It may be that the quality of early training by the parents results in the induction of this extreme anxiety in the child, which in turn results in the production of a psychotogenic agent as a physiological concomitant of anxiety[4] in the hereditarily prone individual, resulting in schizophrenia. On the other hand, it may be that the parents are not at all involved in the sequence of events leading to schizophrenia.

In the present paper, the author has attempted to explore further the pathogenic role of parents and to obviate theoretically derived biases by employing objective measures which tap both "attitudinal" variables (obtained from paper and pencil measures) and the quality of ongoing interaction. The use of these two types of objective measures (paper and pencil, and interactional) represents a set of converging operations[5] whereby some of the findings obtained through the use of one measure may be checked by the use of another.

Three hypotheses describe the conditions of family interaction that were considered by early researchers to be of significance for the production of schizophrenia. These hypotheses, which are tested in this study, derive largely from Levy's concept of maternal domination and overprotection.[6]

According to the first hypothesis, the mother usurps much of the familial authority, which, customarily, in the nonpathogenic home, rests with the father. The composite picture of the mother is that of an aggressive, domineering matriarch whose dicta are rarely challenged by the passive, acquiescent, psychologically absent father. It would be expected that such a mother would view herself and be viewed by her husband as more aggressive and dominating than would the mother of the nonschizophrenic. It would also be expected that such a mother would display more dominating behavior in interpersonal interaction with her husband. Similarly, it would be expected that the father would see himself as more passive, more compliant than the fathers of nonschizophrenics and that this view would be corroborated by his wife's view of him and by his objective interactive behavior. It would be expected further that both parents would devalue their own personal worth, the mother revealing those deficiencies which ordinarily lie beneath her facade of aggressivity and competence [7] and the father, perhaps simply agreeing with his wife's previously expressed opinions about himself.

According to the second hypothesis if the mother of the schizophrenic has a massive power orientation and the father is indecisive and weak, immature, passive and inadequate, it would be expected that this mother would behave in a hostile and denigrating manner toward the father in an attempt to consolidate her own position of power and that the father would inhibit or repress any hostility he might harbor toward his spouse either for fear of retaliation or as a result of his dependency on her. Most of the descriptive studies and many of the studies stressing quantification in this area have strongly averred that the mother of the schizophrenic is a dominating strong individual and the father a weak, retiring and passive person. Some researchers (e.g., Hajdu-Gimes) invoke this polarization of parental behavior as an etiological essential. This view is also stressed by Tietze, Gerard and Siegel, and Kasanin.[8] Lidz, despite having located a contingent of strong fathers, notes that few of his fathers presented masculine images that were even vaguely satisfactory.[9] The Block group noted in their cluster analysis study that they were able to isolate a group of mothers of autistic children who were characterized as "Machiavellian and egocentric," and they mention this type of mother's "power orientation."[10] The Bateson group, in discussing the double bind theory, stress the mother's primary responsibility for the double bind, commenting that the weakness of the father precludes his supporting the child against this development. Lidz, Cornelison, Fleck and Terry found among their subjects a group of fathers of schizophrenics who seem to represent the paradigmatic father which the "schizophrenogenic mother" notion would imply: "These men are very passive and demand little for themselves, acting the part of lesser siblings in the family and accepting their wives as grown-up authorities. . . .

While they offer their wives passive support . . . they are unable to assert needs of their own or to express any ideas concerning the raising of children." [11] Given these descriptions, it is not illogical to make a theoretical leap to the assumption that if the situation were as these authors describe, then there should be little or no disagreement among the parents of schizophrenics.* If the dominant-mother, passive-father situation were to prevail in the homes of chronic schizophrenics, it would have to follow that decisions would be arrived at more readily in such a family situation than in one where authority was not as polarized, by virtue of the meaning of the words "dominant" and "passive."

According to the third hypothesis there is a reversal of the customary coalitions in the family of the schizophrenic. In psychoanalytic parlance, there would be a trend toward identification on the part of the son with the aggressor-mother, to the exclusion of the father. Insofar as the parents' responses to the Semantic Differential can reflect these interpersonal identifications, it would be expected, according to this hypothesis, that the mother of the schizophrenic would evaluate herself and her son more similarly than would the mother of the nonschizophrenic, while the father

* Lidz, Ellison and Hamilton, and Frazee all have noted, however, that in some instances the fathers of schizophrenics are not so passive and retiring as the aforementioned authors felt they were. Related to this is the work of Farina who found, generally, that mothers of schizophrenics tend to be dominant for those cases falling into the poor premorbid category, while fathers of schizophrenics tend to be more dominant in cases falling into the good premorbid category. The other studies mentioned do not clarify, in most cases, whether they are considering good or poor premorbids (or process-reaction, or acute-chronic). Langfeldt and other of the Scandinavian students of schizophrenia make the point that the poor premorbid types are indeed suffering from the disorder of schizophrenia while the good premorbids are suffering from related disorders (schizophreniform). Relating the work of Farina and the view of Langfeldt one might be led to the notion that maternal dominance occurs only in cases of "true" schizophrenia. However, it is evident in the Farina work that, at best, maternal dominance was shown only very minimally in the poor premorbid ("true") group, conflict between parents being the most obvious phenomenon. The results obtained by Farina using primarily "structural" measures, parallel the results of my own study using primarily "contentual" measures, the factor of importance apparently being not with whom the authority rested, but whether it could be shared without conflict in these families.

of the schizophrenic would evaluate himself and his son less similarly than would fathers of non-schizophrenics.

Thus, usurpation of authority by the maternal figure, unilateral denigration of the paternal figure by the mother, and the latter's preternormal association with the male child would delineate the "schizophrenogenic mother" notion. The father in such a situation would, according to this conception, accede to the mother's demands, view her as powerful and competent, and allow himself to be estranged from his child.

METHOD

The strategy of this study is to determine whether the interactional patterns hypothesized are more often characteristic of the parents of male chronic schizophrenics than of a control sample of parents. Briefly this was done by having 20 pairs of parents of "normals" rate various relevant concepts on Osgood's Semantic Differential.[12] In addition, each pair of parents was asked to discuss and reach an agreement about 10 items of the Parent Attitude Inventory [13] which they had previously answered in divergent fashion. These discussions were tape recorded and were later assessed by the Bales method of analyzing interaction in small groups.[14] The data derived from these instruments were used to test the hypotheses outlined.

Subjects

The experimental subjects employed in the study were the natural parents of 20 white, male, chronic schizophrenics. The patients included veterans who were inducted during World War II or subsequently, and whose psychosis became evident between the ages of 17 and 30. Chronicity was determined by a relatively continuous hospitalization period of two or more years. Only those patients for whom both initial and subsequent hospital diagnoses contained some derivative of the word "schizophrenia," and for whom no mention of brain injury or other complicating feature was made, were considered. The distribution of patients among the subclassifications of schizophrenia was the following: chronic undifferentiated: 6, paranoid: 6, hebephrenic: 4, simple: 1, catatonic: 1, unclassified chronic: 2. The requirement that the parents of each patient be alive and cohabiting may have biased the results somewhat.

The control group consisted of 20 pairs of parents of veterans who had never been hospitalized for psychiatric disorder. These subjects were obtained through the cooperation of various veterans organizations.

The groups were equated with respect to the variables of age, socioeconomic status, education, and number and sex of siblings. Information on these variables was obtained through a questionnaire and through observation of the home and dwelling area of the subject. Socioeconomic status was assessed by use of the revised scale by Warner, Meeker, and Eells.[15] A series of t-tests done on the subject groups indicates that no significant differences existed between experimental and control groups on the matching variables (see Table 1). The subjects were apportioned

Table 1
Means of Matching Variables

Subjects	N	Age	Years married	Age son studied	Total no. sons	Number daughters	Years educ.	Warner scale values
Exper. Males	20	60.80	34.20	29.00	1.70	1.05	9.80	46.60*
Cont. Males	20	58.30	35.60	31.20	1.70	1.30	10.75	46.70*
Exper. Females	20	58.85					9.35	
Cont. Females	20	56.40					10.25	
t value bet. males		0.97†					1.07	
t values bet. females		0.13					1.01	
t value bet. familes			0.63	1.09	0.19	0.66		0.03

* Based on occupation, source of income, house type and dwelling area—weighted values were 4, 3, 3, 2 respectively.

† None of the t values indicated achieved statistical significance utilizing two-tailed probability levels.

among three urban areas: Chicago, St. Louis, and Champaign, Illinois, in an attempt to reduce any effects of regional factors which might supervene despite social-class equalization.

The investigator conducted the procedures with the parents in their homes. Their cooperation was secured by means of a letter on the stationery of the hospital. The cooperation of the control parents was obtained through the veterans organizations of which their sons were members. A letter stating that subjects were needed for a study concerning child-rearing preferences was employed in contracting control subjects so that the onus of being experimental rather than control subjects could be maintained, to a degree, for both parents of schizophrenics and parents of non-schizophrenics. A token payment was offered to the subjects and the routine nature of the interview was stressed so as to make it as nonthreatening as possible to them. Of the group of schizophrenic veterans who were in three hospitals surveyed, only one in seven had parents who qualified for and agreed to participate in the experiment. This, of necessity, limits the generalizability of the findings. The major basis of failure to qualify was the death of one or both of the parents. Only four sets of otherwise eligible parents refused to participate in the study.

Assessment Devices and Procedures

The Parent Attitude Inventory, the Semantic Differential and the Bales method of analyzing interaction in small groups were the primary instruments employed in this study. The Parent Attitude Inventory is a series of true-false items similar to the Shoben (1949) scale and to the PARI.[16] The Semantic Differential included six concepts assaying self-perception and interpersonal relationships among the family members. These were identical except for variations in concepts due to the sex of the respondents. These concepts were, for the male: MYSELF, MY SON, MY MARRIAGE BEFORE WE HAD CHILDREN, MY WIFE WHEN WE WERE FIRST MARRIED, MY MARRIAGE NOW, MY WIFE NOW. Of the scales used to characterize each of the concepts, six loaded most heavily on the "evaluative" factor, and five on the "potency" factor. The Bales method permits the categorization of interaction between individuals into four groups of activities, two of these being task oriented (adaptive-instrumental) acts, and two involving social-emotional (integrative-expressive) acts. In the present study, only verbal behavior was scored so as to allow the investigator to remain as uninvolved as possible in the discussions. The reliability of the Bales method as applied to the discussion data obtained from the parents was assayed by comparing the results of two independent scorers. Scoring was found to be reliable at the .01 level for each of the 12 Bales categories as measured by Pearson (or phi) coefficient and the Spearman-Brown Prophecy formula.

Procedure

The testing procedure consisted of having each parent complete, independently, the initial fifty items of the Parent Attitude Inventory, subsequent to which each parent was given the Semantic Differential. The investigator discreetly compared their responses on the Parent Attitude Inventory, selecting the first 10 items on which disagreement between the parents was indicated (i.e., a statement marked "true" by one parent, "false" by the other). They were then asked to discuss these items, one at a time, as they would in any family discussion, with a view toward agreeing on a single opinion (true or false), if this were possible. The examiner occupied himself during these discussions so as to obviate attempts by one or another of the participants to include him as a third discussant. These discussions were tape-recorded and were later assessed by the Bales method.

RESULTS

The results, in brief, do not support the "schizophrenogenic mother" notion. Role reversal was not found to be a major factor in the parental background of schizophrenics, and bilateral rather than unilateral expression of hostility between those parents seemed to be characteristic. In addition, reversal of natural coalitions was not found.

Hypotheses Relating to Role Reversal

According to the "schizophrenogenic mother" concept, whereby the mother is seen as the family ruler, we would expect the experimental group females (EGF's) to rate the Semantic Differential concept MYSELF as more potent and more dominant than would control group females (CGF's). Based on the notion that the mothers of schizophrenics present a facade of aggressivity and competence to hide low self-esteem [17], it would also be expected that the experimental group females (EGF's) would rate the concept MYSELF evaluatively less positively than would control group females (CGF's). Similarly, we would expect that EGF's who, according to theory, dominate their spouses, would rate the concept MY HUSBAND NOW low in potency, especially on the single potency scale which has its poles "dominant" and "submissive." Furthermore, according to this theory, it would be predicted that experimental group males (EGM's) would rate the concept MYSELF low in potency, dominance and evaluation, while rating the concept MY WIFE NOW high in potency and dominance.

Of these Semantic Differential measures, only two approach statistical significance. Experimental group males (EGM's) tended to rate themselves significantly higher on the dominant-submissive scale than did control group males (CGM's) ($p <$ .025). A higher score indicates a trend toward submissiveness. A single scale, of course, cannot be considered a highly reliable indicant; however, it does tend to give minimal support to the passivity hypothesis. Contrary to prediction, it was found that EGM's tended to view themselves as being evaluatively better than CGM's. The mean evaluative rating for EGM's was 2.48, while for CGM's it was 2.99 ($p <$ .025). Superficially, these

99

Table 2

Bales Data Related to Role Reversal

	Females		Males	
	N.	Score	N.	Score
Index of "Dependency":				
$(7+8+9)/(4+5+6)+(7+8+9)$:				
Schizophrenics	20	0.12	20	0.14
Normals	20	0.12	20	0.13
rpb		0.00		0.04
Direction		—		Predicted
Percentage of Total Communica-				
tive Acts:				
Schizophrenics	20	48.8	20	51.2
Normals	20	47.7	20	52.3
rpb		.22*		0.06
Direction		Predicted		Predicted
Index of Directive Control				
$(4/4+6)+(5/5+6)$:				
Schizophrenics	20	0.86	20	0.98
Normals	20	0.94	20	0.93
rpb		0.18		0.10
Direction		Opposite		Opposite
	Exper. Group ‡	Control Group ‡		
"Winner" in PAI Discussion:				
Male wins	2.95	4.10		
Female wins	2.05	4.40		
Wilcoxon T	34.5†	79.0		
Direction	Opposite			

* 0.10
† .025
‡ Ties reduced the number of pairs for each group to 18

findings may be interpreted as representing a trend toward "overconfident humility" on the part of the fathers of schizophrenics. Conjecture aside, however, role reversal is not supported by these Semantic Differential data.

The Bales indices related to role reversal are shown in Table 2. According to the maternal dominance, paternal passivity theory, it was predicted that the experimental group females (EGF's) would score lower than their control group counterparts on the index of "dependency,"* and higher than the CGF's on the per-

* An index derived from the Bales categories by the writer.

centage of total communicative acts and on the index of directive control. It was expected, too, that the experimental group males (EGM's) would score higher on the index of "dependency" and lower on the percentage of total communicative acts and on the index of directive control than would the control group males (CGM's). The indices employed in assessing the Bales data are ratio scores utilizing various of the Bales categories. As Table 2 shows, none of the indices significantly discriminated between normal and control subjects, although the percentage of the total communicative acts contributed by the mother tended to be higher for EGF's than for CGF's ($p < .10$). The respective percentages for these groups were 48.8 and 47.7. In neither case, however, did the females produce a majority of the communicative acts.

An additional analysis was done to assess whether EGF's would win more decisions than EGM's in settling differences of opinion on Parent Attitude Inventory items, as might be expected by the "schizophrenogenic mother" theory (see Table 2). By use of the Wilcoxon matched-pairs signed-ranks test, regarding each experimental group family as a matched pair and then repeating the process for the control families, a strong trend indicating that EGM's tended to win a greater number of arguments than their wives was found ($p < .025$) while no significant difference was found in number of decisions won as between male and female control subjects.

The data relating to the problem of role reversal, then, do not lend support to the maternal dominance, paternal-passivity contention held by many investigators in this area. Instead, there appears to be some evidence that the father attempts domination.

Hypotheses Relating to Marital Discord

It was predicted that mothers of schizophrenics would view their husbands, and behave toward them in a negative, hostile manner, in order to sustain their presumably dominant position,

101

while the fathers, whether through fear or dependency, would overinhibit any hostile feelings they had for their wives. Accordingly, the parents' estimations of each other (MY HUSBAND NOW, MY WIFE NOW) were compared on their Semantic Differential ratings for "evaluation." The expectation was that EGF's would rate their husbands as evaluatively less good than would controls, while EGM's would rate their wives as evaluatively better than would controls. The parents' ratings of the concept MY MARRIAGE NOW on the evaluative and potency scales were also compared. In this case, the expectation was that the EGF's, as part of the denigrating attitude they hold toward their husbands, would rate their marriages as evaluatively less good and weaker than would CGF's, while EGM's described by theory as cowed and passive, would rate concept MY MARRIAGE NOW as evaluatively better and stronger than would CGM's. None of the Semantic Differential measures significantly differentiated the experimental group subjects from those in the control group.

In Table 3 are found the Bales data relating to marital discord. It would appear from these data that mothers of schizophrenics do harbor negative feelings toward their husbands as would be expected from the "schizophrenogenic mother" concept. However, the proposition that fathers of schizophrenics are passive and retiring before the onslaughts of the mothers is not substantiated. Rather, the situation appears to be one of bilateral denigration on the part of the parents. The Bales index of expressive-malintegrative behavior, which is the ratio of negative social-emotional expressions to positive social-emotional expressions showed, as predicted, that the EGF's expressed a significantly greater proportion of negative comments toward their husbands during the discussion than did CGF's. Of the total number of socialemotional comments produced by the EGF's, 54.1% were negative. The comparable figure for the control group females is only 29.4% ($p < .001$). Contrary to prediction, it was found that the fathers of patients tended to express significantly more negative

102

Table 3
Bales Data Related to Marital Discord

	Females		Males	
	N	Score	N	Score
Index of Expressive—Malinteg. Behavior $(10+11+12)/$ $(10+11+12)+(1+2+3)$:				
Schizophrenics	20	0.54	20	0.49
Normals	20	0.29	20	0.22
rpb†		0.54*		0.58*
Direction		Predicted		Opposite
Index of Difficulty of Communication $(7/7+6)$:				
Schizophrenics	20	0.14	20	0.17
Normals	20	0.13	20	0.13
rpb†		0.04		0.12
Direction		Opposite		Opposite
Number (Mean) of Disagreements on 10 PAI Items:				
Schizophrenics	20	4.4		
Normals	20	1.2		
U		47*		
Direction		Opposite		

* .001.
† One-tailed probability levels are employed—d.f.= 38.

social-emotional comments than did their control counterparts. Of the social-emotional comments made by EGM's, 48.6% were of a negative nature as compared to 21.7% negative comments made by the CGM's ($p < 0.001$).

The results derived from the expressive-malintegrative index concerning the patients' parents are in startling contrast with the relatively benign picture of parental interrelationships derived from the Semantic Differential data. Occurring in the relatively "naturalistic" setting of a family discussion, the results of the expressive-malintegrative index seem weighty in characterizing these parents in interaction. One might then be led to question the validity of the Semantic Differential for use in problems of this nature where "social desirability" seems strongly involved.

It was predicted, on the basis of the notion that the father of the schizophrenic would defer to his wife's opinions in a discussion, that the experimental group subjects would be able to agree

103

more readily on a single answer for the Parent Attitude Inventory discussions than would the control group subjects. As Table 3 shows, this prediction did not hold. It was found that the experimental group parent pairs were, on the average, unable to choose a single response (true or false) or compromise on some intermediate answer in 4.4 of the ten discussions of Parent Attitude Inventory items in which they engaged. In contrast, the control group pairs ultimately disagreed on a mean number of only 1.2 of their 10 discussions ($p < .001$). It is, perhaps, more telling to note that the total number of disagreements recorded for the control subjects was contributed by only six pairs of parents, while among the experimental subjects, nineteen of the twenty pairs contributed at least one disagreement to the total number recorded for that group.

An additional analysis utilizing the initial scoring of the Parent Attitude Inventory items was employed. Following the "schizophrenogenic mother" concept it would be expected that the mothers of schizophrenics would show themselves to be the more "deviant" of the two parents.

Of the first thirty-five items on the Parent Attitude Inventory, six items were found to produce relative unanimity of opinion among parents of nonschizophrenics. The frequencies for responses of males and females were pooled within each response category for the control group. The true-false frequencies for the control group were then tested against the true-false distributions of the experimental group males for each item, and subsequently, against the true-false distributions of experimental group females. In this manner, it could be determined whether EGF's or EGM's held the more "deviant" attitudes. A series of chi-squared (fourfold) analyses was employed and it was found that the fathers of schizophrenics deviated significantly from controls or tended to do so on three of the six items, while the mothers of schizophrenics deviated or tended to deviate from the controls on four of the six items. On the basis of these findings, neither sex appears to hold more "deviant" attitudes than the other among the experimental group parents.

Hypotheses Relating to Reversal of Natural Coalitions

It was predicted that the female experimental subjects, presumably dominating and controlling all the family members, would be more prone than control females to perceive their sons as more similar to themselves. The results of the t-test of differences between differences on the concepts MYSELF and MY SON rated for evaluation by the EGF's indicate that this hypothesis is a tenable one. (MYSELF score was 2.44 while MY SON was 2.63 for EGF's; comparable scores for CGF's were 2.58 and 1.87 $p < .005$). It was also predicted that the fathers of schizophrenics, presumably estranged from their sons, would view themselves as less similar to their sons than would normals. This prediction was not confirmed, in that the experimental group males tended to regard their sons as similar to themselves (MYSELF, 2.48; MY SON, 2.42) while the control subjects viewed their sons as less similar to themselves (MYSELF, 2.99; MY SON, 2.03 $p < .001$). However, it may be that the son's illness obscured measures of similarity based on evaluation. The trend is patent for parents of relatively normal sons to regard them highly and for parents of disturbed sons to devaluate them somewhat. However, the fact that *both* the parents of schizophrenics regard the son in approximately the same light in respect to their own self evaluations would still tend to indicate that the hypothesis concerning the reversal of natural coalitions is not a tenable one.

Hypotheses Relating to the After-the-Fact Nature of the Study

The emergence of an extreme illness such as schizophrenia no doubt has many ramifications for those associated with the victim. Accordingly, two attempts at control of parental attitudes in relation to the presence of mental disease in the family were instituted. The first is embodied in the requirement that the schizophrenic be hospitalized for at least two years, during which time a portion of the negative attitude associated with hospitalization could presumably dissipate. The second attempts to measure the

105

interpersonal impact of these attitudinal variables via the Semantic Differential. All the subjects were asked, in addition to indicating their contemporary evaluation of their spouses and of their marriages, to rate the following concepts: MY HUSBAND (WIFE) WHEN WE WERE FIRST MARRIED, AND MY MARRIAGE BEFORE WE HAD CHILDREN. Comparisons were made between experimental and control group husbands and wives, and were considered from both the evaluative (good-bad) and potency (strong-weak) aspects. No significant differences were found in the attitudes the parents of schizophrenics demonstrated toward one another over time, as compared with the control subjects. The previously mentioned reservations concerning the validity of the Semantic Differential as herein employed may apply to these results, however.

DISCUSSION

The findings of the present study yielded little support for the maternal dominance, paternal passivity picture among parents of male schizophrenics. Bilateral, rather than unilateral expression of antagonism seems to be a prominent feature in these homes, and role reversal is not evident.

The question of social class is frequently raised to collate seemingly incongruous experimental findings and to explain why both passivity and serious oppositionism are noted as hallmarks of the fathers of schizophrenics. Unfortunately, this factor serves, largely, to confuse the issue further. Thus Lidz, Cornelison, Terry and Fleck found that the fathers of higher status schizophrenic patients were, by and large, overbearing and antagonistic.[18] On the other hand, Sanua,[19] attributes Frazee's [20] finding that a majority of the fathers in her sample were cruel and rejecting and not passive to the fact that she selected her sample from a "working class" population. In contrast, Kohn and Clausen report that schizophrenics at all levels *tend* to see the mother as the principal authority figure, while, among a nonpatient control sample, this tendency is present only at the lower socioeconomic level.[21] The differences in method between the studies may serve to attenuate the importance of the enigma they pose, but one would remain hard pressed to generalize about the variables involved. For the largely lower-middle class subjects surveyed in the present study, no clear dominance-submission pattern was observed for either experimental or control subjects. The factor discriminating these groups appeared to be not with *whom* the authority in the family rested, but *whether* it could be shared without conflict.

The divergent views of the father presented in the literature may relate to the contention of Farina and of Rodnick and Garmezy that parental attitudes and dominance vary with the premorbid adjustment of the schizophrenic sons.[22] Farina employed primarily "structural" rather than "content" measures of dominance and conflict. All seven of the dominance measures in the Farina work significantly discriminated between the parents of schizophrenics with "good" and "poor" premorbid adjustments, the "goods" showing father dominance and the "poors" mother dominance. Controls (the parents of tuberculous patients) fell between the "goods" and "poors" in these comparisons. Of great interest, is the finding that controls and "poors" did not differ significantly on any of the dominance indices. It was also found that "goods" and controls did not differ on any of the ten conflict indices while "poors" and controls differed significantly on seven of the ten indices. It may be that researchers have indiscriminately studied "good" and "poor" premorbid schizophrenics without distinguishing them. The patients involved in the present study, having been hospitalized for a period of from two to fifteen years, would *ipso facto* fit the "poor premorbid" category, since this is a prognostic rubric. As such, the results obtained in the present study parallel those found by Farina for comparisons between "poor premorbids" and controls.

Two other related variables arise as possible explanatory factors for the divergent views of the father of the schizophrenic that have been mentioned, those of age and length of marriage.

Mothers of schizophrenics *tend* to recall their husbands as being weaker than control mothers do during the initial phase of the marriage (MY HUSBAND WHEN WE WERE FIRST MARRIED—POTENCY). Later a shift seems to result whereby mothers of patients contemporarily evaluate their husbands as being *stronger* than control group mothers do (MY HUSBAND NOW—POTENCY). None of these trends was statistically significant. If this perception of the father of the schizophrenic is a true one, it may be that the parental antipathy found in these families only gradually develops.

At any rate, the results of this study seem to indicate that, in so far as family environmental factors are significant in the development of schizophrenia, *both* parents are involved. The child would, thereby, be subjected to chronic anxiety, originating in his estrangement from both parents. Mowrer attributes the development of neurosis, the chief characteristic of which is anxiety, to the intermediate identification pattern which presumably results from the child's inability to achieve rapport with either parent.[23] One possible speculation derived from these findings might be, then, that neurosis and schizophrenia derive from similar *environmental* (i.e., parental) determinants, but that additional factors, perhaps of a hereditary-constitutional nature are involved in the latter.

SUMMARY

The present study was undertaken to assess the role of the parents in the development of schizophrenia. Specifically, the maternal dominance, paternal passivity theory was assayed. According to this theory, role reversal between parents, denigration of the father by the mother, and reversal of the natural father-son coalition were predicted. It was assumed that in such a home the son's identification would more likely be with the mother and that chronic anxiety resulting from social criticism would ensue in the child, which might in turn be involved in the development of schizophrenia.

Reversal of role did not appear to be a significant factor among parents of schizophrenics. No clear pattern of dominance-submission was indicated in the interaction between these parents, although fathers tended to prevail in the decision-making process. The hypothesis that the mothers of schizophrenics would demonstrate hostility toward the father was substantiated. But the expectation that the father would overinhibit hostility was disproved. Bilateral rather than unilateral expression of hostility was strongly indicated during the discussions. Despite the fact that little difficulty in communication was found to exist between the parents of schizophrenics, they were markedly unable to arrive at a decision by discussion. The hypothesis that mothers of schizophrenics would view their sons as more like themselves than controls would was confirmed. However, the supposition that fathers of schizophrenics would view them as less similar to themselves was not upheld.

The results tend to support the notion that hostile atmosphere is established in the home of the potential schizophrenic so that identification with either parent is precluded and the child is isolated within the family. It was pointed out that both parents, rather than the mother alone, contribute to the so-called "schizophrenogenic" character of the family.

CHAPTER FOUR

RESOLUTION OF INTRAFAMILIAL
ROLE CONFLICT IN FAMILIES OF
SCHIZOPHRENIC PATIENTS.
I: THOUGHT DISTURBANCE *

PAUL M. LERNER

A MOUNTING LITERATURE strongly suggests that the schizophrenic patient emerges from a family milieu which differs in significant and systematic ways from that of the nonschizophrenic. Several of these studies have drawn attention to the more stylistic aspects of family interaction, with the intent of linking specific family transactions to disorder-specific aspects of schizophrenia.

Wynne, Ryckoff, Day and Hirsch suggested that families with a schizophrenic offspring related to each other in a manner characterized by "pseudomutuality." [1] That is, each member brought into the total system a primary investment in maintaining a "sense of relatedness." This predominant absorption in fitting together, the authors maintained, led to the use of family mechanisms by which deviations from the family role structure were excluded from recognition or delusionally reinterpreted.

Lidz, Cornelison, Terry and Fleck described the schizophrenic's

* Reprinted from the Journal of Nervous and Mental Disease, 141:342-351, 1965. A condensation of a dissertation presented in partial fulfillment of the requirements for the Ed.D. degree, University of Illinois, 1964.

family environment in terms of a "training ground for irrationality." [2] The authors reported that families in their sample used communication patterns which distorted and denied what should have been obvious interpretations of the environment, including the recognition and understanding of individual members' impulses and affective behavior. The ability of one or both parents to conceal in their communications disturbing family features, the authors termed "masking."

Although these studies are compelling and highly consistent with the clinician's experience, they are basically clinical reports and, as such, show both the advantages and disadvantages of this research methodology. That is, most are studies in depth, and rather than conclusively substantiating a specific theoretic position, may be more fruitfully viewed as generators of tenable hypotheses to be further researched using more rigorous methodology.

Nevertheless, these reports are suggestive methodologically in that the investigators have attempted to link family interactional patterns directly to disorder-specific aspects of schizophrenia. Such a strategy permits the drawing of inferences with respect to such issues as why the patient abandons reality testing and how he is to abandon reality testing. That is, the schizophrenic's proneness to withdraw through symbolic distortion becomes a central concern through the utilization of this strategy.

The present study is designed to investigate the relationship between one dimension of intrafamilial interaction, resolution of intrafamilial role conflict, and one disorder-specific aspect of schizophrenia, severity of thought disturbance. Although only one dimension of family interaction will be investigated, this interpersonal transaction is conceptualized as one significant aspect of a total family milieu, a milieu which it is conjectured "affords training in irrationality." Therefore, if the family milieu of the schizophrenic patient is related to the genesis of this disorder, then parents of schizophrenic patients and parents of controls should differ with respect to the processes they employ in resolving intrafamilial role conflict, and the excessive use of specific processes should be related to the severity of thought disorder present in the patient offspring.

The following hypothesis was generated and tested: There are consistent and systematic differences among parents whose schizophrenic sons reveal markedly severe thought disorders, parents whose schizophrenic sons reveal less severe thought disorders, and parents of "normal" controls in the processes they use to resolve intrafamilial role conflict.

METHOD

Subjects

The sample consisted of 36 pairs of parents divided into three groups of 12 couples each. Grouping of these parents was determined by the type of illness and severity of thought disorder of their biological sons. Two of the parent groups (experimental groups) had sons who met the following criteria: age between 18 and 40 years, a psychiatric diagnosis of schizophrenia uncomplicated by clinical indications of organic brain pathology or mental deficiency, and possessing both biological parents alive and under the age of 65 years. Ratings of thought disturbance were obtained from the Rorschach protocol of each schizophrenic patient using the Genetic Level Score as devised by Becker.[3] Parents of the schizophrenic patients were dichotomized into groups of Highs and Lows on the basis of their son's score. (The lower the genetic level score the more severe the thought disorder.) Table 1 summarizes the Genetic Level Ratings for the two groups

Table 1
Rorschach Genetic Level Scores

Subjects	Number of Responses		Mean Genetic Level Score	
	Range	Mean	Range	Mean
High genetic level group	10–24	15.8	3.5–4.4	3.8
Low genetic level group	7–38	15.1	1.0–3.3	2.6
T value between groups		0.62*		3.4†

* Nonsignificant at the 0.05 level, two-tailed test.
† Significant at the 0.01 level, two-tailed test.

Table 2
Ranges and Means of Matching Variables

Subjects	Number	Age		Son's age		Length of son's current hospitalization		Hollingshead Scale	
		Range	X	Range	X	Range	X	Range	X
High genetic level group, males	12	61–50	56	30–19	27.2	1–6	2.4 months	18–77	51.3
Low genetic level group, males	12	59–47	54	31–18	26.5	1–6	3.2 months	20–68	52.2
Controls, males	12	58–49	54.2	31–21	27.8	1–8	4.1 months	37–63	50.6
High genetic level group, females	12	60–48	53.5						
Low genetic level group, females	12	58–47	52.2						
Controls, females	12	56–46	52.7						
F value between males			0.48*						
F value between females			0.36						
F value between families					0.32		3.2		0.28

* None of the F values indicated achieved statistical significance utilizing two-tailed probability levels.

of schizophrenic patients. The third group, a control group, consisted of 12 sets of parents whose sons were currently hospitalized for a nonpsychiatric illness.

The initial contact with each family was made by letter. The communication employed was sent to all families under the aegis of the hospital from which the names were obtained. It stated that an interview was to be held with the parents of hospitalized patients as part of an effort to obtain more background information which might subsequently be used in treating, or otherwise aiding, the patient. The routine nature of the interview was stressed so as to make it as nonthreatening as possible to these subjects. A self-addressed postcard accompanied each letter and on this card the parents were requested to indicate a convenient appointment time. Of all the families contacted, 75 per cent were eventually included in the final sample. This high a percentage of inclusion tends to negate the possibility that the variable "willingness to participate" contributed a contaminating bias. The major self-report causes of subject defection in these groups included illness of one parent and too great a traveling distance to the hospital. The parents were equated as groups on the variables age, son's age, length of son's current hospitalization, and socioeconomic status (Hollingshead Scale). Table 2 summarizes the composition of the sample.

Procedure

The major source of data was a situational test conducted with the parents under standardized conditions using Strodtbeck's "revealed difference" technique.[4] This method consists of identifying differences of opinion between two participants, and then requiring the respondents to resolve these differences through the media of verbal discussion. In this study, the parents, individually, were administered a questionnaire on which they were requested to indicate their agreement or disagreement with a solution offered for each of 30 family problem situations. The 30 problem situations were grouped under three major headings: childrearing, husband and wife relationship and style of life. After both parents had individually marked their choices, they were requested to reconcile their differences on ten items, and indicate a final best choice from the standpoint of their family. The joint interview was tape recorded and this material furnished the basic data for testing the experimental hypothesis.

Assessment devices

In accord with the research strategy suggested by Wynne and Singer, the assessment devices included a measure of thought disturbance and two measures of family interactional patterns.[5]

EVALUATION OF THOUGHT DISORDER

Severity of thought disorder was operationally defined in terms of Becker's Rorschach Genetic Level Score.[3] This score was derived directly from Werner's developmental theories and the empirical studies of Friedman, Siegel and Hemmendinger.[7] In studying the issue of perceptual regression in schizophrenia, Friedman developed a Rorschach scoring system which would presumably reflect levels of perceptual development as suggested by Werner's "differentiation-integration" formulation. In comparing adult normals, schizophrenics and children of various ages on his measures, he found support for the hypothesis that the structural aspect of schizophrenic perception was, in many ways, similar to, though not identical with those of children. Evidence that the Genetic Level Score is a valid indication of thought disturbance was provided by Becker who obtained an $(r = .599, p = .01)$ between this measure and a proverbs-vocabulary discrepancy score. In this study, the Rorschach was individually administered to each schizophrenic patient by the principal investigator. Each patient was examined shortly after an appointment time with his parents had been arranged, but previous to the actual interview.

115

EVALUATION OF RESOLUTION OF
INTRAFAMILIAL ROLE CONFLICT

In the literature one is unable to find either an attempt at quantifying, or a systematized investigation of, the variable "resolution of intrafamilial role conflict." However, the theoretic formulations of Parsons and Bales, and the clinical studies of Spiegel, Lidz *et al.* and Wynne *et al.* suggest the possibility of deriving a method of analysis which is in accord with the theoretic structure taken in this study.[8]

Parsons and Bales have used the concept of "social role," and the "equilibrium-disequilibrium" formulation to observe and describe the ways in which individual family members become involved in the family as a superordinate system of behavior. These constructs have been employed in characterizing the interaction of two members as they adjust to each other, as well as in describing the transactions of a plurality of members as they interweave in the special type of control which a going system imposes on its participants.

A summary outline of the scoring system with example is given in Tables 3 and 4. A discussion of the process categories is presented below: however, the reader is referred to the original work for a more detailed discussion as to rationale and category construction.[9]

Process categories for resolution of intrafamilial role conflict: The basic unit to be assessed consists of the entire situation containing the verbal transactions of the mother, father and interviewer.

Compromise is characterized by a restoration of equilibrium involving a change in the goals each participant initially desired. Each settles for somewhat different complementary roles than those with which he started. The change in role expectations is bilateral and the techniques used are based on mutual insight. Compromise can be regarded as a new adjustment on the basis of a redistribution of goals. Spiegel suggests that if compromise is

Table 3
Process Categories for Resolution of Intrafamilial Role Conflict

Category	Description	Example
Compromise	The family arrives at a mutually acceptable position which is different from the position of either spouse as indicated on the questionnaire. In cases in which there is agreement with the proposed position on the questionnaire, conditions or qualifications have been added. In cases in which there is disagreement with the proposed solution on the questionnaire, an alternative solution has been offered and mutually accepted. The parents' understanding and acceptance of the compromise can be indicated by their offering of an example of how they would apply the new solution.	1. (Father) "I think I would not. If it was the boy's own fault then I would let him take his medicine, but if something had happened that he was really excusable, I would help him." (Mother) "I feel the same way, only if he needs to be helped. Like now he isn't able to work so I would make his payments. But if it was his fault then I would ask him to earn it himself."
Role induction, mother	The mother comes to accept the unchanged position of the father. In cases in which there is agreement with the solution offered on the questionnaire, no conditions or qualifications are specified. In cases in which there is disagreement with the solution offered on the questionnaire, no alternative solutions are offered.	14. (Father) "I would join the one I felt was right for me. That is what I would do." (Mother) "Well, I feel that way too. I feel like he does."
Role induction, father	The father comes to accept the unchanged position of the mother. In cases in which there is agreement with the solution offered on the questionnaire, no conditions or qualifications are specified. In cases in which there is disagreement with the solution offered on the questionnaire, no alternative solutions are offered.	24. (Mother) "The husband should go to the cupboard and help himself. That's what I feel." (Father) "And I always do if you are not there."
No agreement	Parents are unable to arrive at a mutually acceptable solution. Includes all situations in which the family recognizes and accepts their inability to agree, in which the problem is avoided, and in which irrelevant material is substituted in place of the present problem.	29. (Father) "I wouldn't think so, any more than if I had inherited the money. I think married people have to give and take." (Mother) "I still think each should spend it the way they like." (Father) "We can't agree on that."
No agreement with distortion	Parents are unable to arrive at a mutually acceptable solution, but indicate that they have agreed. Includes situations in which agreement is reached on a substituted problem. Differs from No Agreement in that the family indicates that they have agreed, but after inspecting the transcript, it's evident that they haven't agreed. Includes agreement on a substituted problem.	14. (Father) "I would join the one for me and, of course, that's the Catholic Church." (Mother) "Yes, the Catholic Church is the proper church for us."

117

successful, then the new solution of the role conflict sinks into the family's normal routine and the conflict disappears.[10]

Role induction, mother is characterized by a restoration of equilibrium by means of a unilateral decision. The mother, be it through persuasion, coercion or bribery, is induced to take a role complementary to that of the father. The father's role remains essentially unchanged. Spiegel noted, that unlike compromise, induction wards off rather than resolves the role conflict.[11] The conflict still remains as an unsettled problem, and the resolution affected is more apparent than real.

Role induction, father is similar to *Role induction, mother* except it is the father who is induced to take the role complementary to that of mother. The mother's role remains essentially unchanged. As in the previous category, this is basically a defensive maneuver, and the disequilibrium warded off is likely to reappear.

No agreement is characterized by the family's inability to restore equilibrium. The conflict remains unresolved and disequilibrium persists. It is this condition, Ackerman maintains, which if allowed to persist, would eventually disrupt and destroy the entire system.[12]

No agreement with distortion is also characterized by the family's inability to restore equilibrium, but differs from *No agreement* in that the family members act as if the conflict had been resolved. It is this ability of one or both parents to conceal the conflict and act as if it did not exist, which Lidz et al. point out, offers to the offspring training in the use of symbolic distortion as a means of coping with an untenable reality.[13]

Process categories for role induction: Although role induction is one method of resolving intrafamilial role conflict, the act of inducing and/or being induced consists of several different types of processes. Spiegel and Farina have identified three of these subprocesses.[14] Thus, each situation initially scored *Role induction, mother* or *Role induction, father* was further rated using one of the three following categories.

Yielding is characterized by a verbal discussion in which both

118

Table 4

Process Categories for Role Induction

Category	Description	Example
Yielding	Both parents state or imply the correct position they selected on the questionnaire; however, as the discussion progresses, one parent leaves his position and comes to accept the spouse's original, unmodified position.	24. (Mother) "No, he should not cook a meal for himself." (Father) "I said yes, well when you're working you know I do." (Mother) "I don't insist upon it. But okay, if he wants to he should."
Passive acceptance of solution	One parent never states or implies his or her original position but simply agrees with the spouse's position. Indicated by either a simple unelaborated agreement or by immediately furnishing support for the spouse's position.	24. (Father) "The husband should go to the cabinet and help himself." (Mother) "And you always do if I'm not there."
Masking	One or both parents state a position which is at variance with that selected on the questionnaire. Differs from Yielding in that the position claimed is different from that actually selected on the questionnaire. Differs from Passive acceptance of solution in that a position is stated.	

119

parents state or imply their original roles; however, through coercion, persuasion or some other means, one parent is induced out of this initial role and induced into a role complementary to the spouse's. This process lacks both the total submission characteristic of *Passive acceptance of solution* and the distortion characteristic of *Masking*.

Passive acceptance of solution is characterized by submission. The role conflict is settled by one parent unequivocally accepting the complementary role enforced by the spouse. Spiegel has suggested that this process is motivated by the alter's anticipation of punishment or gratification from the spouse.[15] In a different context, Farina successfully used this index for distinguishing patterns of dominance and submissiveness between parents of schizophrenic patients and parents of controls.[16]

Masking is characterized by the withholding of correct information or the substitution of incorrect information pertinent to the settlement of the problem. It includes pretending, censoring, lying, deceiving and distorting. Lidz *et al.* have described this process as an altering of facts in the service of emotionally determined needs.[17] They suggested that habitual masking confused the preschizophrenic, for he was taught to ignore the obvious and to distort his perceptions so as to match those of the parents.

In pilot work, the joint interview transcripts of ten parents were scored in accordance with the general directions (note Tables 3 and 4) in order to obtain a preliminary assessment of the procedure. The records of five parents were used for practice and discussion of scoring problems between two raters, and the remaining five were scored independently. Thus, five transcripts which yielded 50 situations showed 88 percent perfect agreement between two judges for the *Resolution of intrafamilial role conflict process categories* and 85 percent perfect agreement between the judges for the *Role induction process categories*.

The joint interview transcripts of all parents included in the final sample were scored by an advanced graduate student in psychology. As all records were numerically coded, the rater was unable to distinguish the experimental group families from the control group families. Because the initial reliability study was based on the transcripts of essentially "normal" families, it was decided to include a second reliability study, however, using cases which would be included in the final sample. Thus, 15 transcripts, 5 from each of the three groups, were independently rated by a second advanced graduate student in psychology. In this analysis, 15 transcripts which yielded 150 situations showed 82 percent perfect agreement between two judges for the *Resolution of intrafamilial role conflict process categories* and 86 percent perfect agreement between the judges for the *Role induction process categories*. Although there were variations from category to category, each appeared sufficiently reliable to warrant its retention.

RESULTS

The present study was designed to evaluate the relationship between one dimension of intrafamilial interaction, resolution of intrafamilial role conflict, and one disorder-specific aspect of schizophrenia, severity of thought disturbance.

Initially, parents of the schizophrenic patients were dichotomized into two groups on the basis of their son's Rorschach Genetic Level Score. This permitted a comparison among the three groups (high genetic level, low genetic level, control) with respect to the relative frequencies with which group members used each of the five conflict resolution process categories and each of the three role induction process categories.

To determine the probability that the three groups differed with respect to the relative frequencies with which members used the conflict resolution categories, a series of chi square tests were

Table 5
Chi-Square Values between Goups for Conflict Resolution Categories

	x^2	P
High genetic level vs. Control	10.24	0.05
Low genetic level vs. Control	35.66	0.001
High genetic level vs. Low genetic level	19.13	0.01

121

made. The resultant chi square values together with the probability of their occurrence are presented in Table 5. A further analysis to determine the probability that any two groups were selected from the same population was made by means of the Mann-Whitney U Test. The P values yielded by this series of tests are presented in the last three columns of Table 6. Presented in the first three columns of Table 6 are the means and standard deviations for each group for each of the five categories.

Table 6
Means, Standard Deviations and Levels of Significance for Groups on
Conflict Resolution Categories

	Means and standard deviations			Levels of significance		
	Control	High genetic level	Low genetic level	Control vs. high genetic level	Control vs. low genetic level	High genetic level vs. low genetic level
Compromise:						
Mean	3.0	1.2	1.2	0.002	0.002	NS
S.D	2.0	3.7	2.4			
Role induction, mother:						
Mean	2.7	3.3	1.8	NS	NS	NS
S.D.	3.3	7.5	4.4			
Role induction, father:						
Mean	1.9	2.8	2.9	NS	NS	NS
S.D.	2.6	7.2	4:2			
No agreement:						
Mean	2.0	2.0	1.3	NS	NS	NS
S.D.	2.4	4.2	4.5			
No agreement with distortion:						
Mean	.4	.83	2.8	NS	0.002	0.002
S.D.	1.5	3.0	3.1			

These findings tend to support the hypothesis that parents of controls, parents of high genetic level schizophrenic patients, and parents of low genetic level schizophrenic patients employ different processes in resolving intrafamilial role conflict. Across all five categories, the resultant distributions yielded by the three groups differed to a statistically significant degree.

These differences in distribution appeared to be a function of two categories, *Compromise* and *No agreement with distortion*. Employment of both categories varied directly with the severity

122

Table 7
Chi Square Values between Groups for Role Induction Categories

	x^2	P
High genetic level vs. Control	2.85	NS
Low genetic level vs. Control	15.32	0.001
High genetic level vs. Low genetic level	10.39	0.01

of thought disturbance present in the patient offspring. That is, *Compromise* was used most frequently by the control group and least frequently by the low genetic level group, with the high genetic level group intermediate. In contrast, *No agreement with distortion* was employed most often by the low genetic level group and least often by the control group, with the high genetic level group again occupying an intermediate position.

To determine the probability that the three groups differed in regard to the relative frequencies with which members employed the three Role Induction Process Categories, another series of chi square tests were made. These values together with their probability of occurrence are presented in Table 7. The means and standard deviations for the groups for each of the three categories are presented in the first three columns of Table 8. The P values yielded by a series of Mann-Whitney U Tests are given in the last three columns of Table 8.

Table 8
Means, Standard Deviations and Levels of Significance for Groups on
Role Induction Categories

	Means and standard deviations			Levels of significance		
	Control	High genetic level	Low genetic level	Control vs. high genetic level	Control vs. low genetic level	High genetic level vs. low genetic level
Yielding:						
Mean	2.3	2.0	1.7	NS	0.002	NS
S.D.	2.2	4.5	3.4			
Passive acceptance of solution:						
Mean	1.6	2.3	1.0	NS	NS	NS
S.D.	3.0	3.2	2.4			
Masking:						
Mean	0.67	1.2	2.5	NS	0.002	0.02
S.D.	2.3	2.0	3.3			

123

An inspection of these tables reveals that, in general, the three groups tended to differ in regard to the relative frequencies with which members used the three Role Induction Process Categories. The most striking differences appeared between the low genetic level group and each of the other two groups. The essential feature setting apart the low genetic level group was the relative frequency its members employed the category *Masking*. The results further indicated that family utilization of *Masking* varied directly with the severity of thought disorder in the patient offspring.

DISCUSSION

In general, these findings supported the proposition that families of schizophrenic patients and families of controls differ with respect to the processes they employ in resolving intrafamilial role conflict. Furthermore, it was found that consistent differences existed between parents of subgroups of schizophrenic patients.

The differences in distributions yielded by the control group, high genetic level group, and low genetic level group were explicable in terms of the categories *Compromise* and *No agreement with distortion*. Of import was the finding that family utilization of both categories varied with the severity of thought disorder manifested by the patient offspring.

Built into the category *No agreement with distortion* was an attempt to capture the family's altering or distorting of facts in the service of emotional needs. Along these same lines, *Masking* was also found to significantly differentiate the three groups, and in this category, a second attempt to assess family use of distortion and denial was made. These findings are consistent with the position of Wynne and Singer who suggest that, "The overall transaction disorder in a family's communication sequence may be comparable stylistically to that found in the vagueness and fragmentation of a severely impaired schizophrenic. That is, the form or structure of the family transactions is stylistically comparable to that of the individual schizophrenic's thought disorder." [18]

These results could also be explained in terms of "pseudomutuality" theory.[19] That is, the family's inability and reluctance to recognize their differences could be accounted for by their need to maintain a sense of relatedness." Within this framework, member's use of distortion and denial could represent family mechanisms evoked by situations, such as intrafamilial conflict, which threaten to destroy the entire ongoing system.

The finding that the three groups did not differ with respect to their use of *No agreement* tends to question Ackerman's assertion that, "Intrapsychic conflict represents an internalized representation of in intrafamilial conflict." [20] This is, the results of this study suggest that intrafamilial conflict in and of itself does not adequately explain the emergence of schizophrenia. In this study what appeared to be critical were the more stylistic aspects of parental interaction such as the family's way of focusing attention, their style of communication and their facility for perceptual distortion.

Methodologically significant to this study was the research strategy of selecting and differentiating patients on the basis of a specific ego function impairment, and then relating this impairment to a specific intrafamilial transaction. The strategy permitted an ordering of the schizophrenic sample on the basis of severity of impairment as well as allowed the drawing of inferences from a pervasive theoretic structure (Psychoanalytic Theory). It is felt that such a procedure could prove fruitful in directing future research concerned with the problem of etiology in schizophrenia.

SUMMARY

The present study was designed to investigate the relationship between resolution of intrafamilial role conflict and severity of thought disorder in the schizophrenic patient offspring. The major source of data was a situational test conducted with parents of schizophrenic patients and parents of "normal" controls using a "revealed difference" technique. Severity of thought disturbance was defined in terms of the Rorschach Genetic Level Score as developed by Becker,[21] while the variable "resolution of intra-familial role conflict" was defined in terms of five process categories: *Compromise, Role induction, mother, Role induction, father, No agreement,* and *No agreement with distortion.* The two Role Induction Categories were further defined by the sub-processes *Yielding; Passive acceptance of solution,* and *masking.*

The results of the study supported the proposition that families of schizophrenic patients and families of "normal" controls differ with respect to the processes they use in resolving intrafamilial role conflict. Furthermore, consistent differences were found between parents of two subgroups of schizophrenic patients dichotomized on the basis of their son's severity of thought disturbance. The findings were interpreted as supporting the concept of Wynne *et al.*[22] of "pseudomutuality" with family use of distortion and denial conceptualized as predispositions to the patient offspring's use of symbolic distortion.

PARENTS WITH A SCHIZOPHRENIC CHILD:
PATHOGENIC TRIAD

IN THIS SECTION are three experiments which investigate a family triad consisting of a schizophrenic patient along with his or her parents who are asked to interact with each other. This design contrasts with those in the previous section in which the patient child was not actually present and inferences were made about the effect of the parents' behavior on their child and the possible responses of the child. Here these inferences are open to test.

While the addition of the patient's presence to the design removes some unnecessary inferences, the triadic approach retains another basic limitation shared by all the studies included in this book. Examination of the relationship between parents and the schizophrenic child and comparisons with a number of different control groups will not tell us whether these relationships were present before the occurrence of the child's illness. Thus, if the investigator is concerned with the question of etiology of the illness, the cross-sectional design demands, inferences and assumptions about the stability of the behavior measured, and the degree to which parents may take on new roles in order to respond to a deviant child.*

The decision to include a third person in the experimental situation has a striking effect on several aspects of these family studies—an effect that is greater than one would expect from the simple addition of one more person. First, the inclusion of three people presents a conception of the family which differs from those formed in the studies in the previous section. Here there is much greater concern with the family as a social system rather than as a collection of individuals who are acting in the presence of others. Concepts related to social structure, such as roles, norms, statuses, and values are introduced, and this perspective leads to measurement of such structural qualities as coalitions, role differentiation, group products, role reversal, impairment of group problem solving, and group or family norms.

A second nuance introduced by the triadic approach to families is its effect on modes of data analysis. Many more comparisons are possible and these comparisons may involve several levels of conceptualization. For example, not only is it possible for the investigators to examine each family member separately (are schizophrenic children like normal children, or, are schizophrenic mothers like schizophrenic fathers) but it is also possible to investigate the family as a whole, without regard for its specific members (are schizophrenic families less conflictful than normals?) and it is further possible to look at individual behavior in a defined family context (are schizophrenic patients more powerful in families in which parental roles are reversed?). The multiplication of analytic questions in the studies of family triads therefore provides for much more interesting and complicated findings but also poses many more logical, statistical and data analysis problems.†

* The problems of interpretation of findings from ex post facto experimental studies are discussed in detail in E. G. Mishler and Nancy E. Waxler, "Family Interaction and Schizophrenia: Alternative Frameworks of Interpretation." [1]

† The problems of levels of conceptualization and levels of data analysis in studies of family interaction are discussed in detail in E. G. Mishler and N. E. Waxler, "Family Interaction Patterns and Schizophrenia: A Multi-Level Analysis." [2]

We have pointed out that each of these three studies has moved theoretically to the level of family structure, introducing, for example, ideas about role differentiation and the effect of the third person's behavior on a coalition. All of the conceptions are related to ones previously described in clinical and theoretical work on schizophrenic families. However, there is a wide difference between the three studies in the degree to which theoretical concepts have actually been operationalized and thus the degree to which findings from the study may be legitimately interpreted as supporting or refuting a theory. We have already pointed to the difficulty of selecting indicators for the often poorly defined concepts in the schizophrenic family theories. However, Singer's study, in this section, provides an example of the way in which a number of theoretical constructions may be explicitly related to a behavior measure and antecedent predictions made, thus allowing a limited but direct test of the theory. Beginning with Lidz' [3] description of sex and generational role reversal in male and female families Singer develops measures of parental dominance to represent generational role-taking, and a measure of support to stand for sex role behavior. He uses these to test a number of concretely stated hypotheses directly drawn from the Lidz theory. While the degree to which his findings may be generalized is quite limited, his attempt to make explicit the links between theories and measures is quite different from the more general and loosely defined inferences of Lennard and Cheek. We point to Singer's explicit use of theories and clinical formulations as an important step toward clarifying concepts as well as toward testing hypotheses.

In the introduction to the previous section we noted that the experimental method requires a degree of clarity with which the clinical method need not be concerned. Decisions about independent and dependent variables, sampling, and experimental procedures must be made. The selection of control variables in the studies in this section represent the different orientations of the investigators. Lennard and Cheek, perhaps due to their interest in etiology, selected a normal control group, that is, families

131

having no psychiatric patients. Lennard also mentions the use of families with asthmatic children as a control for those with chronic illnesses, although these data are not presented. Singer has chosen to ask a different question which is concerned with the reasons for the presence of only one schizophrenic child in a family. This has led him to select as his control group the parents of the schizophrenic patient when they are interacting with a well sibling of the patient.

A second potential control variable, shown to be important in Farina's study, is the distinction between different types of schizophrenia. None of the present investigators separates his sample of patients in any way, although it appears that Singer's sample is probably an "acute" sample (having less than one year of hospitalization). While the most common distinctions made within groups of schizophrenic patients are the process-reactive or the chronic-acute distinctions, Lennard's study points to another type, the diagnosis called "childhood schizophrenia". The patients in his sample range in age from nine to fourteen and thus it is probable that some if not all of these fall into the "childhood schizophrenia" category. Goldfarb writes, ". . . although a sizeable proportion of childhood schizophrenics later are diagnosed as schizophrenic in adolescence or adulthood, childhood schizophrenia is not the usual precursor of the schizophrenias of later onset nor should the two be regarded as equivalent." Thus it is not clear that family patterns from a sample of children diagnosed as schizophrenic should be comparable with those of schizophrenics whose illness developed later in life. The fact that none of the investigators clearly makes a distinction between subtype of schizophrenia nor controls for them allows the possibility, which is suggested in Farina's study, that the differences between control families and some schizophrenic families that do exist in reality will not appear in the data.

Another important control variable that is introduced into the design of these studies is the sex of the schizophrenic child. Among the theorists, Lidz has hypothesized that parental roles in the families of females differ from the families of male patients.

While early studies focused on male patients only, both Cheek and Singer include male and female patients and analyze their findings within these controls. Cheek also adds a second control variable which is not used in other studies but which is potentially very important; this is the situation in which data are gathered. Half of her data is collected in the hospital setting and the other half in the family's home, which then allows for testing the effect of the two settings. While there is some evidence that family role-taking changes from situation to situation [5] and we might expect that families will behave differently in the hospital than in their home, Cheek reports no significant differences between the two situations.

Besides a clear definition of control variables, the experimental technique allows for selection of a large sample of subjects. One major contribution of Cheek's research is to demonstrate that over a reasonable length of time it is possible to collect a large sample of families; her sample of 67 schizophrenic families and 56 normal families is by far the largest of any of the studies. The advantages are great; measures are more stable and there are many more possibilities for controlling variables statistically. Thus more weight can be attached to findings.

The experimental procedures used in these triadic studies are similar to those used in the studies of parental dyads. Variants of the revealed difference method or a set of standard topics are used to generate discussions between the three members and these discussions are tape-recorded. Coding of relatively small units of interaction from the tapes or from typed transcripts then follows.

Each of the investigators uses one or more coding systems that combines the semantic and structural approach. Cheek and Singer use different modified Bales category systems. Singer includes, as well, several measures derived from the family's task performance. This latter score adds a new dimension not found in the other studies in that the family score is based on the degree to which the family reaches an objectively defined "right" answer. This kind of measure is clearly useful in determining the schizophrenic family's problem solving ability, a quality mentioned in several family theories. Lennard's measures are composed of several separately applied codes or counts of actions. The advantage of being able to intercorrelate these independently coded measures is evident in his correlations of the "who speaks" and "to whom" variables which add to our understanding of the family coalition patterns.

There is also evidence in the development of measures of increasing concern with the "process" of interaction. Lennard, more than the others, builds into one of his measures a sequence of events that is scored as a whole. For him an intrusion is an act directed by a third person toward a member of an on-going interacting coalition; he finds "that the ratio of intrusion attempts by patient-sons is lower than that for sons in control families," suggesting that perhaps the schizophrenic family discourages the child's initiating behavior. The interest in family process is clear in clinical and theoretical work, and Lennard's use of this indicator provides evidence that it is possible to develop objective measures of process that result in interesting differences between types of families.

It is in their data analysis techniques that these three studies differ most from each other. The introduction of a third person naturally moves the investigators to become concerned with the family as being a system or as having a defined structure. The interest in these more complex questions calls for more complex modes of analysis which are quite different from the simple counting of behavioral output in the parental dyad studies. We can point to the techniques actually used in the studies as a way of showing the kinds of problems of interpretation that arise in a number of family studies.

Cheek's technique of analysis consists of comparing interaction profiles of fathers in normal families with those of fathers in schizophrenic families, while making separate comparisons for male and female patients. In other articles [6] the same comparisons are made for mothers and patients. For example, the schizophrenic mother is found to be less supportive than her normal counterpart, while the schizophrenic father is more supportive than other fathers. From these two patterns Cheek concludes that in the schizophrenic families there is less differentiation of parental roles than in the normal families and that this supports theoretical formulations about parental role difficulties in families of schizophrenics. However, since mothers and fathers within the same family are never compared (only profiles for the whole set of mothers or fathers), is seems questionable to draw a conclusion about family structure from the comparisons of a sample of individuals taken out of the contexts of their families. The leap from an individual level of measurement (e.g., interaction profiles of individuals) to a sociological level of theory and interpretation (e.g., role differentiation) is confusing and would not be necessary if distinctions between these levels of analysis were more clearly understood.

Singer's mode of analysis and Lennard's less explicit approach take into account the differences in levels of conceptualization and use measures that are more appropriate for each level. Singer is also interested in role differentiation between parents and the relation of degrees of differentiation to the presence or absence of the schizophrenic child. Yet the measure he chooses to stand for parental role differentiation is a "within family" measure; within each family the number of mother-dominant responses is subtracted from the number of father-dominant responses, and the family then characterized according to this score. His findings do not support the Cheek findings in that, on the average, in all family situations the father is more dominant than the mother. Using a technique that clearly links the conceptual level with the measurement level, it is possible to ask further questions which cannot be asked when individual output is the sole source. For example, what is the patient-child's behavior in families having mother-dominant as compared to father-dominant parental roles?

As Singer's research shows, the attempt to work with several conceptual levels, and thus to take into account family structure along with individual behavior, provides a more complex and interesting set of findings. Taking advantage of the numerous comparisons that are possible also brings the findings much closer to the level at which a clinician might describe them or a family member might experience them.

In these studies the levels at which the data are analyzed obviously affect the interpretations of the findings and set limits on the kinds of statements it is possible to make about families and their members. Another aspect of these studies that influences the conclusions drawn from the findings is the assumption the experimenter makes about the etiological significance of his data. Lennard and Singer take opposite stands on the etiological problem; Lennard assumes that the family patterns measured after the patient's illness are stable, long-term ones that probably have had an effect on the child's development. This leads him to interpret the low rates of communication between father and mother in the schizophrenic families in an etiological framework: "Deficits in communication between father and mother, for example, would lessen the child's opportunity to learn or internalize the respective role statuses involved. The inability of a schizophrenic to perform in a variety of role relationships may in part be attributed to his having been raised within a family structure in which he has had insufficient opportunity to observe the operation of family role relationships." [7] An equally probable explanation, of course, is that the parental dyad has broken down as a result of inability to cope with the child's deviant behavior. In Cheek's work, also, the etiological assumption limits explicit attempts to rule out other possible explanations. Singer clearly excludes the possibility that etiological evidence can be obtained from his experimental design and looks only for evidence that certain interaction patterns exist empirically in the schizophrenic families after the fact of the illness. His interpretation does not include statements about the time order or stability of the patterns he finds.

The extent to which levels of statistical significance are taken seriously by an investigator also has a subtle but determining effect on the conclusions he draws from his findings. Cheek, for example, bases her conclusions on non-significant trends as well as on a limited number of statistically significant findings. Singer, on the other hand, interprets as meaningful only those findings that reach statistical significance and assumes that all others can be explained by chance variation. Naturally, since two of the people present remain the same (the same parents are present in both sessions), this latter policy, limits the number of "findings", particularly in Singer's work, where the design implies a large number of similarities across groups. Thus, while it is important for future work to pay attention to trends in the data since these trends may lead to formulation of new hypotheses and better measures, it is also important to avoid premature conclusions about schizophrenic families when, empirically, these conclusions are not clearly warranted.

In our introduction to the studies of parental dyads we were able to compare and contrast the findings from the three studies, showing which findings are replicated and, thus, which qualities of interaction are probably important discriminators between schizophrenic and control families. Some of the findings from these studies recall those of studies in the previous section. We noted that Caputo measured marital discord with an index derived from Bales categories and found, contrary to his prediction, that fathers of schizophrenics expressed more negative socioemotional comments than did normal fathers. Cheek's results add some support to this finding since in her study fathers of schizophrenic children disagree significantly more often than do normal fathers.

Our major impression of the findings from these studies, however, is that when the experimental design is complicated by the addition of a third person with the design's accompanying a wider range of concepts, measures, and modes of analysis, it becomes increasingly difficult to make useful comparisons across sets of findings. For example, both Lennard and Singer measure participation rates of family members; yet the concepts that these stand for are quite different. For Lennard, rate of participation and the person to whom the communications are addressed represent the "role saliency" of the family member; for Singer, participation is an indicator of "dominance." Even with this conceptual difference it is impossible to compare statistical findings for these concepts across studies since in one instance schizophrenic parents are compared with their normal counterparts and in the other they are compared with each other. Other findings are even more difficult to compare since not only do the conceptual formulations differ but so do the measures; for example, is Lennard's "inner-state communication" tapping the same qualities as Singer's "support" behavior? The fact that findings from studies having similar designs and purposes cannot be reasonably compared marks the absence of a firm research tradition in this area and also indicates that up to this time there has been little interest in building upon the work of others in order to develop a sound, empirically based theory. A conscious attempt by investigators to replicate measures and techniques of analysis, even within different research designs, is a requisite if work in the future is to be cumulative rather than merely an accumulation of disparate findings.

CHAPTER FIVE

INTERACTION IN FAMILIES WITH
A SCHIZOPHRENIC CHILD *

HENRY L. LENNARD
ARNOLD BERNSTEIN
and MAURICE R. BEAULIEU

THIS PAPER,[1] a report on one of a series of studies concerned with therapeutic and disturbed communication processes, has three interrelated objectives:

1. To develop a quantitative methodology for the study of family behavior process in families with a severely disturbed child.

2. To compare interaction patterns in a group of families with a child diagnosed as "schizophrenic" with interaction patterns in a group of "control" families.

3. To formulate and explore tentative hypotheses about the meaning of differences, if any, found in the characteristics and sequences of interaction among the two groups of families.

Each of the three objectives for this study will now be elaborated:

1. To Develop a Quantitative Methodology: Family-oriented clinicians have made major contributions in calling attention to

* This paper originally appeared in the Archives of General Psychiatry, 12:166-183, Feb. 1965. It has been revised since then in collaboration with Dr. Arnold Bernstein. The research reported in the paper was aided by a Research Career Scientist Award (7 Ko3 MH 18697) to Dr. Lennard by the National Institute of Mental Health.

distinctive features of intrafamilial process in families with a schizophrenic member. Descriptions of such families by Ackerman, Bateson, Bowen, Goldfarb, Lidz, Wynne, and others are an important source of hypotheses on how such families differ from others, and how family interaction may contribute to the development or maintenance of the schizophrenic disorder in a family member.[2] Yet we are certain that these investigators would also agree that the current hypotheses might well benefit from further specification and systematic documentation.

The clinician specializes in a concern for the dramatic and the pathological. When he assumes the role of researcher, this concern may still prevail. However, our interest has been to study the recurrent processes of intrafamilial communication on an act-to-act basis. Thus, each communication is scrutinized as to its form and content, and sequences of communications are identified. The advantages of this approach seem analogous to those of epidemiological research in medicine. The epidemiologist, not profoundly skilled in particular medical specialties, cannot approximate the level of understanding brought to the study of the sick individual by the clinician-specialist. Yet he argues that the type of insight available to him through systematic data collection from many cases is not accessible to the individual-oriented clinician.[3] The effect of thalidomide on embryo deformity may serve as one illustration. One would hardly expect even the most brilliant of diagnosticians to have been able to identify which of the many agents consumed by one mother might be implicated in the production of the deformity in the embryo. It was information on drug-consumption patterns of *many* mothers which provided the significant hypothesis. Our position is a similar one to that advanced by the epidemiologist. We tentatively suggest that the kind of methodology employed here may yield a level of insight different from and, hopefully, complementary to that provided by clinical study.

Patterns of interaction process, for a number of reasons, appear not to be fully accessible to impressionistic judgment, no matter how informed or skilled. This has been evident to social scientists for some time and is strikingly demonstrated by the pioneering research of R. F. Bales on the structure and function of group processes. As Bales says: [4]

Both changes in behavioral process that occur much more quickly than the average tempo of social interaction, and those that occur much more slowly, tend to elude conscious awareness and control . . . a quantitative approach may help to bring within cognitive grasp changes and relationships that otherwise escape attention.

2. How to Compare Family Interaction Patterns: The purpose here is to compare a group of "schizophrenic" families [5] with a group of control families with respect to kinds and sequences of communication through the utilization of quantitative methods for the study of family processes. The methodological problem of comparing samples of family interaction process gathered within an experimental setting will be discussed later in "Methodology." At this time, we wish to identify the framework within which the comparisons are being made and the kinds of variables that are used in our study of family processes.

Some of the variables selected for systematic examination stem from a consideration of the family as a small communication system. Thus, we are mainly concerned with amount, rate, and direction of intrafamilial communication, and the availability and strength of communication channels between family members.

Other variables derive from a concern with the family as a regulation and control system that determines the appropriateness, direction, and rate of behavior of its members. Of special interest is behavior which is self-initiated, especially the volume and rate of self-initiated entry by a third family member into ongoing interaction between any two other family members. We wish to learn about the response to this entry both when requested and when not requested by the interacting dyad.

We subsume the rate, direction, and success of such efforts to participate in interaction under the concept of intrusion and consider intrusion a significant characteristic for attention in studies of family process.

A third perspective views the family as a socialization system concerned, among other things, with enabling the child to identify and articulate inner states. We are concerned with how parents elicit and pattern motives and feelings on the part of the child. Of particular importance here are frequency and character of communications in which the parent interprets the child's experiences, motives, and feelings.

The method of quantification used in the comparisons of the two groups of families represents an adaptation of general social research methods, especially content-analytic methods, to the study of communication through time. Some of this methodology was developed in the senior author's (H. L. L.) research on communication patterns—through time—in psychotherapy,[6] and some was applied in preliminary studies of family therapy data.[7]

Since we are well aware (see "Methodology") of the heterogeneous character of our sample, both in the schizophrenic as well as in the control groups, it is realistic to expect some variability within each group of families, in the types and sequences of communication in which we are interested. The kind of comparison attempted here should, however, permit one to assess whether some patterns are distinctly more prevalent within families in the schizophrenic group than in the control group.

3. To Explore Tentative Hypotheses About the Meaning of Differences: Methodological problems inherent in meeting the objective of interpreting differences in the two groups of families are outlined, as has been mentioned, later in this paper. At the very least, two still-to-be-documented premises are involved: (1) that current family interaction patterns resemble past family interactions, especially in the schizophrenic families; and (2) that these patterns preceded the development of the schizophrenic illness of one of the family members. Granting these two assumptions, one can then formulate and assess hypotheses on how kinds and sequences of communication currently noted in schizophrenic families may have contributed in the past to the development of the disorder in the child.

For the purpose of generating hypotheses, patterns of communication can be viewed, at different times, as independent as well as dependent variables. In thinking of the former one can, for example, speculate on the effects of a particular mode or sequence of parental communication on the development of the child's sense of autonomy and self-direction. On the other hand, we can also look at patterns of communication within the family as indicators of intrafamily relations, perceptions, attitudes, and feelings.

In examining patterns of communication, we are not restricted to working with already current hypotheses, but also wish to derive new hypotheses from an examination of comparable segments of family interactions.[8] It is hoped that the emphasis on process in this study has, in some measure, made this possible.

Procedure

The group of "schizophrenic" families consisted of ten families in which the son had been diagnosed as schizophrenic, borderline schizophrenic, or psychotic. All the patients were males between 9 and 14 years of age who came from working-class, Jewish families with at least one other sibling. The diagnoses for seven of the children were made at the Child Guidance Clinic of Kings County Hospital in New York City; for two, at the New York State Psychiatric Institute; and for one at Rockland State Hospital. Although it was not feasible for our staff to review the diagnoses, descriptions in the case records did suggest that the sample included very highly disturbed children. Nevertheless, the patients may well have comprised a heterogeneous group of psychological disorders.

For example, the record of one child contains descriptive phrases such as "fragile ego," "identity problem," "isolation of affect," "paranoid fears," etc. In another record, we find descriptive phrases such as "borderline case with fluidity of ego boundaries with possible schizophrenic and dissociative tendencies."

Each sample of family interaction was obtained from a 45-minute discussion among father, mother, and son. While it may be argued that a discussion among all members of the family would provide a more accurate representation of family process, we were inclined toward Bowen's view that "the primary family members involved in the family conflict are the father, the mother, and the patient," and that in effect, father, mother, and the identified patient form the family group of most interest to study.[9] Moreover, since the consequence of differences in the number of members of a family upon the patterns of intrafamily communication is undetermined, it seemed wiser to control for family size at this exploratory stage of research.

The seven control families were volunteers recruited from a public housing project located near Kings County Hospital. Families eligible to reside in this project were limited to an income of $7,000 per annum. The cooperation of the families was enlisted by a member of the project's committee, who contacted families meeting the study criteria and offered $10 as payment for participation. A psychiatrist conducted a screening interview with each child in the control group to ascertain that there was no apparent major psychological disturbance.

The "schizophrenic" families were taken to the one-way vision screen room by one of the investigators, who explained that they would be asked to discuss three topics for 15 minutes each, and that at the end of each 15-minute period, the investigator would return to learn what they had concluded, as well as to assign them a new topic. They were also told that their conversation was to be recorded. The topics for discussion were: (1) Would you discuss whether or not a boy might have some duties to perform around the house, and, if so, what they might be? (2) When a boy needs a helping hand with his homework, do you think it is better for mother or for father to help out? (3) Here is a list of jobs that a boy might think of doing later in life (typed on a card): fireman, teacher, reporter, dentist, pilot, and engineer. Would you discuss these occupations among yourselves and list, in order, the three you think best. These topics were all formulated on a level that permits their discussion by a child of nine, and they also required the participation of all three family members.

144

All of the sessions were tape-recorded and subsequently transcribed verbatim. Each individual's statements appeared in the transcript in the sequence in which it occurred, the typist taking special note of all instances in which one family member interrupted another.

Each statement in the verbatim transcript of a session was coded along a variety of dimensions, such as who originated the statement, toward whom the statement was directed, categories of implicit and explicit agreement and disagreement, etc.[10] We selected the statement as the unit of analysis for coding purposes. The statement provides a unit that is both manageable (for IBM analysis) and "natural" in the sense that it involved a minimum of arbitrariness in delineating the unit.

The use of the statement as a basic unit makes it possible to combine statements in a number of ways for comparative purposes. For example, it is possible to compare within any session the differential frequency of given types of communications by each family member over specified time intervals, and to compare the communication patterns of one family member with that of the other two family members. On another level of analysis, it is possible to compare the communication pattern of a particular status in the family (e.g., son) with the communication pattern of the same status in the other families, either control or schizophrenic. These comparisons can be made for the session as a whole, or between specified time intervals within a session. On still another level, it is possible to compare the patterns of communication in the schizophrenic families with the control families as a whole.

METHODOLOGY

Methodological Limitations of This Approach

If the objectives of this study were confined to describing current family interaction patterns, the list of methodological limitations enumerated below would be less extensive. However, it is clear that while descriptions of current ongoing processes yield valuable information,[11] such descriptions often reflect the assumption (though often hedged) that current interaction patterns reflect past interaction patterns, that these patterns preceded the development of the illness of one of the family members, and that indeed these identified characteristics of communication contributed in a significant manner to the development of the schizophrenic disorder.[12]

Since we, too, take this position, it appears justified to enumerate the methodological limitations which the approach described here involves.

Methodological Problems

1. THE ISSUE OF STABILITY AND CHANGE IN FAMILY INTERACTION PATTERNS

How stable are family interaction patterns over time, especially over a span of years? The problem more specifically is which patterns are stable and which change over time—which patterns were present in the family *before* the development of severe mental disorder in one of its members?

There are two divergent viewpoints that have been advanced in relation to this issue. One, derived from clinical impression and analytically oriented theory, proposes that "disturbed" families are much less prone to change in the structure of family organization and quality of interpersonal relationships than are "well" families.[13] It is thus conceivable that a pattern currently identified as characteristic of the schizophrenic families and not of the control families may have been present at some past period in the well families. The second position sees almost a reverse process operating. The proponents of this viewpoint, frequently investigators skeptical of the possible etiological role of familial behavior patterns, suggest that patterns currently identified in the schizo-

146

phrenic families represent reactions to the illness or deviance of the child. In this sense, they postulate that family systems containing a severely disturbed member are capable of major change in characteristics of intrafamily process subsequent to the development of illness in one family member.

In the light of the issues raised by these questions, some investigators would feel that comparison of "current" family interaction processes would not permit one to claim, with any degree of confidence, that family processes currently characteristic of schizophrenic families preceded and contributed to the development of the disorder. However, to satisfy the requirements of such criticism, one would require kinds of data most difficult to collect; data on family processes in a large number of families, at many points in time, with families selected in such a way that some would be likely to develop a mentally ill member. Stability and change in interaction patterns would then be determined for this large group of families.[14]

2. WHAT IS A SAMPLE OF FAMILY PROCESS?

What slice of family life need one study in order to make valid inferences about the current structure of family organization and about kinds and sequences of interaction processes which characterize the family at this point in their lives? Some investigators suggest that weeks or months of observation of a family in a variety of settings are required before such inferences can be made. Others claim that a great deal of significant data is provided by observing family interaction over an interval of minutes.[15]

It appears to us that this question cannot be explored without reference to the specific parameters of family structure and communication process one is studying. If one is concerned with establishing which family members are not speaking with each other, then *any* situation which would provide them an opportunity to speak with each other may constitute an adequate

147

sample for this dimension. The issue here is one of distribution or prevalence of given kinds of behavior. The study of behaviors which are almost always required in any situation involving all family members (such as speaking with each other) pose a different sampling problem from the study of occasional and periodic behaviors. For example, if one were to be interested in family behavior directed toward socializing a child to his sex role, the question of arriving at a valid sample of such behaviors would be a more serious one. In order to decide on a sample, one would have to know how such socializing acts are distributed over time and within settings. If such acts, for example, are likely to occur —on the average—once a week, and only within the home, then any observation of family process of less than one week and outside the home would be misleading. However, systematic information that could be used as a guide for such determinations is not available and not likely to be for some time. The investigator is thus forced to use his judgment regarding probable distribution of given behaviors and whether the sampling decision made will provide him with a representative picture of the family process variables with which he is concerned.

Repeated observation of the same families that yield comparable results would help increase his confidence in the soundness of his judgment.

3. CAN ONE SAMPLE SCHIZOPHRENIC FAMILIES?

Since the issue of sampling has been introduced, a brief reference to another "sampling" issue is in order. This issue, ably discussed in a 1962 paper by Haley,[16] is concerned with whether the schizophrenic families studied are in any way representative of such families. In order to sample, one must be able to identify the size and characteristics of a "universe" from which a sample can be drawn in accordance with one's specifications. This is enormously difficult. If one were to consider one's universe as all families with a child diagnosed as schizophrenic in New York

City, and if one would be able to locate some descriptive information on these families (a major effort not at all certain of success), there would still be the problem of unreliability in diagnosis.[17] This, however, does not resolve the problem of defining a universe of families with a schizophrenic child. For the latter objective, one would have to identify cases not in treatment. This clearly is most difficult on a large scale.

4. SPECIFICITY OF PATTERNS

Will a study, limited to a comparison between interaction patterns in schizophrenic and control families, which identifies differences in the patterns of intrafamilial interaction in the two groups of families, yield any information on the specificity of these patterns? If, for example, schizophrenic families exhibited a major deficit in father-son communication (as our study suggests), is it not possible that families with members disturbed or impaired in some other way (delinquent, reading problem, psychosomatic illness) manifest a similar communicational skew? Perhaps any pattern found to characterize schizophrenic families in any sample is merely the reflection of a general attribute of all families with a severely disturbed or deviant member. In that case, what inferences can be drawn about the possible contributory role of such identified patterns in the etiology of the disorder? This is a serious problem and one which must not be lost sight of in interpreting results of the kind of research reported here.

The most effective way of determining specificity consists in the comparison of family interaction data from families with diverse disorders in their offspring. Investigators doing family research have increasingly attempted to do this. In our work, as mentioned already, we have collected data on another group of families, matched on demographic variables with the two groups reported on here. Each family in this group has a boy from 8-14 years of age, suffering from intractable asthma. Analysis of this data is under way.

Another way of attacking the specificity issue lies in the de-

149

termination of the "theoretical fit" of the interaction data and findings to current clinical judgment and theory about familial determinants of schizophrenia and about the nature of the disorder. For example, if, on the one hand, clinical observation characterizes such patients as unable to discriminate correctly among bodily sensations and inner states and, on the other hand, family interaction studies reveal a flow of messages from mother to patient, suggesting, evaluating and (perhaps) misinterpreting the patient's experiences, motives, and wishes, then may it not be reasonable to hypothesize specific relationships between such mother-child interaction patterns and a schizophrenic outcome?

5. DIAGNOSIS OF SCHIZOPHRENIA

Throughout this paper the terms "schizophrenic" and "schizophrenic families" are employed. We should, therefore, emphasize at this time that we share, with many of our colleagues, a great deal of uncertainty about this diagnosis and its applicability. We are intrigued by Goldfarb's research effort to separate schizophrenic children with organic impairment from those with no such involvement.[18] Yet, as mentioned earlier, we were not able to separate our group in this manner. We accepted the diagnosis as it appeared in the record in the participating institutions. We are very much aware of the possibility that some of the children may have "organic" impairment and that others might be reclassified if the diagnosis were to be made in another institution. However, it was not possible, within the limitations of this study, to undertake any further diagnostic refinement.

Some inferences for interpreting data, however, are to be drawn from the diagnostic problem. First, one should not be surprised if one or more families do not share in the patterns characterizing most of the schizophrenic families (one, in particular, looks quite different). And second, one should try to use statistical measures which are more sensitive to tendencies in the aggregate data (such as the median) rather than measures more likely to be influenced by one or two strong deviant cases.

6. EFFECT OF STUDY CONTEXT ON "NATURAL FAMILY INTERACTION"

Whenever a segment of family interaction is subjected to study, the question inevitably arises as to what effect the family's awareness of being recorded and observed has upon the "natural" patterns of family interrelationships.

This is a complex issue which deserves careful study rather than statements of opinion and controversy. Introspection into our own behavior in a diversity of situations reveals clearly that, in some measure, setting does, indeed, influence behavior. One would expect, therefore, the study setting to exert some effect. But the crucial issue is in what respect and how strongly family behavior is altered as a result of the family's being studied.

The problem is made more difficult by the not-to-be-overlooked assumption, stressed by Haley, that the behavior of the schizophrenic and control families would probably be affected in different ways as a result of being studied.[19] The parents in the schizophrenic family who are participating in the research on the basis of services provided to their "patient" child may feel more "accused and defensive" (Haley) than the control parents. They may tend to be more guarded and "less natural."

One would, nonetheless, wonder whether there is enough "give" in the structure of interaction patterns in schizophrenic families to permit any major modification in their interpersonal behavior. To change form and content of behavior implies that new modes of interrelating are possible and available to the individual. If family interaction patterns in such families are, however, as stable and as rigid as has been claimed, then conscious efforts at change would not be too successful.

Which types and sequences of behavior the researcher has selected for study, of course, enter into any consideration of the effect of the study condition.

Granted that family members may wish to present themselves in a more favorable light than they might with no one listening, need one assume that they would attempt to modify or be able to modify such recurrent patterns of behavior as the rate of communication from father to son, which happens to be a variable of interest in our research? We think not!

To the extent that the families were unaware of our special interest in specific communication patterns, and to the extent that the patterns we were concerned with probably are of long duration, we may be less concerned with the distortion in family interaction that might be introduced as a result of the investigation.[20]

7. CAN "SIGNIFICANT" VARIABLES BE MEASURED?

This enumeration of methodological considerations would not be complete without reference to the measurement problem. This problem is especially relevant in a research in great part derived from social science concepts and methods.

Clinicians have often pointed out that a quantitative approach to the study of interpersonal process is premature, if at all feasible in the foreseeable future. The significant phenomena, from this point of view, lie in the feelings experienced and projected by the participants in the situation: in the unconscious images and motives which—so it is claimed—can only be discerned by the skilled clinician in a personal encounter with the subjects.

Without sharing this extreme position, the researcher must admit that there are aspects of interpersonal process which, at the present time, are not accessible to quantitative assessment. For example, Bateson's most provocative double-bind hypothesis, which refers to incongruences between feelings and behavior, does not appear accessible to rigorous evaluation at this time.[21] The development of methods for reliable inferences about feelings, whether on the basis of verbal, vocal, or kinesic communication, is still in its beginning. Despite these considerations, research into interpersonal processes—in the family, in therapy, and in other groups—is proceeding. There are a number of reasons for this. First, if the disturbances in interaction in the schizophrenic family are as constant and pervasive as has been claimed, then it should be possible to discern these by measures of interaction, however gross and formal.[22] Second, it has been variously pointed out that redundancy is a characteristic of biological and social phenomena. Some support for redundancy in family interaction has been developed by one of us (H.L.L.).[23] We therefore assume that communications between family members on levels not yet accessible to measurement may be duplicated on a level accessible to measurement. And, finally, it is only through plodding effort that one can distinguish the "merely very difficult from the impossible."

FINDINGS

The Family as a Communication System

1. DISTRIBUTION OF COMMUNICATION

First we wished to ascertain whether the total volume of communication and its distribution among family members were significantly different in schizophrenic than in the control families.

As Figure 1 shows, there are no consistent differences between the schizophrenic and the control families in the median number

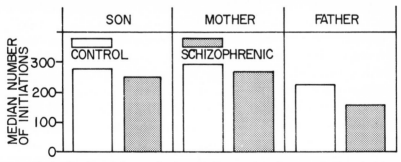

Fig. 1   Number of Communications: Median number of communications (uninterrupted verbal utterances) by son, mother, and father during group discussion. (N equals ten schizophrenic families and seven control families.)

of communications during the discussion period.[24] While the sons and mothers emit almost the same number of communications in the schizophrenic families as in the control group, the median number of communications by the fathers was found to be lower in the schizophrenic families.

2. CHANNELS OF COMMUNICATION

Epstein and Westley postulate that "communication among the members is necessary to the successful functioning of the family . . . it should be obvious that needs cannot be satisfied, problems solved, or goals reached without communication." [25] To the extent that the fulfillment of a group's goals and the satisfaction of a group's members is dependent upon communication among group members, the effectiveness of a group will depend on whether the members of the group feel free and are able to communicate with each other. The ability to communicate within a system is ultimately dependent upon the availability of channels of communication within that system. Without such channels of communication, transmission of information is impossible.

In a triadic group consisting of a father, mother, and son, there are three bi-directional channels of communication: (1) father ⟨—⟩ son, (2) mother ⟨—⟩ son, and (3) father ⟨—⟩ mother. Hence, there are six directions in which communications can flow. Figure 2 charts the direction of flow and the utilization of the six channels of communication in our schizophrenic and control families.

It can be seen that the configuration of communication flow is markedly different in the group of schizophrenic families than in the group of control families. In the schizophrenic families, the son addresses significantly fewer (at the .025 level) communications to the father and also receives fewer communications from him than in the control families; thus, the father-son channel is under-utilized. The father-mother channel of communication also appears to be grossly under-utilized. In contrast the mother directs more communications to the son and receives

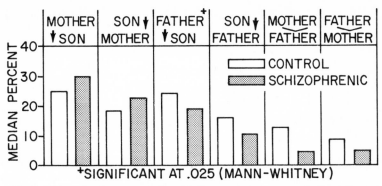

Fig. 2.   Channels of communication: Median percent of communications directed by son, mother, and father to each other during group discussion. (*N* equals ten schizophrenic families and seven control families.)

more from him in the schizophrenic families than in the control families.

There appears to be a consistently lower utilization of four channels of communication in the schizophrenic family system, all of which involve communications with the father. These findings correspond very closely to the description by Fleck *et al.*[26] and others of the "unusual passivity" of the fathers of schizophrenics. Our findings also bring to mind Epstein and Westley's hypothesis that "when a parent is the focus of such impaired communication, it is an indication that he or she is a source of pathological disturbance in family functioning." [27]

It may be suggested that, to a certain extent, the proportion of communications flowing to and from each of the participants in the family system reflects the saliency of each of the participants, or his status, in that system. Thus, one might conclude that all three role relationships appear to have somewhat more equal salience in the control families than they do in the schizophrenic families; while in the schizophrenic families, the mother ⟨—⟩ son role relationship seems to be dominant. These differences lend some support to Lidz's statement to the effect that one problem to avoid in small groups, including the family, is the formation of sub-groups or dyadic coalitions in order that the participants can remain opened to multiple communication and affiliation.[28]

155

Our data confirm the clinical hypothesis that in many schizophrenic families in which the identified patient is a male, one dyadic unit (mother$\longleftrightarrow$ son) operates to the exclusion of the other family role relationships.

It seems reasonable to suppose that adequate family functioning requires just as much that all of the possible family role relationships obtain, as sociologists maintain, as that all statuses in the family are occupied. Broken families and families in which role relationships are defective can be considered to be inadequately differentiated in structure and function. Inadequate family differentiation may be correlated with individual differentiation and is, perhaps, both in the present and in the past, responsible for the latter. Role-learning occurs, as Parsons and Bales imply,[29] both through participation in a family sub-system and through observing the operation of other family sub-systems. Deficits in communication between father and mother, for example, lessen the child's opportunity to learn or to internalize the respective role statuses involved. The inability of a schizophrenic to perform in a variety of role relationships may partly be attributed to his having been raised within a family structure in which he has had insufficient opportunity to observe the operations of multiple family role relationships.

INITIATION AND CONTROL OF INTERACTION
IN DISTURBED FAMILIES

Clinicians have observed that certain phenomena appear to be characteristic of families within which there is a schizophrenic child. For example, Fleck et al.[30] refer to what they call "the narcissistic communication barrier" that they regard as present in schizophrenic families. "Certain mothers—or fathers—are quite incapable of responding spontaneously to their children's behavior unless the parent has evoked such behavior. Thus, a parent may respond to a young child's behavior only if it is elicited by that parent." [31] Hilde Bruch [32] also observes that the word "impervious" occurs with striking frequency in studies describing schizophrenic families, and she regards it as important to determine whether a given behavioral act should be regarded as an "initiation" or a "response." This notion of initiated communication versus responsive communication is reminiscent of Skinner's distinction between operant and respondant behavior.[33]

In two previous pilot studies, with very small samples,[34] we found that the identified schizophrenic patient had very little success in "intruding" upon mother$\longleftrightarrow$ father interaction. Perhaps, in this connection, we could speak of "permeability" or "lack of permeability" in the dyadic interactions or coalitions that form during family interaction as a function of the ease with which a third member can intrude himself into an ongoing dyadic communication sequence. One question raised by this pilot work was whether the lack of response to intrusion and the lack of permeability was attributable to "unresponsiveness" on the part of the parents, or to the strength of the bond between the parents that excluded the child. Our present finding with respect to the deficit in communication between father and mother in schizophrenic families tends to support the former hypothesis.

The transition from childhood to healthy adulthood requires the acquisition of the capacity for self-initiated or autonomous behavior.[35] As in other social systems, participation in the family system places constraints upon the rate, direction, and type of behavior permitted among its members. Moreover, each individual family tends to develop and maintain its own definitions about how much and what kind of behavior is permissible by its members during family interactions, though these definitions are supposed to be subject to revision when changes take place in the statuses of the family members.

Of great interest, then, would be an examination of the way in which different kinds of families deal with the occurrence of efforts at self-initiated behavior on the part of their children. Children's efforts to gain their parents' attention or to redirect parental dialogues represent a frequent and typical form of self-initiated behavior. Such instances of intrusion provide readily quantifiable examples of the way in which families reinforce,

157

control, and allocate the initiation of communication. We refer to such an entry by a third person into a two-person interaction, which is not requested or elicited by the persons in interaction, as an *intrusion*. We constructed measures of the frequency, success, and duration of the effect of such intrusions for each member of our sample of families. We then determined for each family member the number of times he initiated efforts to intervene, the number of times he succeeded in becoming part of an ongoing interaction between two other family members, and the degree of success of his efforts.

By focusing on any pair of family members who are intruded upon, we could determine how responsive or impervious they are to the intrusion of any third family member, especially how permissive parents are of intrusions by their child. We also attempted to assess the rates and types of intrusions characteristic of a family as an indicator of the extent to which self-initiated behavior is tolerated and encouraged within any given family system, and to compare our schizophrenic and control families with respect to these parameters.

For the purpose of coding, a statement will be characterized as an *intrusion* if the person making the statement is (1) neither the target nor the initiator of the previous exchange, and (2) if the previous exchange involves the other two persons in the triad. An exchange is defined as a sequence of two statements during which ego directs a communication to alter, and alter responds with a communication to ego. An intrusion may be regarded as successful only if it yields at least one communication directed to the third person by either of the interactors. The *degree* to which an intrusion is regarded as successful is measured by the number of interactions that it yields. Thus, an intrusion that results in four exchanges with the family member attempting to redirect interaction is regarded as more successful than one which results in only two exchanges. An unsuccessful intrusion does not result in any exchange with the "intruder"; rather, the ongoing interaction continues uninterrupted.

158

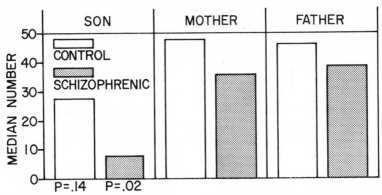

Fig. 3   Median number intrusions. (*N* equals ten schizophrenic families and seven control families.)

Figure 3 compares the median number of intrusions that occurred in the control and schizophrenic families.

It can be seen that considerably less intrusions occur in schizophrenic families than in control families. It is particularly clear that mothers and sons in schizophrenic families attempt considerably fewer intrusions than mothers and sons in the control families. In addition to the difference in the absolute number of intrusion attempts, it also appears to be the case (see Figure 4) that the *proportion* of the mothers' and sons' statements which are attempted intrusions is lower in the schizophrenic than in the control families.

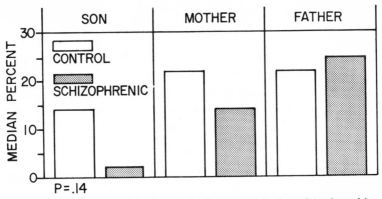

Fig. 4   Median percent of intrusions (Index A): percent intrusions$=\dfrac{\text{intrusions of A}}{\text{all statements by A}}$.

Since the absolute number of attempts at intrusion may simply reflect the fact that there are different amounts of interaction among the participants in family discussion, and fewer exchanges between any two family members upon which to intrude (for example, see Figure 2, the deficit of interaction between mother and father in schizophrenic families), the data was reanalyzed to control for number of "opportunities" to intrude into the interactions between the two other family members. This was done by computing the ratio between the number of intrusion attempts and the total number of intrusion opportunities (e.g., total number of exchanges between mother and father divided by number of intrusion attempts by son). Figure 5 shows, nevertheless, that the ratio of intrusion attempts by patient-sons is lower than that for sons in control families.

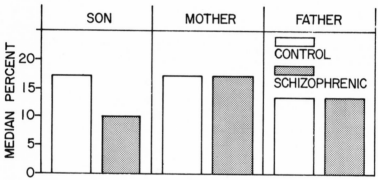

Fig. 5   Median percent of intrusions (Index B): percent intrusions=$\dfrac{\text{intrusions of A}}{\text{interactions of B to C plus interactions of C to B}}$.

Thus, it would appear that a deficit in self-initiated behavior (as measured by intrusion rates) is characteristic of the patient-son status in schizophrenic families. This is reflected in the extremely low absolute number of intrusion attempts (see Figure 3); the proportionate number of intrusion attempts (see Figure 4); and the lower ratio of intrusion attempts to intrusion opportunities (see Figure 5). Since our data (see Figure 1) do not indicate any significantly lower participation and volume of activity by our patients, this finding regarding lower intrusion rates cannot be considered to be an artifact of the generally lower activity level that is commonly thought to be characteristic of the schizophrenic disorder. Rather, it seems to us that the differences in the intrusion patterns reflect the way in which schizophrenic families regulate and inhibit certain types of behavior.

It will be recalled that the parents of schizophrenic patients are believed to discourage those forms of behavior for which Hilde Bruch's term "initiating" seems to be so appropriate (behavior in which the child redirects the focus and content of communication).[36] The discouragement or non-reinforcement of self-initiating behavior should certainly lead to its reduction or extinction over time. We would hypothesize that the reduced intrusion rates that we found reflect the product of this process.

To test the hypothesis that self-initiated behavior receives less reinforcement in schizophrenic families, we analyzed the degree to which attempted intrusions were "successful." How frequently does the dyad intruded upon respond to the third person's statement, and how frequently do they ignore it and continue to interact among themselves? Figure 6 shows the median number of successful intrusions in our schizophrenic and control families.

It can be seen that the median number of successful intrusions by all members of our schizophrenic sample is significantly lower (.025 level) than for the controls. Accordingly, it may be con-

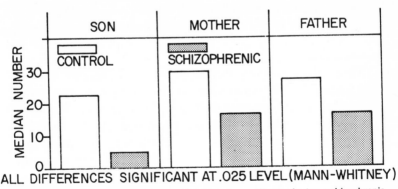

Fig. 6 Median numbers of successful intrusions. (N equals ten schizophrenic families and seven control families.)

cluded that the opportunities to experience success (reinforcement) in controlling and directing interactional sequences are highly limited in the schizophrenic family context. Thus, it appears that the members of a schizophrenic family seem to be more impervious to communications issuing from others who are not in response to communications initiated by themselves. Ronald Laing suggests that "the other who is felt to be unresponsive or impervious to the self as agent, or is in fact unresponsive, tends to induce by this imperviousness a sense of emptiness and impotence in the self." [37]

The Family as a Socialization System

THE PROCESS OF SOCIALIZATION

Interaction involves unceasing interpretation and evaluation by each participant. Monitoring and labeling of intentions, motives, and feelings enables participants in social interaction to engage in appropriate interpersonal behavior. Monitoring processes ordinarily occur "within" individuals and are not communicated. Indeed, it may be quite dysfunctional for the flow of interaction to permit their expression.

Accurate identification and interpretation of inner states followed by appropriate forms of action are essential for the care of an infant or a young child. During the first years of life, the mother and, to a lesser extent, the father, are at first required through appropriate tension-reduction actions, and later through verbal communications and representations, to identify, interpret, and respond to the inner states and experiences of their child. Hilde Bruch stresses that accurate identification and appropriate response to communications emitted by infants is critical for "the development of self-awareness—self-effectiveness." [38] Lack of reinforcement, improper identification of or inappropriate response to a child's experiential states can be expected to cause perplexity. The child subsequently finds it difficult to differentiate among bodily states and may mislabel them.

162

When a mother learns to offer food in response to signals indicating nutritional needs, the infant will develop the engram of "hunger" as a sensation distinct from other tension or needs. However, if the mother's reaction is continuously inappropriate, be it neglectful, oversolicitous, inhibiting, or indiscriminately permissive, the outcome for the child will be perplexing confusion in his biological clues and later in his perceptions and conceptualizations. When he is older he will not be able to recognize whether he is hungry or satiated, or suffering from some other discomfort. . . .[39]

As a child develops and matures, he is expected to gradually assume this monitoring function for himself, and the amount of labeling communication issuing from the parent diminishes. Such information as "You are angry," "You feel sad," supplied by a mother is then no longer necessary or *appropriate* to identify the state of tension or discomfort in the child, but may in fact be dysfunctional. A striking aspect of the transcripts of conversations between mothers and their schizophrenic patient-sons was the pervasiveness of this type of communication as the mother's center of interest.

Illustrations from our transcripts are provided below as typical of such types of conversation.

Example 1:

Mother: Did you get any other feelings besides, uh, what was it? Getting mad, or you couldn't stand it. Was that the sole feeling you had?

Patient: I don't. . . .

Mother: Or was it a feeling of maybe, uh, and jealousness, jealousy?

Patient: Yeah, I imagine that is partly, partly jealousness—I mean jealousy. Partly I'm sure, part of it is jealousy.

Mother: Yeah.

Patient: Yeah.

Mother: Did you recognize it a certain uh . . . feeling against Pop?

Example 2:

Mother: What do you call it, er, er, ant . . . not antagonism, that's not the word. What is that other word? Um, still, there's a hostility underneath occasionally . . .

163

Patient: Shakiness like, er . . .

Mother: Maybe a little hostility towards me sometimes which crops up. Er . . .

Patient: Do you have to use hostility?

Mother: A little, er, bitterness, maybe . . .

Patient: Yeah, that's . . .

Mother: A little . . .

Patient: That's better, or, or . . .

Mother: A little . . .

Patient: I, I think bitterness . . .

Mother: Bitterness?

Patient: Yeah, er, the bitterness is something which I create myself.

Mother: Yes.

Patient: And you, and, and, er, I know it.

These illustrations call to mind the concept of "engulfing and intrusive communication" described by Fleck and Lidz [40] as follows:

> . . . engulfing communication bespeaks the failure of a parent to establish ego boundaries between himself and an offspring. There may be a veritable barrage of cues from parent to child to elicit responses vital to the parent's emotional needs of the moment without any perception of the child as a separate person with his own emotional life. . . .

Lidz and Fleck [41] go on to say that the mothers of schizophrenic children have "a tendency to confuse the child's needs with her own needs projected on the child; failure to recognize ego boundaries between herself and the child." This observation corresponds to the views of Bowen [42] who writes:

> We have used the term projection to refer to the most all-pervasive mechanism in the mother-child relationship. It has been used constantly by every mother in every aspect of her relationship with the patient. . . . [He describes a patient who] had never been able to know how she felt. She has depended on her mother to tell her how she felt. When occasionally she had a feeling that was different from what the mother said, she discounted her own feeling and felt the way the mother said she felt.

164

THE MEASUREMENT OF "LABELING"

In reading through our family transcripts we became aware of what appeared to us to be an unwillingness or inability upon the part of the parents of patients to abandon their monitoring function and to discontinue the labeling (or mislabeling) of the patient's inner states, motives, feelings, and needs. We shall treat all communications that refer to the inner states (interpretations and evaluations of feelings, experiences, etc.) of a person as Level II communications (labeling) to distinguish them from what we shall call Level I types of communication, which consist of non-evaluative references to human action, to events, or to other factual matters. Some examples of the two types of communications have been extracted from the transcripts and are shown below:

Examples of Level I Communications:

Mother: Your grandmother and your grandfather when they came to the United States, they knew nothing about English. They knew nothing about the history of the United States.

Mother: Yeah, but a scientist, they can find something which can alleviate the suffering of millions or thousands. Like with all these vaccines that they discover. They rid the world of the most, the scourges of mankind.

Examples of Level II Communications:

Mother: You feel that you're very sensitive?

Mother: That's what you'd learned, and you weren't actually afraid. The only thing that you were afraid of was that you were really hurt. Is that right?

Mother: You only want to be good when you have to get something, huh kid?

Mother: Remember, you said your head was shaking so, you were getting terrible pains in back of your head. You haven't had those pains since you're here.

165

Mother: You won't get sick. Don't talk it into yourself.

Mother: I'm sure you don't hate everybody here.

Mother: Well, you mean maybe you feel a little lonely with Bob around because you can't actually play with him?

We attempted to classify all statements made by the mothers of our patients into Level I or Level II types of communication. We found the median percent of Level II (labeling) communications for the mothers of patients to be 21 percent, while it was only 10 percent in the control families. This means that the mothers of patients devote more than twice the proportion of their communications to Level II as compared to the control mothers. The difference between the structure of the communications issuing from the control mothers and the mothers of patients is even more striking if one determines whether the content of their Level II communications revolve about themselves or others—their own inner states and feelings, or those of their sons. Figure 7 shows that the median proportion of labeling references about alter is about 0.90 for the mothers of patients, while it is less than 0.40 for the control mothers (p equals .06).

That these findings represent the product of the parents' unwillingness or inability to desist from their "monitoring" function and their persistence in labeling (or mislabeling) is also supported

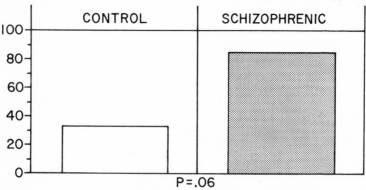

Fig. 7 Median percent of level II (labeling) communications about alter by mother
(ratio = $\dfrac{\text{level II communications about alter by mother}}{\text{all level II communications}}$.

(*N* equals ten schizophrenic families and seven control families.)

Table 1.   Frequency of Changes in Levels of Communication

PARENT = PATIENT PAIR	NUMBER OF TIMES PARENT CHANGES FROM:		NUMBER OF TIMES PATIENT CHANGES FROM:	
	LEVEL I TO LEVEL II	LEVEL II TO LEVEL I	LEVEL I TO LEVEL II	LEVEL II TO LEVEL I
A	41	10	I	33
B	17	3	4	18
C	61	28	18	51
D	21	0	0	21

by some of our previous findings derived from the analysis of recorded conversations between four patient-parent dyads.

Table I shows the number of times each member of the four patient-parent pairs changed the frame of reference from Level I to Level II, and from Level II to Level I. It can be seen that the patients in each pair persist in changing the Level from II to I, while the parents consistently change the Level from I to II. This means that the parents direct the conversation toward the discussion of the patients' inner states, while the patients try to direct the conversation to other topics. For example, the following dialogue:

Patient: Did you bring my laundry?

Mother: How do you feel today?

Patient: Do you have my laundry?

Mother: You look sad.

Patient: I'm O.K.

Mother: Are you angry with me?

Patient: Yes.

One cannot rule out the possibility that this excessive preoccupation with the patient's feelings and subjective states may be

167

a reaction to the child's disturbance rather than, as we tend to assume, being antecedent to the onset of the schizophrenic disorder and therefore possibly implicated in its development. Longitudinal data on a large number of families would be required to provide a definitive answer to this question, or possibly an analysis of a control group of families in which there was a child suffering from a serious disorder other than schizophrenia. (We have undertaken such a comparison with data on family interaction process collected from ten families with a child diagnosed as "intractably asthmatic.")

Nevertheless, our findings are highly suggestive and, at this time, we tend toward the assumption that the failure on the part of parents to relinquish control over a patient-child's inner processes is characteristic of a schizophrenogenic context, and we believe that the kind of interpersonal environment created by excessive Level II communications (especially if they reflect projections and mislabelings) is contributory to the genesis of the schizophrenic disorder. Our findings, arrived at through our quantitative content-analytic approach, are strongly supported by and lend support to clinically derived formulations to the effect that the mother in schizophrenic families employs symbolic communication to exercise control over her patient-child through the quality and structure of her communications.

These findings prompt us to offer a few speculative comments about sequences in personality and system control processes. We assume that in "normal" development the parents, especially the mother, through a set of mechanisms not yet explicated, make it possible for a child to learn to identify and evaluate his own feelings, experiences, and motives. In time, the child can correctly interpret his own experience and is able to reject inaccurate versions when they are offered to him by others. Accompanying this increased awareness of inner states and their appropriate symbolic representation is the ability to set adaptive interpersonal processes into motion when the relief of discomfort requires actions on the part of another person. Thus, the child replaces his parent as a "regulator" of system process when conditions of intrapersonal or interpersonal disequilibrium require it. If a parent fails to induct his child into this control function, or if the child fails to achieve it, the child may remain dependent on the parent (as he has been as an infant) for restoration of intrapersonal or interpersonal equilibria.

Both with regard to psychic monitoring and especially with reference to labeling communication, there appear to be optimal modes and levels (amounts) in specific social relationship systems and for different developmental phases of these systems (e.g. the family). The investigation of the vicissitudes of labeling communication is compatible with the "system" conception of familial interaction. The occurrence of labeling may be used as an indicator of the type of homeostatic and control mechanisms that are operating in parent-child relationships and the changes that such mechanisms undergo as the statuses of the members of the system (e.g., the child) change.

CHAPTER SIX

THE FATHER OF THE SCHIZOPHRENIC: THE FUNCTION OF A PERIPHERAL ROLE *

FRANCES E. CHEEK

Daughter: You can't speak for all mothers, mother, because you really don't . . .

Mother: No I can't speak for all mothers but . . .

Father: But wouldn't you think that a mother has the welfare of the child . . .

Daughter: Excuse me, you butted in while I was speaking.

Father: Oh, It's supposed to be a three-way discussion.

Father: Why should the daughter . . .

Mother: (Talking at the same time) What did you want to say, Ann?

Daughter: I don't want to say something but . . .

Father: But what . . .

Daughter: You know what we said before about . . .

Father: I'm not speaking about you. I'm talking in general.

Daughter: I'm not talking about that. I'm talking about . . .

Mother: That you interfered while she was trying to say something.

* Reprinted from the Archives of General Psychiatry, 13:336-345, Oct. 1965.

Father: Well, I'm supposed to be in this discussion too.
Daughter: Of course you are.
Father: But you want to leave me out.

Mother: But I wonder whether the girls realize that by not cooperating, but not in many ways . . . that they hurt the mother. Why? Why do they want to hurt the mother when the mother is so good to them?
Father: What about the father?

What about the father? Mr. R, his wife, and daughter Jan are taking part in a study of family interaction with schizophrenics. The family is discussing, somewhat disjointedly it would appear, typical problems that might come up in a family where a young adult has been hospitalized for a mental illness and is now at home and convalescent. Jan is 22 years old and has recently returned home from a hospitalization for a schizophrenic episode. Her father, Mr. R, is voicing for us a sentiment that has echoed through our tape recordings and has emerged from our IBM machines complete with statistical significance, a sentiment of exclusion from the family group.

What about the father of the schizophrenic? Since Frieda Fromm-Reichmann first so designated her in 1948, the "schizophrenogenic mother" has been the object of a proliferation of studies. Seldom have the characteristics of the father of the schizophrenic been granted much attention. On those occasions that he has been studied, it is noteworthy that as little consistency in findings has appeared as has been characteristic of the studies concerned with the mother. At times he has been described as passive and ineffectual [1] but upon occasion as harsh and dominating.[2] It has recently been suggested that the characteristics of the father might be related to the sex of the schizophrenic. Thus, fathers of females have been described as narcissistic and proud, fathers of males as passive and ineffectual.[3]

On the other hand, less confusion and contradiction have been evidenced with regard to the structural characteristics of the

171

family of the schizophrenic. An almost constant feature of the reports of both clinicians and researchers has been a symbiotic relation of the mother and schizophrenic. The father has thus quite generally been regarded as peripheral to the family group,[4] though Lyman Wynne and his associates [5] have also described an invidious mother-father coalition which excluded the schizophrenic.

It was my feeling that in order to clarify these contradictory findings an approach must be taken that would provide both objective and systematic information about the family environment of the schizophrenic. The objectivity was necessary in order to eliminate subjective coloration by either family members or investigators with regard to the nature of family interaction. A circumspect and systematic approach was essential in order to examine the interrelatedness of aspects of the family environment. Thus, for instance, if the role of the father did prove to be peripheral as other studies had indicated, what relation might this aberrant role structure have to other aspects of the family environment? Might it perhaps reflect in some way the effect of schizophrenic interaction on the family, might it even serve some useful function for them?

In order to provide this objective and systematic approach, the Bales Interaction Process Analysis technique and the social system theoretical framework of Talcott Parsons were used to study the interaction of 67 families with young adult convalescent schizophrenics, 40 male and 27 female, with the interaction of 56 families with nonpsychotic young adults, 31 male and 25 female. To study outcome in relation to family characteristics, the adjustment of the schizophrenics was also evaluated at the time of the interaction interview and one year later.

In a highly structured setting, mother, father, and convalescent young adult schizophrenic were asked to discuss together certain problems about family relations on which they were in disagreement. The discussions were tape-recorded and subsequently coded with a revised version of the Bales Interaction Categories.[6] Profiles of the interaction of father, mother, and schizophrenic were derived.

Additionally, each of the three family members was asked to fill in privately a questionnaire which examined his or her normative expectations and actual perceptions of how all three might behave in relation to one another in handling certain typical family problems. The solutions offered for the questionnaire problems were based on Parsons' types of deviant behavior and mechanisms of social control.[7]

The questionnaire was used as a way of introducing the interaction sessions in a structured fashion. However, it also made possible a comparison between the results obtained with the two different techniques, both of which were based upon the same systematic theoretical framework.

In previous papers we have described the rationale and methodology of the study,[8] the findings regarding the mothers,[9] and the findings regarding the schizophrenics [10] and their adjustment on convalescent status.[11] In this paper the findings with regard to the fathers are presented and an attempt is made to assess the functional significance of these findings in terms of the total family situation.

The study was conducted at the Bureau of Research in Neurology and Psychiatry located at the New Jersey Neuro-Psychiatric Institute at Princeton. It was begun in July 1958, with a grant from the Russell Sage Foundation.

It was decided to work with young adult convalescent schizophrenic patients, both male and female, between the ages of 15 and 26, unmarried and living at home with their natural fathers and mothers, all three being literate and English-speaking. The schizophrenics must also have been released from a mental hospital with a diagnosis of schizophrenia (without organic complications) after September 1957. In order to locate a large enough sample, and also to eliminate a possible bias by the selection of patients from any one hospital, the release records of all 16 state, county, and private mental hospitals in the state of New Jersey were scanned for suitable patients. One hundred and fifty-seven were located in this way.

Over a period of ten months, letters were sent out to each patient requesting that he or she come with his or her father and mother to the hospital where the patient had been hospitalized in order to take part in a study of the sorts of problems that might arise in families where a patient was convalescing from a mental illness.

At the hospital, father, mother, and schizophrenic son or daughter each filled in privately a 20-question questionnaire in which were presented problems that might arise where a young person lived with his or her parents, as well as three possible solutions to each problem. The three family members were asked to check which of the 20 problems had, in fact, come up in their own situation, which of the solutions offered for each problem seemed best to them in the case where a young adult had been hospitalized for a mental illness and had now returned to his or her family (normative expectations) and also which solution best described what would probably happen in their own family if such a problem arose (actual preceptions). Ten of the problems concerned the behaviors of the subject towards the parents, and the solutions might indicate that the behavior of the subject toward the mother or father was "active rebellion," "passive rebellion," or "conformity." The other ten dealt with the behavior of the parent towards the subject and the solutions might indicate that the behavior of the mother or father towards the subject might be "support-permissive," "enforcement of role conformity," or "withdrawal, ignoring." These solutions were based upon Talcott Parsons' types of deviant behavior and mechanisms of social control.[12]

The filling out of the questionnaire was followed by two recorded discussions of 15 minutes each by the three family members on two questionnaire problems on which they had covertly disagreed. The interviewer was not present during these discussions. After the discussions, in an interview with the mother, the convalescent adjustment of the patient was evaluated by means of a 40-item 4-point rating scale. Information was obtained regarding such matters as patient performance of household routines, work and peer group adjustment, remaining symptomatology, etc. One week later, in the home of the patient, two more 15 minute discussions between the three family members were recorded. Detailed instructions were prepared for the interviewers in order to ensure rigor in the conduct of the sessions and systematic notes on the progress of the interview were made at both hospital and home interviews on a prepared schedule. Later, information was abstracted from the hospital case-records on a prepared schedule regarding the early background of the patient, course of illness and hospitalization, treatment, etc.

Of the 157 families who had been located and contacted, 57 took part. In order to augment the sample the investigators returned to two of the state hospitals and located an additional 30 suitable patients. The original procedures were repeated and 10 of these 30 were added to the sample to make a total of 67. Forty of the final sample were male and 27 were female.

In order to compare the results obtained with the schizophrenics and their families with other families where there had been no hospitalization of the young adult for a mental disorder, it was now necessary to locate and study a comparable group of "normal" young adults in the same way. Suitable normal families were located in factories, university groups, the New Jersey 4-H Club, by private referrals, etc. Fifty-six normal families, 31 with male young adults and 25 with female young adults, were studied with procedures identical to those used with the schizophrenics.

One year after the original interviews, each mother of a schizophrenic was contacted by telephone and an interview with her in the home requested. At this interview the investigator once again questioned the mother regarding the convalescent adjustment of the patient, using the 40-item rating scale.

The data obtained was now processed in the following fashion. The hour of interaction data available for each schizophrenic and normal family was coded from the tape with a 20-category variation of the 12 Bales Interaction Categories developed by Edgar F.

Borgatta.[13] The hour was reduced to 48 minutes to eliminate certain timing problems (the last three minutes of each of the four 15-minute discussion sessions were eliminated) and profiles of the activity of each family, father, mother, subject, and total group, in each of the 20 categories, as well as a total interaction category, were now derived.

The data was then analyzed in the following fashion. One hundred and fifty-eight variables including questionnaire, interaction, interview note, developmental, demographic and adjustment variables characterizing each schizophrenic and normal family were selected for analysis. For the schizophrenics, an additional seven variables concerned with chronicity, length of hospitalization, the follow-up adjustment measure, etc, were added.

It was decided to study the interrelationships among these variables for the schizophrenic group separately, the normal group separately, and for the two groups combined. Hence three product-moment correlation matrices were now prepared. Also, as previous studies had suggested that there might be significant differences in the family environment of male and female schizophrenics, it was decided to investigate separately the significance of the variables relating to the illness status and sex of the young adult. By a two-way analysis of variance [14] it was possible to study whether on any particular variable families with schizophrenics differed from families with normal young adults (schizophrenic vs normal), families with female young adults differed from families with male young adults (male vs female), and families with schizophrenic females differed from families with normal females in the same or in a different way than families with schizophrenic males differed from families with normal males (interaction between illness and sex variables).

An important consideration was, of course, the stability of the interaction patterns of the families, and this was examined by an analysis of variance between the four interaction sessions (two at the hospital, two at the home) on all the interaction variables for the schizophrenic and normal families separately. Significant

Table 1

Means and F-Ratios for Mother-Subject (MS), Father-Subject (FS), and Mother-Father
(MF) and Agreement on Normative Expectations (NE) and Actual Perceptions (AP)
for Families With Female and Male, Schizophrenic (Sch) and
Normal (Nor) Subjects

Agreement	Families with female subjects		Families with male subjects	
	Sch	Nor	Sch	Nor
On normative expectations:				
Mother-subject	11.89	12.56	11.73	12.10
Father-subject	10.93	13.04	11.03	11.97
Mother-father	11.67	13.68	11.45	12.84
On actual perceptions:				
Mother-subject	10.59	11.72	11.18	10.61
Father-subject	9.59	11.84	10.28	11.23
Mother-father	9.93	12.80	10.03	11.29

F-ratios	MS		FS		MF	
	NE	AP	NE	AP	NE	AP
Sch-nor	—	—	8.71 *	8.35 *	11.96 *	12.99 *
Male-female	—	—	—	—	—	—
Interaction	—	—	—	—	—	—

* Significant above the 0.01 level.

differences in the interaction did not appear over the four sessions, suggesting stability of the interaction characteristics.

Such stability is also suggested by the work of other investigators who have found the interaction characteristics of subjects to remain stable over time [15] and in the context of reconstituted groups,[16] though O'Rourke [17] found differences in the interaction of families who were studied in their homes and also in more formal research settings. It would appear that this important question of representativeness of such samples of interaction must require further careful study. For discussion of these matters, papers by Haley [18] and Lennard [19] are recommended.

RESULTS

Let us first look at the findings regarding the fathers which appeared in the questionnaire study. The patterns of agreement of the family members concerning the solutions to the 20 ques-

Table 2

Means and F-Ratios of Questionnaire Responses for Fathers of Female and Male
Subjects in Schizophrenic (Sch) and Normal (Nor) Family Groups

Means	Fathers of female subjects		Fathers of male subjects	
	Sch	Nor	Sch	Nor
Normative expectations:				
Support-permissive	4.67	2.92	4.30	3.85
Role enforcement	4.67	6.92	4.48	5.53
Withdrawal	0.67	0.16	1.23	0.63
Actual perceptions:				
Support-permissive	4.48	3.44	4.73	3.48
Role enforcement	4.07	6.12	3.90	5.77
Withdrawal	1.37	0.44	1.33	0.74

F-ratios	NE			AP		
	SP	RE	W	SP	RE	W
Sch-nor	19.09 *	27.68 *	8.00 *	12.13 *	23.83 *	12.00 *
Male-female	—	—	8.33 *	—	—	—
Interaction	—	—	—	—	—	—

* Significant above the 1% level.

tionnaire problems offer us suggestive evidence regarding the character of the relatedness of father, mother, and schizophrenic.

Patterns of Family Coalition Reflected in Attitudinal Similarity

As we have said earlier, the three family members were asked to indicate privately which of the three solutions offered to the 20 problems seemed to be the best solution (normative expectation) and what would most likely happen in their own family (actual perception). Attitudinal similarity was then used as an index of closeness of relationship so that the degree of similarity between the questionnaire responses of mother-father, mother-subject, and father-subject might reveal the relative closeness of the various pairs. In Table 1 these agreements are shown.

The normal families show higher mother-subject, father-subject, and mother-father agreement on both normative expectations and actual perceptions, though only the father-subject and mother-father differences are significant.

Thus, the father of the schizophrenic differs significantly from

178

the father of the normal in his agreement with the mother and subject, and this difference in attitudes suggests that the father of the schizophrenic may occupy a peripheral position in the family. It is of interest that mother-subject agreement is lower in the family of the schizophrenic, which suggests that mother-schizophrenic closeness or symbiosis may result as a sort of default. In other words, it would appear that it is not that the mothers are so close, but rather that the fathers are so far.

In the families of the schizophrenics, mother-subject agreement is higher than father-subject or mother-father agreement. This also suggests a stronger mother-subject coalition in the families of the schizophrenics. In the normal family the mother-father coalition is strongest. These differences hold both for families with male and female schizophrenics.

Withdrawal of the Father Revealed in the Questionnaire Responses

Let us now look at the content of the questionnaire responses. In Table 2 we see the comparison between fathers of schizophrenics and of normals, male and female, in terms of "support-permissiveness," "role enforcement," and "withdrawal."

Fathers of schizophrenics are much higher on support-permissiveness and lower on role enforcement than fathers of normals on both normative expectations and actual perceptions. They are also much higher on withdrawal than fathers of normals on both normative expectations and actual perceptions. In the paper describing the characteristics of mothers of schizophrenics we have reported the questionnaire data for the mothers. In general, the patterns for mothers were very similar to those of the fathers, the mothers of schizophrenics being slightly more support-permissive and less role enforcing than the fathers of schizophrenics. However, the mothers of schizophrenics did not show as much withdrawal in normative expectations and actual perceptions as the fathers. Thus, the F-ratios for fathers on normative expectations and actual perceptions of withdrawal are 8.00 and

179

8.33 respectively, while for mothers there was no significant difference on normative expectations and the *F*-ratio was 3.9 on actual perceptions. This suggests more withdrawal on the part of the fathers.

The Interaction Profiles

We now turn to our actual observations of the fathers of schizophrenics and of normals in interaction with the mothers

Table 3
Interaction Profiles (Means of Scores) of Fathers of Female and Male,
Schizophrenic and Normal Young Adults

| | Group means | | | |
| | Females | | Males | |
Interaction Categories	Sch (N = 27)	Nor (N = 25)	Sch (N = 40)	Nor (N = 31)
Positive social-emotional:				
Social facilitative (2)	3.7	3.9	4.2	4.3
Acknowledgment (4)	16.6	12.1	13.9	12.9
Agreement (5)	6.9	8.0	6.1	5.9
Negative social-emotional:				
Projected hostility (10)	0.8	1.6	1.1	0.9
Disagreement (16)	2.3	4.3	3.1	3.5
Overt hostility (19)	4.7	4.4	8.7	5.0
Egodefensiveness (20)	0.7	1.0	0.7	1.0
Tension behaviors:				
Signs of tension (17)	36.0	26.4	30.4	27.7
Tension release (3)	5.8	3.7	3.1	4.7
Task behaviors:				
Procedural suggestion (6)	15.2	16.0	13.4	15.9
Suggesting solution (7)	0.2	0.1	0.2	0.1
Giving opinion (8)	70.2	69.4	62.0	71.7
Self evaluation (9)	0.1		0.2	0.2
Giving information (11)	13.6	15.0	13.2	18.4
Explaining, clarification (12)	128.6	120.7	113.5	114.4
Asking for information (13)	3.9	3.6	3.9	5.5
Asking for opinion (14)	7.3	4.9	6.8	4.4
Asking for suggestion (15)	1.2	0.9	0.8	1.0
Total interaction (21)	317.7	296.4	285.2	297.9

and young adults. The interaction profiles of the fathers derived from our tape recordings are shown in Table 3, while the *F*-ratios from the two-way analysis of variance (sex and illness status of the young adult) appear in Table 4.

Table 4

F-Ratios Derived From Two-Way Analysis of Variance of Interaction Scores of
Fathers of Female and Male, Schizophrenic and Normal Subjects

Categories	Sch vs Nor	F-Ratios M vs F	Interaction
Positive social-emotional:			
Social facilitative (2)			
Acknowledgment (4)	(2.8)		
Agreement (5)			
Negative social-emotional:			
Projected hostility (10)			
Disagreement (16)	4.9 *		(2.1)
Open hostility (19)			
Ego-defensiveness (20)			
Tension behaviors:			
Signs of tension (17)			
Tension release (3)			(3.7)
Task behaviors:			
Procedural suggestion (6)			
Suggesting solution (7)			
Giving opinion (8)			
Self evaluation (9)		(3.7)	
Giving information (11)	(2.5)		
Explaining, clarification (12)			
Asking for information (13)			
Asking for opinion (14)	3.8 *		
Total interaction (21)		(2.4)	(3.0)

* $P < 0.05$.

In general, the interaction profiles of the fathers of schizophrenics do not differ from those of the fathers of normals as
much as the interaction profiles of mothers of schizophrenics
differ from those of mothers of normals, as previously reported. Of
the 21 variables examined, only two significant differences from
normal fathers appeared, whereas the mothers of schizophrenics
showed four significant differences from mothers of normals in
their interaction. In the discussion of the interaction profiles
which follows, all the variables are commented upon, but those
showing significant differences are specially noted.

A. TOTAL INTERACTION

While the mothers of schizophrenics proved to be significantly
underactive as compared to the mothers of the normals, the

fathers of schizophrenics do not differ significantly from fathers of normals in terms of total activity.

It is, however, of interest that the fathers of female schizophrenics are much more active than the fathers of female normals, while the fathers of male schizophrenics are much less active than the fathers of male normals. Here we may have a reflection of "proud, narcissistic" fathers of female schizophrenics and "passive, ineffectual" fathers of male schizophrenics.

B. POSITIVE SOCIAL-EMOTIONAL BEHAVIORS

Fathers of schizophrenics show higher total social-emotional behaviors than fathers of normals, a contrast to the mothers of schizophrenics who were lower in this respect than mothers of normals. The fathers of the female schizophrenics are especially high, though they are oddly low on category 5 (agreement) and very high on category 4 (acknowledgment). This suggests that the fathers of the schizophrenics in their positive expressions are relatively indirect, for acknowledgment means less forthright support than agreement. This may be a kind of "yes, dear" supportiveness.

C. NEGATIVE SOCIAL-EMOTIONAL BEHAVIORS

The fathers of schizophrenics, both male and female, are lower on disagreement and ego-defensiveness. The difference in terms of disagreement is significant though the interaction F-ratio of 2.1 reflects the fact that while fathers of female schizophrenics are much lower on disagreement than fathers of male schizophrenics, there is not much difference between fathers of male schizophrenics and fathers of male normals in this respect.

On projected hostility fathers of male schizophrenics are higher than fathers of male normals, though fathers of female schizophrenics are lower than fathers of female normals. On overt hostility fathers of male schizophrenics are much higher than fathers of male normals, while fathers of female schizophrenics are only slightly higher than fathers of female normals. However, these differences are not statistically significant.

D. TENSION BEHAVIORS

Fathers of both male and female schizophrenics are higher on signs of tension (category 17) than fathers of female and male normals, though the differences are not significant. Tension release is higher in fathers of female schizophrenics than in fathers of female normals but lower in fathers of male schizophrenics than in fathers of male normals. It may be that the fathers of the male schizophrenics release some of their tension in overt hostility, as the high rates of overt hostility might suggest.

E. TASK BEHAVIORS

One difference only is significant here. Fathers of schizophrenics are higher on asking for opinion and this may reflect a peripheral role in the family. As we have seen in the questionnaire study, the fathers of the schizophrenics were much less close to the family in their opinions than the fathers of the normals. The peripherality of their role is also suggested by the low rate of the fathers of schizophrenics of giving information in the interaction.

The "passive, ineffectual" father of the male schizophrenic is suggested by the low rate of procedural suggestion in this group; fathers of female schizophrenics are only slightly lower in this respect than fathers of female normals.

Summary of Interaction Profile Data

While the interaction profiles of the fathers of schizophrenics do not differ from those of the fathers of normals as much as the interaction profiles of mothers of schizophrenics differ from those of mothers of normals, the differences which do appear suggest the peripherality of the role of the father, also indicated in the questionnaire responses. Thus, fathers of schizophrenics are high on asking opinion and low on giving information.

183

Table 5

Correlations Between Questionnaire Responses and Interaction Data for
Fathers of Schizophrenics and Normals *

	Fathers of schizophrenics			Fathers of normals		
	Positive sanctions		Negative sanctions	Positive sanctions		Negative sanctions
	04 †	05	16	04	05	16
Normative expectations:						
Support-permissive	0.11	0.10	—0.06	0.07	0.08	—0.13
Role enforcement	—0.12	—0.16	00	—0.12	—0.04	0.10
Actual perceptions:						
Support-permissive	0.19	0.18	0.08	0.10	—0.14	—0.12
Role enforcement	—0.26 *	—0.16	—0.10	—0.09	0.13	0.05

* Normals, 0.30 significant at 5%; and schizophrenics, 0.24 significant at 5%.
† 04 acknowledgment; 05 agreement; and 16 disagreement.

However, another and perhaps significant clue with regard to the role of the fathers of schizophrenics has appeared in the interaction profiles. The mothers of schizophrenics were lower on positive sanctions than the mothers of the normals. The fathers of the schizophrenics appear to be higher on positive sanctions than the fathers of the normals. We will return to this point later.

The interaction profiles also suggest differences related to the sex of the schizophrenic. The low rates of procedural suggestion and total interaction in the fathers of the male schizophrenics could reflect the "passive, ineffectual" father of the male described in the literature, while a "narcissistic, proud" father of the female schizophrenic may be reflected in the high rates of total activity and "normal" rates of procedural suggestion. While fathers of both male and female schizophrenics show high rates of tension (especially the fathers of females), the fathers of females also show high rates of tension release in laughter, while the fathers of males show low rates of tension release in laughter but high rates of overt hostility.

However, these are trends rather than statistically significant differences. The major lines of differentiation appear to lie along the schizophrenic-normal dimension without regard to the sex of the schizophrenic.

184

Word and Deed

Now, let us return to our observation that more positive sanctions are given by the fathers of the schizophrenics. In the paper describing the mothers we reported that while the mothers of schizophrenics were low on support behaviors in the interaction, their questionnaire responses showed high support-permissiveness. However, when the correlations between interaction data and questionnaire responses were examined, it was found that high support-permissiveness of the mothers of schizophrenics was associated with low interaction rates of disagreement rather than high interaction rates of agreement. The mothers of normals, on the other hand, when high on support-permissiveness in the questionnaire were high on positive sanction in the interaction, while no relation to disagreement appeared. Thus, it would seem the mothers of the schizophrenics were permissive rather than actively supportive.

We have already noted that the fathers of schizophrenics were high on support-permissiveness and low on role enforcement on the questionnaire. Let us now look at the correlations between questionnaire data and sanctioning patterns in the interaction of fathers of normals and schizophrenics. These correlations are shown in Table 5.

Our pattern here is not so striking as that associated with the mothers, but it does appear that support-permissiveness in the father of the schizophrenic is associated with more positive sanctions and role enforcement with fewer positive sanctions, while negative sanctions do not appear to be related to these attitudes. In the fathers of the normals the relation between attitudes and behavior in this respect is not strong. Thus, the support-permissiveness of the father of the schizophrenic would appear to take the form of active support, while that of the mother of the schizophrenic takes the form of permissiveness.

185

Convalescent Outcome in Relation to the Role of the Father

We have previously reported characteristics of the father of the schizophrenic which were related to poor outcome of the patient on the one-year follow-up. The questionnaire, interaction, and interview variables describing the fathers were correlated with the follow-up adjustment scores. It was found that where the father was low in agreement (category 5), tense (category 17), and active (category 21) in the interaction, expressed perceptions of role enforcement on the part of the parents on the questionnaire, and, surprisingly, was rated by the interviewer as highly cooperative in the interview, the schizophrenic did poorly.

In this paper we have reported evidence which suggests that the father of the schizophrenic plays a peripheral role in the family, that he is less role-enforcing and more support-permissive than the normal father. Also, his support-permissiveness takes the form of active support, whereas the mother of the schizophrenic tends to be permissive but not actively supportive.

In terms of convalescent outcome, the schizophrenic seems to do worse where the father is in many ways more like the normal father, that is to say, more involved in terms of activity and cooperativeness, more role-enforcing and less supportive. That is to say, the peripheral, supportive, non-enforcing role of the father of the schizophrenic appears to serve some useful function for the schizophrenic.

COMMENT

The investigation of the role of the father of the schizophrenic by an examination of the interaction of father, mother, and schizophrenic with a combined observational and questionnaire approach has in general supported the findings of other investigators in this area.

Thus, many studies have reported a close, symbiotic relationship between the schizophrenic and his or her mother with the father playing a peripheral role. In this study we used agreement between family members on responses to the questionnaire as an indicator of closeness. Schizophrenics and their mothers turned out to be slightly lower in agreement than normals and their mothers; however, a symbiotic mother-schizophrenic relation was suggested by the fact that the fathers of the schizophrenics were much lower in agreement with both the mothers and schizophrenics than fathers of normals with their wives and offspring. Thus, our data suggests that the closeness of mother and schizophrenic may arise by default; not that the mothers are so close but that the fathers are so far.

The peripheral role of the father of the schizophrenic was also suggested in the interaction profiles by their high rates of asking opinion and low rates of giving information. However, the profile of the father of the schizophrenic differed less from that of the father of the normal than the profile of the mother of the schizophrenic differed from the profile of the mother of the normal. This suggests more behavioral aberrancy in the mother, either caused by, or perhaps a cause of, the schizophrenia. It is hardly surprising that the family member closer to the schizophrenic shows the greater behavioral aberrancy.

With regard to the studies that have described fathers of schizophrenics as "passive and ineffectual" or alternatively "harsh and demanding," our findings lend support to the theory that the sex of the schizophrenic may be related to discrepancies that have been noted. In their low procedural suggestions and low total activity rates in the interaction, the fathers of the males suggest the "passive, ineffectual" father, while the "narcissistic, proud" father of the female may be indicated by high rates of total activity and "normal" rates of procedural suggestion.

However, in addition to supporting some previous hypotheses and findings regarding the role of the father of the schizophrenic, our study has suggested certain other features of this role not previously noted. These features, which relate to parental social control mechanisms, may provide a means of understanding not

187

only what the role of the father of the schizophrenic is, but also *why* it takes this form.

The behavior of the schizophrenic is characteristically difficult to control. Parsons has suggested that, in response to the presence of deviant behavior, control mechanisms appear to reduce strain and to reequilibrate the system.[20] Our questionnaire data showed both mothers and fathers to be much more support-permissive and less role-enforcing than the parents of normals. Also, in the interaction fathers and mothers of schizophrenics are much lower on disagreement than fathers and mothers of normals, suggesting a family atmosphere of permissiveness.

However, while these findings suggested that mothers and fathers of schizophrenics were more permissive than normal parents, an interesting difference between the mothers and fathers of schizophrenics in terms of supportive behaviors appeared. In their interaction the mothers of schizophrenics were lower on supportive behavior than the mothers of normals, while the fathers of schizophrenics were higher. And when the correlations between the interaction and questionnaire data were examined, it turned out that mothers of schizophrenics were less supportive but more permissive than fathers of normals, while fathers of schizophrenics were somewhat more supportive.

Our study also suggested that the permissiveness and supportiveness of the parents of the schizophrenic might be related to the outcome of the illness, for the schizophrenics did poorly in situations where the father and mother were more role enforcing on the questionnaire and where the mother showed more disagreement in their interaction and the father less supportiveness. Also, where the father was more involved with the family, the schizophrenic did poorly.

What do these findings suggest? Parsons has pointed out that in the American family the mother is typically the expressive and the father the instrumental leader.[21] In the family of the schizophrenic, these roles are distorted. In the expressive area there is a lessened differentiation, for while the mothers are less supportive than mothers of normals, the fathers are somewhat more supportive than fathers of normals. The low supportiveness of the mother might be either a reaction to the defective response of the schizophrenic to her socializing attempts, or a "characteristic" behavior which might be a factor in the etiology of the illness. Similarly, the high supportiveness of the father might be an attempt at compensation for the low supportive behavior of the mother, a general acquiescence to the family situation, or, indeed, a "characteristic" behavior.

With regard to the instrumental role of the father, the situation we have observed in the family of the schizophrenic is of particular interest. The father's role tends to be peripheral; the more actively involved and role enforcing he becomes, the worse for the schizophrenic. Perhaps inasmuch as roles cannot be enforced as in the normal family, this instrumental role of the father becomes inappropriate and, indeed, damaging. He is forced to abandon this role and hence moves to the periphery of the family. The only role he is allowed is a somewhat supportive one to compensate for the low supportiveness of the mother. Or perhaps just to say, "Yes, dear" to the whole situation. And it is where the father does not take this supportive and/or compliant role, where he becomes more involved and tries to enforce rules, that the schizophrenic becomes sicker.

In terms of these findings it is of interest that Parsons has related the etiology of schizophrenia to a lessened differentiation of parental sex roles in the family.[22] Our study suggests that this lessened differentiation does, in fact, exist, and that in the case of the father at least, it serves a useful function for the maintenance of the schizophrenic within the family. However, our study does not tell us whether or not this distortion of parental roles has been a cause of, or a reaction to, the schizophrenia.

In this connection it is interesting to note that our profiles of the male and female schizophrenic patients showed a surprising sex role reversal, the males being passive and withdrawn as compared to the normal boys, while the females were overactive and dominating as compared to the normal girls. This sex role reversal might be related to the distortion of parental sex roles.

Thus, our study suggests that fathers of schizophrenics play a peripheral role in the family. However, our findings also suggest that it is exceedingly important that they do play such a role, for their typical role of instrumental leader would be inappropriate, and probably damaging, in this context.

CHAPTER SEVEN

FAMILY INTERACTION WITH SCHIZOPHRENICS AND THEIR SIBLINGS *

SHLOMO SHARAN (SINGER)

A perspective on schizophrenia is emerging in which the illness is viewed as symptomatic of pathological interaction patterns in the entire family.[1] The empirical foundations for these family theories rest upon data from sources such as family therapy sessions, interviews, and the observation of families living on the wards of hospitals. However, there are to date only a handful of studies undertaking an experimental exploration of the complex issues surrounding the family life of schizophrenic patients.

The present experiment selected three aspects of current family theories for investigation. These were: (1) impaired problem solving within the family; (2) the formation of rival intrafamilial dyads; and (3) parental role-reversals and the crossing of sex-generation boundaries. If such behavior patterns are indeed manifest, are they associated exclusively with a schizophrenic child, or do they also pervade family interaction in the presence of a non-schizophrenic sibling? Are the normal children also involved in the same pathological family interaction as their schizophrenic

* Reprinted from Journal of Abnormal Psychology, 71:345-353, 1966.

siblings? If the family is schizophrenogenic, how does it happen that all of the siblings are not diagnosable as schizophrenic patients? [2] Clearly the presence of a normal child in the same family with a patient presents a challenge to the family theories. It also provides a unique opportunity for the systematic differentiation of those patterns of family behavior which may be specific to the parent-patient interaction in contrast to the parents' interaction with their nonpatient-child. The major task of the present study was directed toward precisely this comparison of family interaction with a patient- and a nonpatient-child. As such, it was a study of intrafamilial relationships and did not purport to provide information about etiological factors in schizophrenia.

Several observers maintain that communication in schizophrenic families serves defensive needs and possesses little instrumental utility for dealing with the environment.[3] On the basis of these observations, it was hypothesized that the family triad involving the patient should manifest impaired problem solving when compared to the triad with the nonpatient-child. Hence the hypothesis:

If disturbed communication in the parent-patient triad impairs problem solving, then the parent-patient triad should solve problems less efficiently than the parent-sibling triad.

The second parameter of pathological interaction which was selected for study in this experiment concerns the competition between the parents for the allegiance of their patient-child. It has been noted that when the family is split into rival dyads, the interaction of its members is marked by chronic conflict, and the parents do not form a mutually constructive relationship with the patient for purposes of problem solving.[4] These observations led to the expectation that, not only would there be considerable expression of mutually deflating and critical remarks in the family during the course of its problem-solving efforts, but that such destructive interaction should be more apparent in the patient than in the nonpatient triad. This expectation was supported by case reports of families with both a patient and a nonpatient-child who resided on a hospital ward for extended periods. The impression was that the intrafamilial conflict was confined largely to the parent-patient interaction.[5]

Two interview studies have addressed themselves to the normal child in the schizophrenic's family.[6] These authors concur that the patients were not singled out for systematic scapegoating or abuse by parents, nor were they subject to unusual physical or psychological traumata. Rather, it appears that the patients were always more passive, more sensitive, and less sociable than their normal siblings. By contrast the siblings always were less submissive and more independent than the patients. These studies indicated that the observations of some family theorists regarding the parental denigration of patients still require systematic, experimental investigation. Therefore, it was hypothesized that:

If the parents do not form a supportive relationship with the patient for purposes of problem solving, then the parents should be less supportive of the patient than they are of his sibling.

Finally, family studies have noted a reversal of roles between the parents of schizophrenic patients, as well as a breakdown in the integrity of the sex-generation boundaries between parents and patients. Fathers of male patients are allegedly passive and aloof from family affairs, while by contrast the mothers are reported to be the more aggressive parent, maintaining an engulfing, symbiotic relationship with their patient-sons. With female patients, the parental roles rotate, with the mothers aloof and withdrawn and in competition with their daughters. On the other hand, the fathers are aggressive, even tyrannical toward their wives, and they maintain an intensive, seductive relationship with their patient-daughters.[7]

Several experimental studies have examined the question of parental role-reversal. Farina and Dunham reported that the fathers of the patients with "good" premorbid adjustment, as well as the fathers of the control subjects (Ss), tended to dominate in their families, while the only tendency for maternal domination appeared in the families of patients with "poor" premorbid adjustment, although this tendency did not achieve statistical significance.[8] Caputo's results also did not support the role-reversal hypothesis: "bilateral rather than unilateral expression of hostility between those parents seemed to be characteristic . . . both parents . . . contribute to the so-called schizophrenic character of the family." [9] Cheek concluded that her results were inconclusive on the issue of parental role-reversal. Mothers appeared to be close to their sons only in contrast to the more peripheral position of the father, but these mothers were also cold, withdrawn, and expressed very little support of their patient-sons.[10] Haley found that the parents of schizophrenic patients tended to interact more with each other than with their child.[11] This finding might be consistent with the hypothesis that the parents form a closer alliance with the normal than with the patient-child. Lennard, Beaulieu, and Embrey interpreted their findings as consistent with the role-reversal hypothesis.[12] Family experiments have thus yielded conflicting results regarding role-reversal in the families of schizophrenic patients.

For the purpose of experimental clarity, the role-reversal hypothesis was subdivided into two parts: (1) the interparental relationship; and (2) the parent-patient relationship.[13] In respect to the interparental dyad, the observations reported by family theorists led to the expectation that the more active and dominant parent should be of the opposite sex of the patient. In a problem-solving situation, the dominant parent's answers should appear more often as the group's solution to the task than the answers of the parent who is of the same sex as the patient. Also, the dominant parent should be expected to participate in the family discussion more than the less assertive parent. Concerning the confusion of sex-generation boundaries, the dominant parent was expected to maintain a more intense and supportive relationship with the patient than the less dominant, same-sex parent did. The hypotheses, therefore, were as follows:

1. If there is a breakdown of parental sex-linked roles, then the patient and dominant parent should be of the opposite sex; and,

2. If there is a breakdown in the parent-child sex-generation boundaries, then the patient and opposite-sex parent should have

a more mutually supportive relationship than the patient and same-sex parent.

METHOD

Subjects

The families of 24 schizophrenic patients, each family including both parents and a normal child in addition to the patient, were selected for study. All families were tested in the hospital while the patient member was hospitalized with a diagnosis of schizophrenia. The hospital staff's diagnosis was accepted as the criterion for including the patient in the category of schizophrenia. None of the patients or siblings had histories of organic impairment or mental retardation, nor had any of the patients been hospitalized for mental illness prior to adolescence, and all patients had been hospitalized for 1 year or less. All normal siblings were functioning adequately in school or on jobs and had no history of psychiatric treatment.

The families were divided into four groups according to the sex of patient and sibling. Each group consisted of six families with the following sex alignments of the children: male patients, female siblings; male patients, male siblings; female patients, male siblings; female patients, female siblings. The mean age of each category of Ss was as follows: patients, 19.8 years (SD 2.4); siblings, 17.2 years (SD 2.6); fathers, 50.2 years (SD 4.1); mothers, 47.2 years (SD 5.0). All patients and siblings were unmarried and residing at home with both parents, except for the period of the patients' hospitalization. Thus, both in age and in marital status, these groups were more homogeneous than in previous studies. In addition, it was more likely that these people still constituted a family, in terms of fulfilling typical parent-child roles, than in research involving elderly parents with married children who had spent years away from home. All families were Caucasian, 15 of Jewish, and 9 of Catholic religious background.

Procedure

The Interaction Testing Technique devised by Roman and Bauman [14] was adopted as the research instrument. As used here, the technique consisted of the Comprehension and Similarities subtests of the Wechsler-Bellevue Intelligence Scale, Forms I and II, providing two comparable sets of standardized questions for use with the parent-patient and parent-sibling triad.

The testing procedure was as follows: All four family members were seated in such a way that they could not see each other's paper. Each one was given a mimeographed copy of the 44 questions from both forms of the two Wechsler subtests. The questions were combined so as to retain their progressive order of difficulty, that is, Question 1 from Form I was followed by Question 1 from Form II, etc. When everyone had answered all the questions in writing, the patient or sibling was asked to leave the room, the sequence of which child left first being alternated. The remaining triad was then given one copy of the questions from only one form of the Wechsler subtests, and they were asked to discuss the questions among themselves and formulate a response acceptable to the entire group. The examiner did not participate in and did not respond to questions during the group discussions, all of which were tape recorded. The instructions were as follows:

I am going to readminister some of the questions which you just answered individually. The purpose is to determine whether the group can do better together than each person was able to do alone. Please discuss each question among yourselves and agree upon the best answer. Try to have everyone participate in the discussion, and have one person write the group's final answer on this paper. There is no time limit.

When the questions from subtests of one Wechsler form had been answered, that child left the room and the same procedure, using the alternate Wechsler form, was followed with the other child. Testing sessions with a family ranged from 1 to 2½ hours, with the mean session being approximately 1½ hours.

Measures

The written responses were scored according to the standard criteria for the Wechsler-Bellevue Intelligence Scale.[15] From these scores a maximum and an actual score were calculated. The maximum score was obtained by selecting the highest score (0, 1, or 2) on each item obtained by any family member during individual testing. This composite score represents the highest score the group would have achieved had it consistently chosen as its collective response the best answer on each item proposed by any of its members during individual testing. The actual score is the score achieved by the group during its collective effort. Using these two scores, an efficiency ratio was calculated reflecting the extent to which the group in its collective effort utilized the resources of its individual members. The formula is:

$$\text{Efficiency Ratio} = 1 - \frac{\text{Maximum score} - \text{Actual score}}{\text{Maximum score}} \qquad [1]$$

The efficiency ratio increases as the difference between the maximum and actual scores decreases.

The information regarding parent-child support was elicited from a systematic analysis of the group discussion adapted by Mills [16] from Bales' [17] (1950) process-analysis technique. Each verbal act is scored in sequence in one of three categories: contributions to the solution of the group problem, and supportive or nonsupportive reactions directed to others, classified on the basis of Bales' criteria. Scorable acts in this study were limited to verbal statements exclusively, and the basic unit for scoring was any statement expressing a complete thought. Supportive statements will hereafter be designated as S, nonsupportive statements as NS.

In order to equate individuals for total production of S and NS statements, ratios were used instead of absolute numbers of such statements. A support ratio was calculated for each parent in relation to the child in each of the two triadic groups. Similar ratios were calculated for patients in respect to each parent. The support ratio formula is simply:

$$\frac{S}{S + NS} \qquad [2]$$

A high percentage indicates high support, a low percentage, low support.

The Wechsler responses and the group discussions were scored and coded blindly by two research assistants. Both coders, working independently, achieved 92% agreement on their coding of 10 pilot groups.

The measure of parental dominance was comprised of two parts: response dominance and total verbal activity. Response dominance occurs when one parent's response offered during individual testing appeared as the group's final response. If the group's answer matched the individual response of either parent alone, that parent was said to be dominant for that response. The total number of statements, as the second index of dominance, automatically results from the application of Bales' method which scores every statement in terms of speaker and listener (who-to-whom), as well as qualitatively.

RESULTS

Hypothesis I. Problem-solving efficiency

PREDICTION

The parent-patient triad will have a lower efficiency ratio than the parent-sibling triad when solving the problems from the Comprehension and Similarities subtests of the Wechsler-Bellevue Intelligence Scale.

A two-factor analysis of variance (with Groups of Families and Triads as the factors) applied to these efficiency ratios failed to yield any significant results. Each group of six families achieved a mean efficiency ratio of at least 85%, so that they fulfilled their problem-solving potential amazingly well. This high degree of efficiency does not conform to the reported descriptions of problem-solving "paralysis" in the families of schizophrenic patients.

The question may be posed whether this same degree of efficiency between the patient and sibling triads may not be an artifact produced by a compensatory maneuver of the parents who reject all of the patient's inadequate responses but accept the more adequate contributions of the sibling. In such an instance both groups could emerge as equally efficient. However, an analysis of the number of each child's individual responses which later appeared as the group's collective response failed to reveal any significant differences.

Hypothesis II. Parent-child support

PREDICTION

Parent-to-patient support ratios will be smaller than parent-to-sibling support ratios.

The difference between each parent's support ratios to the patient- and nonpatient-child was calculated. Neither the group of 24 fathers nor the group of 24 mothers showed a mean difference significantly different from zero. An inspection of the individual parent's support ratios to the patients and to their siblings revealed that many parents supported, or failed to support, both children in similar measure, while other parents did differ in their treatment of each child. However, the variability in the amount and direction of the differences was too great for any significant trend to emerge considering the size of the population. Thus, the evidence does not conform to the descriptions in the literature of marked differences in the interaction of parents with patients in contrast to the parents' treatment of their nonpatient children.

199

Hypothesis III. Parental role-reversal

PREDICTION A

Interparental reversals:

1. Mother's individual test responses should appear more often than father's as the group response in the triad with male patients.

2. Father's individual test responses should appear more often than mother's as the group response in the triad with female patients.

3. Mother should produce a greater number of statements than father in the triad with male patients.

4. Father should produce a greater number of statements than mother in the triad with female patients.

5. Mothers' individual test responses should appear more often in triads with male patients than in triads with female patients.

6. Fathers' individual test responses should appear more often in triads with female patients than in triads with male patients.

The means and standard deviations of the number of parental responses appearing as the final group response to the Wechsler items are given in Table 1. In each family-patient triad, the dif-

Table 1
Parental Response Dominance in Patient Triads

Group	N	Father		Mother	
		M	SD	M	SD
Male patients	12	5.42	4.52	3.08	3.03
Female patients	12	5.58	4.50	3.33	2.35

ference between the response dominance of the parents was calculated by subtracting the number of dominant responses of the mother from those given by the father. Table 2 presents the mean differences for the families grouped according to the sex of the patient, as well as for all families disregarding the patient's sex. All these mean differences revealed that the father's individual responses appeared as the group response more often than did the

Table 2
Difference between Parental Response Dominance in Patient Triads

Group	N	M Diff.	SD Diff.	t
Male patients	12	2.34	5.52	1.47
Female patients	12	2.25	6.55	1.19
All patients	24	2.30	5.92	1.90*

* $p < 0.10$.

mother's in all groups, regardless of the patient's sex. However, since none of the differences reached statistical significance, no evidence was found in support of Predictions A1 and A2 to the effect that parental response dominance would alter as a function of the patient's sex.

The number of parental statements made in the triads with the different sex patients was also analyzed with no significant findings. The mean number of statements made by the patients' fathers was consistently greater than the mean number of the mothers' statements, but the difference did not reach statistical significance. These "negative" findings also fail to support the predictions (A3 and A4) that the parents will be differentially active, verbally, as a function of the patient's sex. Both parents were equally active in terms of total speech production when in the presence of both male and female patients. Moreover, the tendency for fathers' statements to be more numerous than mothers' in both groups indicates that there was certainly no trend in the direction of less paternal than maternal participation in the group discussion.

Statistical analysis of the difference between the mean response dominance of the two groups of fathers (of male and female patients) and between the two groups of mothers failed to yield significant results. Therefore, no support was found for Predictions A5 and A6.

PREDICTION B

Parent-child sex-generation confusion:

1. Mother's support ratios to male patients should be larger than father's.

201

2. Father's support ratios to female patients should be larger than mother's.

3. Mother's support ratios to male patients should be larger than the support ratios of mother to female patients.

4. Father's support ratios to female patients should be larger than the support ratios of father to male patients.

5. Male patients will have larger support ratios to mothers than to fathers.

6. Female patients will have larger support ratios to fathers than to mothers.

Table 3

Parent-to-Patient Support Ratios

Group	N	Father			Mother		
		M	SD	t	M	SD	t
Male patients	12	29.67	14.09	2.15*	33.89	21.08	.39
Female patients	12	43.70	17.69	2.15*	31.18	12.17	.39

* p < .025, one-tailed.

Table 3 presents the mean and standard deviations of the parent-to-patient support ratios. Predictions B1 and B2 deal with the parental support to patients. In each family-patient triad, the difference between the parents' support was calculated by subtracting the mother's support ratio from the father's. Table 4 gives the mean differences for families grouped according to the sex of the patient. With a significant mean difference of 12.52, the results support Prediction B2 to the effect that the father supported the female patient more than did the mother. Although the mother did support the male patient more than the father

Table 4

Difference between Father's and Mother's Support Ratios to Patient

Group	N	MDiff.	SDDiff.	t
Male patients	12	−4.22	25.21	.58
Female patients	12	12.52	20.46	2.12*

* p < 0.05, one-tailed.

did, the —4.22 mean difference was not significant. Thus, the hypothesis of sex-generation confusion received only partial corroboration from the data gathered in this study.

Table 4 gives the comparisons for between-group differences (Subhypotheses B3 and B4). Prediction B4 is upheld since the group of fathers with female patients achieved a significantly higher mean support ratio than did the group with male patients. Again, no comparable finding emerged regarding the behavior of mothers toward their patient-sons in contrast to the support mothers offered their patient-daughters. Whatever crossing of generation boundaries occurred in the families was restricted to the father-daughter relationship, and was conspicuously absent in the mothers' relationships with their patient-sons.

The data which bear upon Predictions B5 and B6, to the effect that patients will support opposite-sex parents more than same-sex parents, did not reveal any significant findings. Patients did not support opposite-sex more than same-sex parents, and it is of interest to note that the female patients who received such marked support from their fathers did not reciprocate by evidencing any preferential support for them as compared to the support they offered their mothers.

Of additional interest was an analysis of the interaction in one family dyad not dealt with in the hypotheses, namely, the child-to-parent behavior.

The means and standard deviations of the child-to-parent sup-

Table 5
Child-to-Parent Support Ratios

Sex of patient		Patient triad		Sex of sibling		Sibling triad	
		Father	Mother			Father	Mother
Male	M	26.82	34.10	Female	M	29.90	22.25
	SD	16.60	22.79		SD	10.13	20.32
Male	M	33.82	40.70	Male	M	24.62	37.42
	SD	17.01	31.06		SD	16.33	12.29
Female	M	47.75	30.08	Male	M	16.18	22.67
	SD	15.70	17.71		SD	12.03	16.56
Female	M	36.58	47.48	Female	M	51.18	24.30
	SD	20.49	15.01		SD	17.30	12.46

Note: 24 patients; 24 siblings.

203

port ratios are presented in Table 5. Inspection of the mean support ratios indicated that the sex of the sibling was an important factor in determining the amount and direction of the difference between the patient and sibling support to each parent. Table 6

Table 6
Difference between Patient and Sibling Support Ratios to Parents' Support Ratios

Families with	N	To father			To mother		
		$M_{Diff.}$	$SD_{Diff.}$	t	$M_{Diff.}$	$SD_{Diff.}$	t
Male siblings	12	20.40	18.15	3.89†	5.35	14.26	1.30
Female siblings	12	−8.84	27.98	1.09	17.52	25.54	2.38*

† $p < 0.01$, two-tailed.
* $p < 0.05$.

provides the results of the statistical analysis of the mean differences, with the families divided according to the sex of the sibling. For each parent, the sibling's support ratio was subtracted from the patient's support ratio. In those families with male siblings, the patients offered significantly more support to their fathers than did their normal brothers, but the patients' support offered to their mothers was not significantly greater than that given by the nonpatient children. In those families with female siblings, the patients offered significantly more support to their mothers than did their normal sisters. The patients' sisters were more supportive of their fathers than were the patients, but this difference did not reach statistical significance. Further analysis of the child-to-parent support failed to reveal any evidence that the patients or male siblings tended to support an opposite-sex parent. However, the nonpatient females did express significantly greater support for their fathers than they did for their mothers: $t = 2.52$, $df = 11$, $p < .05$.

The final analysis concerns the difference between the number of S and NS statements exchanged among family members during the discussions. The intratriad statements were subdivided into their respective dyadic interactions: parent-to-child, child-to-parent, and interparental. The t tests revealed that in each case the NS

Table 7
Difference between Nonsupportive and Supportive Statements

Dyad	M Diff. *	SD Diff.	t†
Patient-to-parent versus sibling-to-parent	−17.83	34.70	2.52‡
Interparental with patients versus interparental with siblings	14.71	35.73	2.02§

Note: Mean difference of the differences.
* two-tailed tests, $df = 23$.
† NS > S statements.
§ $p < 0.10$.
‡ $p < 0.05$.

statements were relatively more numerous, at the .01 level for the patient-to-parent dyad, at the .001 level for all other interactions, with patients and siblings alike. These findings convey some impression of the interfamilial dissension expressed during the group discussions but without proper control groups no estimate can be made regarding the extent to which the schizophrenic family is unique in this respect.

Of special interest here are the differences between the quality of interaction of the various family members in the patient and sibling triads, such as parent-to-patient contrasted with parent-to-sibling; patient-to-parent contrasted with sibling-to-parents, etc. In each family the number of S statements exchanged between any two members was deducted from the number of NS statements. The difference found for each of the relationships within the sibling triad was then subtracted from the difference found in the parallel relationship within the patient triad in the same family.

A t of 2.52 ($p < .05$) reveals that the extent to which the NS statements predominated over the S statements was greater in the sibling-to-parent than in the patient-to-parent dyad. Also, the NS statements were relatively more numerous in the interparental dyad when the patient was present than when the nonpatient was the third party: the t of 2.02 approaches the .05 (2.07) level. Thus, the sibling was more critical of his parents than was the

205

patient, while the interparental conflict was more pronounced in the presence of the patient- than in the presence of the non-patient-child.

DISCUSSION

Contrary to the prediction, both parent-patient and parent-sibling triads exhibited an equal degree of efficiency in the solving of experimental problems. Similarly negative were the results relevant to the prediction that parents would address more S and fewer NS statements to their normal than to their patient-child. Parents were found to display great regularity in their support or nonsupport of both children. The findings concerning the presence of parental role-reversal also failed to substantiate predictions. Although the differences were not statistically significant, fathers' responses predominated over mothers' in groups with both male and female patients, and no reversal of roles was evident. In terms of verbal productivity, both parents were equally active, and no evidence was found with this measure to support the hypothesis of the aloof, passive father. These negative findings concur with reports from other behavioral experiments with families which also failed to corroborate the role-reversal theory.[18] In a study of psychological test protocols, the fathers of schizophrenic children were described as "driving" personalities.[19] The accumulating evidence thus suggests that there need not be any breakdown of the traditional parental roles associated with the emergence of severe pathology in a family member.

The second part of the role-reversal hypothesis predicts greater mutual support between patients and opposite-sex parents than between patients and same-sex parents. The results offered partial corroboration of the hypothesis. Fathers were more supportive of their patient-daughters than were patient-daughters' mothers, and these fathers were even more supportive of their daughters than were other fathers of their patient-sons. There was, therefore, a particularly strong attachment between fathers and female patients, but no similar trend was apparent in the mother-son relationship. This is contrary to the hypothesis as well as to the findings reported by Lennard et al.,[20] though it is consistent with the experimental findings reported by other investigators, as noted above.

In contrast to the regularity manifested in the parents' S statements addressed to both children, the children, on their part, evidenced distinct differences in the amount of support they addressed to their parents. Both children behaved similarly toward one parent, but differently toward the other parent. The normal children were far more critical of a same-sex parent than were the patients toward the identical parent. Both children were equally critical or supportive of the parent who was of the opposite sex of the sibling. Thus, the parent of the same sex as the normal child became the focus of divergent allegiances on the part of the children. In this manner the family may become divided into rival dyads, as suggested by some observers.[21] However, no evidence was found for the contention that patients tend to support an opposite-sex parent more than their same-sex parent. Even though the fathers exhibited marked support of their patient-daughters in contrast to that offered these girls by their mothers, the female patients did not reciprocate by expressing preferential support for their fathers over their mothers. Remarkably enough, it was the normal daughter who displayed greater support for her father than for her mother.

An analysis of the number of S and NS statements exchanged by family members revealed that, as with the ratios, parents did not vary in the relative number of such statements they addressed to both children. However, of great interest was the finding that the relative number of S to NS statements did differ in the child-to-parent and in the interparental dyads as a function of which child was present in the group. The patients were more supportive of their parents than were the siblings, and there was a corresponding change in the interparental support in which the parental discord was more marked in the presence of the less critical patient than it was in the presence of the more critical sibling. In this sense, the patient was associated with greater interparental conflict than was the normal child while he appeared to be more directly involved in conflict with the parents, or with one parent at least, than was the patient. This finding highlights the importance of the interparental relationship in the study of the patients' families, as is emphasized by Lidz [22] and others.

Consequently, these families manifested a shift in the balance of their various dyadic interactions as a function of the child's patient or nonpatient status. The behavior of the family members was interrelated in what may be characterized as a system-in-equilibrium, in which the children expressed varying degrees of criticism toward their parents, while the parents' expression of mutual criticism altered as a function of the child's behavior. Whether the more passive or active posture of the patient and sibling was a cause or effect of the parental posture, and whether this parameter was relevant to schizophrenia, cannot be established from these data.

There was a confluence of findings pointing to mother's generally unsupportive behavior in these families. As noted, she was less supportive of her patient-daughter than was the father. It was learned, too, that the normal daughter supported her father more than she supported her mother, so that she may have found her mother to be critical and unaccepting. Cheek described the mothers in her study as reminiscent in many ways of the so-called schizophrenogenic mother.[23] The hypothesis suggested here, however, is not intended as a reversion to the theory of the schizophrenogenic mother. Rather, it emphasizes how a rejecting mother's attitude influences the emotional atmosphere in the entire family.

The measures employed in this study were subject to a number of limitations, the most salient of which was, perhaps, the highly structured nature of the task and its relationship to intelligence factors. Furthermore, the number of statements expressed during a discussion may not provide a completely reliable index of parental dominance since a verbally productive parent may still be submissive in other ways. These findings point to the need to delineate more precisely the relevant parameters of what is globally referred to as a dominant or submissive parent. It is also possible that the behavioral experiment, with its cross-sectional framework, was too artificial to assess the subtle nuances of enduring family relationships which could play an important role in the emergence of mental illness.[24]

PARENTS, PATIENT AND SIBLING:
THE FAMILY TETRAD

INTRODUCTION

The two studies in this section are similar in research design, but in other respects represent markedly different theoretical and methodological approaches to the study of families and schizophrenia. Both Stabenau *et al* and Reiss include the well sibling of the diagnosed patient in their experimental situations and this brings them a step closer to the study of the natural family unit. From this shared focus on the family tetrad the two investigations diverge in their respective theoretical concerns and research strategies. Yet the two approaches, the first following a hypothesis-generating and the other a hypothesis-testing model of reseach, are complementary, each having different advantages and disadvantages. For this reason it is interesting to group them together and to compare them with each other.

Stabenau *et al* are concerned with many different qualities of families of schizophrenics that may distinguish them from normal and other types of families. As is typical in hypothesis-generating research, a number of different methods and sources of data are used. In our discussion we shall ignore their measures of individual psychological characteristics since our focus is on family interaction. In contrast, Reiss limits his attention to the ways families approach the solution of a common cognitive problem; he attempts to relate the different approaches to specific cognitive and perceptual changes in the members. His work assumes, and makes explicit, the hypothesis that there is a relationship between the cognitive dysfunctions, which are characteristic of schizophrenic patients, and the cognitive style of their families.

Different approaches to the measurement of variables and the analysis of data follow from these overall differences in research orientation. Since the Stabenau group's work is largely exploratory, no explicit hypotheses are stated. Therefore, the interaction measures used are not specifically linked to particular concepts or theories. Reiss states a set of specific hypotheses and develops new measures that are directly related to the concepts in the hypotheses. The advantages and limitations of each of these approaches will be pointed out as we examine the study designs, methods, and findings.

In addition to their common decision to include four members of a family in the experimental situation, the types of control families used in both studies are similar although the reasons for their selection differ. Stabenau *et al* include families of schizophrenic patients, juvenile delinquents, and normal children, the delinquent families selected to control for the effect of chronic psychological disorder in the child. Reiss selected families of schizophrenics, normals, and those with children who, upon hospitalization, had been diagnosed as "character disorders". The latter were used to control for the effects of hospitalization. It is in these two studies that we first find the systematic use of two non-schizophrenic control groups, each introduced to allow for the measurement of the effect of an important variable that has, up until the present, only been assumed to be significant. Here it is possible to test whether the child's psychological symptoms or whether the definition of the child as deviant is as predictive of a family pattern as is a specific symptom or form of deviance.

We have referred to Farina's study in particular as evidence for

214

the importance of another control variable—the type of schizophrenia. Neither Reiss nor Stabenau systematically differentiates within the patient samples. However, these experimenters bring to our attention two important issues concerning the selection of schizophrenic patients. Stabenau views both the validity of the psychiatric diagnoses of patients and the validity of the assumption of "normality" of the control cases as being problematic and open to question. In earlier studies the tendency has been to take hospital diagnosis as given; Stabenau, instead, uses the MMPI administered to all subjects to verify the classification of the family members. Reiss' work points to another dimension of schizophrenia that may turn out to be as useful in discriminating between types of families as is the process-reactive distinction. This is the paranoid-nonparanoid dimension. Since his sample is largely a paranoid one it is impossible to test for differences between these sub-types. However, other work concerning attention and perception in schizophrenia suggests that this is a variable that is important in explaining a patient's individual performance.[1]

We have previously indicated a number of experimenters' concern with controlling or measuring other variables that may affect the family's performance in an interaction situation. In these two studies, variables such as age, education, and social class are taken into account. The Stabenau group took great care to match the three sets of families on these three variables by drawing families from a larger sample. In both studies the attention paid to the selection of families in order to rule out extraneous effects makes the findings proportionately stronger than the small sample size —five families of each type—suggests. However, the basic difficulty with small samples remains; interesting and more complex analyses of data are not possible and the degree of generalization is limited.

The Stabenau group used the well-known and fairly standard method of revealed differences to generate interaction among family members. Reiss invented an entirely new experimental procedure that effectively structures the family's problem-solving attempts in an easily measurable form. In his study, the family members sit in booths that isolate them from visual contact with each other and can communicate only by written messages that are restricted in form and content to possible solutions to the experimental problem. The specific task that Reiss designed is closely related to his guiding hypothesis about the schizophrenic family's difficulty in dealing with cognitive problems and the relationship between family and individual cognitive dysfunctions. It is a pattern recognition task in which family members are asked to discover together the principle that underlies a series of examples given to them at the beginning of the session by the experimenter. The procedure allows everyone in the family a chance to test his own hypothesis, learn from the hypothesis-testing of every other member, and to influence every other member. In addition to the family's solution of the problem, Reiss also obtains from individual members their private solutions at two points in time, before and after the family interaction.

The experimental tasks used in these two studies demonstrate that interesting and theoretically relevant findings may be obtained from families working under widely different conditions. When the situation is structured only in terms of the topic for discussion and by an expectation that the family come to an agreement, as in the revealed difference procedure, the experiment "makes sense" to the family and they are able to adapt easily to the requirements of the situation and talk together. When the experimental situation differs radically from a family's usual experience, as in Reiss' study, family members are also able to adapt to these requirements and their responses are meaningful and relevant to the problem under investigation. While this latter experimental situation is clearly more artificial than those used in other studies, Reiss' success in securing the cooperation and participation of families should encourage other experimenters to consider the use of highly controlled and refined experimental procedures when these seem appropriate to the hypothesis under study.

The hypothesis-generating and hypothesis-testing orientations of the two studies lead toward two different strategies of measurement, each with certain values and limitations. The family inter-action tapes collected by the Stabenau group were subjected to two different measurement procedures. First, tape recordings and typescripts were reviewed for evidence of distinctive patterns of role-taking, affect expression, and modes of communication. The patterns subsequently found are reported as differentiating char-acteristics of the three types of families. This approach—an over-all "clinical" evaluation of the family discussions—is a valuable source of concepts and ideas for future measurement and research. However, in addition to usual problems of reliability, this evalua-tion apparently was not done blind, a factor which may have contributed to a list of family qualities that too easily fit stereo-typed views of the three types of families. These listed qualities, while suggestive, would be more useful to other researchers as sources of ideas for more precise measurement and study if the specific cues that were used to generate them had also been described. Stabenau's second measurement technique is similar to a number of earlier studies. Five aspects of interaction—for example, the total number of speeches—were objectively counted and averaged. None of these is directly related to an explicitly-stated hypothesis although each is interpreted as standing for a common quality of groups, for example, as an index of leader-ship, and each is assumed to be related to the more general family qualities noted in the typescript review.

While the Stabenau study suggests a number of interesting aspects of interaction for future, more rigorous research, Reiss' study provides examples of specific measures that are linked di-rectly to a limited set of hypotheses. This strategy has the consid-erable advantage of permitting the testing of hypotheses, but at the same time it may sharply limit the possibilities of new and un-anticipated findings. This risk is reduced because the experiment reported on here is only one of a series of independent but closely-related studies. By using the data from a set of experimental studies of the same families, Reiss is in a position to explore in depth a number of aspects of cognitive functioning at a family and individual level. The measures that Reiss uses are described in the body of his paper in sufficient detail that another investigator might replicate his measures. These measures are all derived from family member's performances on the private "before" and "after" questionnaires and from the messages sent by the members in the cooperative hypothesis-testing phase of the task. There are measures of the degree and type of change in concept formation from the "before" questionnaire to the "after" questionnaire. These measures indicate whether and how the family problem-solving situation that intervened between the two had an effect on the individual's cognitive performance. Specifically, did the individual learn from the other members of his family, or did the family problem solving experience serve to blur or lower his performance level? A second set of scores is derived from the joint family problem-solving situation and measures several aspects of the intervening process, such as whether family members simply copy the performances of others, whether they learn from the ideas behind others' hypotheses, and whether they are willing to take the risk of being wrong. All of these measures are closely tied to the specific requirements of the task and come from a relatively small amount of raw data, most of which is in a form that can be directly counted or compared without further preparation.

In previous sections we have mentioned the increasing complexity of data analysis problems as more members of the family are added to the design. While the increase in the amount of data calls for greater efficiency and control over data analysis procedures, the major problem is to distinguish clearly between different conceptual and empirical levels of analysis. Both Stabenau and Reiss are aware of the problem that several levels of family organization are measurable and that these have different conceptual meaning. Stabenau compares families as a whole along several interaction variables and also compares individuals within a family with each other to obtain information on intrafamily role differentiation. Reiss' study is a good example of how different conceptual levels may be linked to data analysis procedures to provide a detailed picture of family member's individual contributions to the problem-solving strategies of the family as a whole. He obtains scores for each member of the family and for the whole family; this allows for comparisons between families as undifferentiated social units as well as for an examination of each member's performance on the task.

One cannot speak of definitive findings in this area of investigation. However, findings may be viewed in terms of their heuristic value, their suggestiveness for further research, and the degree of clarification they bring to old problems and questions. In these respects both studies make contributions, but in different ways which are related to their differences as hypothesis-generating and hypothesis-testing studies. The wide net cast by Stabenau and his co-workers results in a varied list of dimensions along which the three types of families are found to differ from each other. Each family type is characterized by a particular set of role relationships, a form and intensity of affect expression, a style of interpersonal control, and a specific level of coherence and continuity in interpersonal communication. The measurement of these variables remains a critical and difficult task. Nevertheless, due to a range of dimensions that may be used to characterize schizophrenic families and to distinguish them from another type of pathogenic family, as well as from normals, the results of this study will be helpful in determining priorities for future research.

Reiss demonstrates the value of applying refined and sophisticated techniques of experimentation and measurement to the problem of the relationship between individual and family cognitive styles. He finds that members of schizophrenic patient families are able to perform as adequately as members of normal families when they work individually. However, their performance tends to deteriorate when they work together; this is true not only for the patient but for all members of the family. For members of these families, their understanding of the basic principle involved in the solution of the problem—their recognition of the underlying pattern that each example represents—becomes blurred rather than sharpened by the experience of testing their own hypotheses and seeing the hypotheses tested by others. Normals tend to improve in the clarity and accuracy of their cognitions as a result of this collective problem-solving experience. Members of schizophrenic families tend to copy each other's performance rather than to learn the abstract idea behind the concrete act; they avoid taking the risks that would be necessary for them to learn. Since the study was aimed at determining relationships between cognitive dysfunctions in schizophrenia, which are already established in much other research, and defects in the family's collective approach to cognitive problems, these findings on the disruptive effect on individual cognitions of the family's working together take on special significance. Reiss' findings apply in general to the family and are not specific to one or another member. Therefore, they support the assumption underlying the other work reported in this volume, namely, that the family as a unit requires investigation if we are to fully understand the pattern of deficits, symptoms, and deviance that is called schizophrenia.

CHAPTER EIGHT

A COMPARATIVE STUDY OF FAMILIES OF SCHIZOPHRENICS, DELINQUENTS, AND NORMALS *

JAMES R. STABENAU, JOE TUPIN,
MARTHA WERNER, and WILLIAM POLLIN

During the past several decades, one major innovation in the study of schizophrenia has been a broadening of the field of investigation, with a change of focus from the psychotic patient as an isolated entity to the patient and his family as an integral unit. Against this background, psychotic behavior has seemed much less incomprehensible. Here at the National Institute of Mental Health we have studied three groups of families, one with one child schizophrenic, another with one child a juvenile delinquent, and the third with a well-adjusted child; in each family there is a same-sexed, approximately same-aged sibling, neither schizophrenic nor delinquent, serving as a control. This paper is

* Reprinted from Psychiatry, 28:45-59, Feb. 1965. Presented May, 1964 to the Joint Meeting of the Amer. Psychoanalytic Assn. and the Amer. Psychiatric Assn. We wish to extend our grateful acknowledgment to Mrs. Josephine Harris and Mrs. Diane Gaston for their assistance in the collation and statistical analysis of the data; also to Arthur Rosenstein, Helen Petersen, and Katherine Kocel who kindly gave their time and energy in blind scoring the Object Sorting Test, and to Donna Greenough (Office of the Chief, Lab. of Psychology, NIMH), Janet Barclay (Section on Personality, Lab. of Psychology, NIMH), Anabel Reese (Adult Psychiatry Branch, Clin. Investigations, NIMH), for their work in making the blind rating of the TAT stories.

221

a report on the results obtained with three techniques: the Revealed Differences Test, the Object Sorting Test, and the Thematic Apperception Test.* From these data combined with certain clinical observations we have defined some of the characteristics which we found to differentiate the three groups of families.

Various investigators have described disorders within the families of schizophrenic patients. These have included disorders in the personality of the parents and siblings,[1] communication patterns,[2] interpersonal relationships,[3] and patterns of differential or

Table 1
Age, Education, and Social Class of 15 Families

Family member	Schizophrenic (5 families)			Delinquent (5 families)			Normal (5 families)		
	Age *	Educa- tion *	Social Class †	Age	Educa- tion	Social Class	Age	Educa- tion	Social Class
Father	49.2	12.8	2.6	52.2	11.4	3.4	47.4	13.6	2.6
Mother	46.6	13.6		44.4	11.8		45.2	13.2	
Index	20.6	9.2		16.2	9.6		19.0	13.2	
Control	20.8	11.8		16.4	10.8		17.8	10.4	

* Mean years.
† According to the Hollingshead-Redlich Index. See August B. Hollingshead and Fredrick C. Redlich, *Social Class and Mental Illness: A Community Study*, Wiley, New York, 1958, p. 66.

increased stress.[4] Each such finding has been represented as having a possible significant relationship to the appearance or form of the psychotic process. Such initial studies, though they have opened up new areas of thought and inquiry, have raised many basic questions. Several of these seem to be of particular importance. Are the behaviors that have been described merely a variation of the human process or are they or any part of them uniquely or differentially characteristic of the families of schizophrenics? A second question concerns what the relationship of such pathology to schizophrenia might be, assuming a relationship exists. Are differences in patterns of family interaction causally related to the pathology in the patient or are they merely a reaction to such pathology? Most schizophrenic patients are members of sibships

* Subsequent reports will consider the sibling comparisons and the etiologic significance of variables obtained from the life-history material, psychiatric interviews, and the other psychological data.

in which the majority of the siblings are not schizophrenic. Does the genetic difference between siblings explain the discordance of psychopathology in the siblings? Are differences in experiential factors more important? Or is a particular pattern or combination of these factors more crucial? One approach to the resolution of such questions is the research design we have utilized in this study and in a study of identical twins and their families.[5]

METHODS

The Sample

Thirty-five families have been studied during the past five years. The first nine of these constituted a pilot group. From the subsequent twenty-six families, three groups of five each were selected for this report solely on the basis of optimal matching for age, sex, sibling order, and social class. Table 1 presents comparative data for these three groups on age, education, and social class, and shows that there was no significant difference between them for any of these variables by analysis of variance.

The three groups of families met the following criteria: In each group the index case was respectively a schizophrenic, a nonschizophrenic delinquent, or a nonschizophrenic, nondelinquent "normal"; the control siblings were neither delinquent nor schizophrenic; no evidence of significant neuropathology was present; the family was intact and the children were raised by their biological parents. All families who were referred and who met these criteria were studied. Both parents and both siblings participated in all phases in the research. The schizophrenic indexes were inpatients; all other subjects were seen during outpatient visits.

All index and control siblings were between the ages of 14 and 28. In each group three of the index cases were male while two were female, and three of the control siblings were younger while two were older than the index siblings. All families were Protestant except that in the N group a father and control sibling were

Catholic, and a father in the D group subscribed to no religious denomination. Because of selection criteria the educational level of the normal indexes was somewhat higher and the age of the delinquent index and control was somewhat lower. The delinquent group also differed from the schizophrenic and normal groups in being approximately one level on the Hollingshead-Redlich index of social class. However, neither these nor any of the other matching variables differed to a degree that was statistically significant.

The rationale for the inclusion of the families of delinquents as controls in a study of schizophrenia was twofold. First, they provided a comparable family constellation which also contained a child with a chronic "psychological disorder"; thus, nonspecific reactions of guilt and shame to socially stigmatized illnesses were present in both groups. Second, the symptomatology of delinquency is, in the main, of an alloplastic nature which offers maximum contrast to the intrapsychic, autoplastic symptomatology of the schizophrenic. The families of normals provided a baseline against which the other two family groupings could be compared.

The index siblings in the S and D families were alike in their failure to cope in the customary way with society; therefore these sets of parents might see themselves as failures. On the other hand, the N families were chosen because of their child's successful adjustment, and the parents might be expected to be proud of his success and the recognition of his achievement. Such feelings of pride and success on the one hand and failure, guilt, and defensiveness on the other are thought to influence the nature of the information obtained, and we therefore have maintained an awareness of this possible bias in evaluating the material.

Diagnosis

The diagnostic judgments were based on interviews by two or more psychiatrists, as well as psychological tests. All S indexes exhibited, in addition to disorder of affect and association, secondary symptomatology of schizophrenia including either hallucinations, marked paranoid delusions, marked regression, or a combination of these. Duration of symptomatology ranged from 6 months to 9 years. The D indexes were referred by a court or other legal agency as delinquents. The specific behaviors leading to this designation—car theft, promiscuity, and running away—are examples of the sociopathic behavior described by Kaufman as characteristic of the impulse-ridden character disorder.[6] The N indexes were nominated by the staffs of a local junior college and a local high school. The criteria used were that the students have a better than average capacity to integrate competence in three major life areas: (1) in their academic work at school, (2) in their ability to maintain interpersonal closeness with a peer, and (3) in their ability to participate in social groups.* These indexes, as well as the control siblings in each of the three groups, showed no evidence of schizophrenia or delinquent behavior. MMPI profiles from twenty-four of the twenty-six indexes and controls who completed the test were entirely consistent with the clinical diagnoses of the index cases and the planned discordance in each of the groups of families. One delinquent index had a high score † on the schizophrenic scale, and one delinquent control was high on both the psychopathic deviate and schizophrenic scales. However, clinically they exhibited no evidence of schizophrenic symptomatology.

In the S group one father had been hospitalized with the diagnosis of manic-depressive illness. None of the other nine parents had been overtly psychotic and none had a history of sociopathic behavior. All of the MMPI scores were within "normal" limits. In the D group one father had a history of intermittent alcoholic toxic psychosis, and he and one other were considered to have sociopathic personality disorders with alcoholism. Three of eight parents in the group who completed MMPI's had scores in the pathologic range on the psychopathic deviate scale. In the N group there was no history of psychosis or sociopathic behavior, and all MMPI's were in the "normal" range.

* These criteria were adapted from Earle Silber et. al.[7]
† That is, greater than two standard deviations above the mean.

Procedures

All interviewing and testing procedures were introduced to each family in a similar manner and sequence. The initial face-to-face contact with the family was a recorded group interview in which two of the research psychiatrists met with the four family members. This was a semistructured interview which considered the family's feelings about coming to NIH and participating in the study, the index's current functioning, differences between the index and control sibling, and an overview of the family's modes of function and interrelationship. Subsequently, each of the four family members was seen by a psychiatrist for a series of recorded individual interviews. Additionally, each family member participated in an extensive series of tests which included the Rorschach, TAT, Object Sorting, and MMPI. During the second family meeting at NIH, the family participated in the Revealed Differences Test.

The Revealed Differences Test employed a procedure similar to that described by Titchener and Golden.[8] Each family member independently checked "yes" or "no" to each of a series of 16 statements and questions dealing with attitudes and opinions concerning individual family values. Some of these were: "Marriage is more important than the work one is doing." "There is nothing a person can't be or do if he really wants to and works hard to achieve it." "Do you believe that sex education is acquired outside the home better than in the home?" On those items where the four family members did not agree, the family was asked to discuss and resolve the differences in their individual answers and come to a common agreement. The investigator left the room, and the family interaction was observed, recorded, and subsequently analyzed. Although initially there was an artificial, game-like quality to the task, the families quickly became personally involved.

The Object Sorting Test was given individually to each subject, employing the method described by Rapaport.[9] First the subject was presented with one of 32 common objects displayed on a tray, such as tableware, toys, smoking utensils, and so on. He was then requested to select from the remaining 31 objects those that belonged with it. After he had done so, the subject was asked, "Why do all these belong together?" He then was asked to make similar groupings for a standard series of 7 objects presented in the same sequence to each subject. In the second part of the test he was presented with 12 different standardized groupings, each having some characteristic in common; and he was again asked, "Why do all these belong together?" The test protocols were scored blindly by three judges (interrater reliability, $r = 0.86$) trained in the Lovibond scoring method.[10] According to Lovibond, scoring criteria measure the degree of inhibition of inappropriate associational linkages and the extent to which nonessential linkages and irrelevant material interfere with the proper formation of categorical abstractions. Scores for each sorting may range from 0 to 3. A "zero" score indicates a clear, conceptual categorization or abstraction, while scores of 1, 2, or 3 indicate increasing degrees of conceptual impairment. Level 3 is characterized by extreme overinclusiveness, and personal, arbitrary, or autistic response. The total score for the 19 sortings may range from 0 to 57. A response was scored as a failure when the subject did not attempt to make a conceptual abstraction, but made a response such as: "I don't know," or "They don't belong together."

Other investigators have used the total impairment score as a way of comparing conceptual thinking among schizophrenics and controls.[11] However, we found the sum of "zero" scores more reliable than total impairment scores. Therefore, in this report the sum of "zeros" or "clear conceptualization" and the total impairment score for each subject will both be used.

The Thematic Apperception Test was analyzed by a technique designed to suit the goals of this investigation. Each subject was tested with 10 cards. For each sex, eight cards were analyzed. Cards 4 and 13MF were not included in the analysis because they did not elicit stories involving parent-child interaction. Cards

227

1, 2, 3 BM, 6 BM, 6 GF, 7 BM, 16 (blank card), and 18 BM were analyzed for the male subjects; and Cards 1, 2, 3 GF, 6 BM, 6 GF, 7 GF, 16 (blank card), and 18 GF for the females. A modified content analysis, with the focus on the pattern of parent-child interactional behavior as revealed in the manifest content of the stories elicited by these cards, was applied to stories narrated by all parents.* Types of interactional behavior were culled from the relevant individual stories and abstracted into higher-order behavioral modal categories with more generalized properties of content, described along the following subvariables: Parental attitudes and interaction, children's reactions, controls and discipline, basic trust, family atmosphere, success, failures and predicaments, and communication.

Three major parent-child interactional categories were defined by the investigators to characterize the modal pattern of the parent-child interaction as narrated in the TAT stories. The stories which did not reveal parent-child interaction were classified as "No parent-child interaction"—for example, peer-sibling or husband-wife interaction. Parent-child interactions which did not fit into the three categories, A, B, and C, were assigned to a nonratable group. The defined categories described behaviors and are not considered as synonymous with the diagnostic groups.

All identifying data were deleted from each of the TAT stories produced by the 30 parents. These stories were then assigned a random code number. Independent raters judged each of the productions using a scoring manual outlining the characteristics of the three categories, A, B, and C, and using operational methods described in another report.[12]

Another quality of the TAT stories that was measured was their clarity or fragmentation. Verbatim typescripts of each story for each of the 30 parents were blindly scored using the following ratings:

0—*Clear.* Story is clear and cohesive. Parts are relevant and association is, in the main, logical.

---

* The TAT responses of the index and control children will be described in another report.

1—Wandering. Main theme is apparent, although a shift in focus may distract. Logical but unnecessary secondary themes or parts reduce cohesiveness.

2—Fragmented. Story lacks continuity because of weak association between parts, illogical progress, or an inconsistency in mood or events.*

3—Blurred. No main theme is present; the story is vague, without clear order, focus, or goal.[14]

RESULTS

Revealed Differences Test

The characteristics which differentiated the interactions of the three family groups in the Revealed Differences Test were both qualitative and quantitative. Following repeated reviews of the typescripts and the tape recordings of these sessions, modal patterns of differentiating characteristics were defined for each of the three groups of families. Although there is variability and overlap between the groups, it is our impression that the modal patterns described in Table 2 do characterize and differentiate the three family groups.

As shown in Table 2, the major differentiating features were found to be in family roles, in the expression of affect, in family interaction, and in communication patterns. Overcontrolled affect, often inappropriate to content and behavior, was exemplified by families with a schizophrenic in which bitter, angry affect inappropriately pervaded the discussion on the question and was accompanied by an equally inappropriate, calm behavioral restraint. In other families with a schizophrenic, though the behavior was that of hostile rejection or exclusion of some members in their attempt to participate in the discussion, the affect was an inappropriate one of controlled, saccharine sweetness. The rigid

---

* Adapted from the classification of schizophrenic thinking by Lyman C. Wynne and Margaret Thaler Singer.[13]

family organization of these families, with distortion of role differentiation and expectancy, was characterized by imbalance in the leadership with frequent isolation, withdrawal, and blockage of assertiveness by the various family members. This rendered some members impotent in the family interaction or resulted in distortions of the socially expected alignments and roles.

In the families with a delinquent, affect was relatively uncontrolled, sharply intense, and at times counterfeit and artificial. Interactions showed a teasing manipulation with frequent open conflict among family members. Family organization was unstable with an absence of clear role differentiation. Members frequently competed for roles or abdicated from their expected roles. Interaction occurred between the parents, but they were frequently at odds with each other.

Finally, in the families with a normal control, affect tended to be appropriate, modulated, positive, and warm. Interaction featured considerable autonomy, a coping rather than manipulative or controlling pattern in dealing with the family members, and a goal of mutual understanding and satisfaction. Family organization was flexible with clear role differentiation and expectancy. Empathic awareness of each other's role was evidenced, and the father and mother tended to interact in a complementary manner.

There was no significant difference between diagnostic groups as to which of the 16 questions and statements evoked disagreement and were discussed. Therefore, we chose the four that were most frequently discussed by all families for a more detailed quantitative analysis. These were: (1) "A seventeen-year-old girl told her parents that at her age some of her personal affairs had become more important than home and family. Do you feel that the girl had the right to consider some things more important than home and family?" (2) "Do you believe that sex education is acquired outside of the home better than in the home?" (3) "There is nothing a person can't be or do if he really wants to and works hard to achieve it." (4) "Marriage is more important than the work one is doing." We systematically analyzed the family discussion of these four questions and statements—using original

230

Table 2

Transactional Observations from Revealed Differences Test

Family characteristics	Schizophrenic	Delinquent	Normal
Roles:			
Family Organization	Rigid	Unstable	Flexible
Pattern	Distortion of role differentiation or expectancy	Absence of clear role differentiation and expectancy	Clear role differentiation and expectancy
Role Stability	Maintenance of inflexible role	Shifting in competition for and assumption of roles	Empathic ability to project self into another role
Parental Complementarity	Father and Mother operate without complementarity	Father and mother interact—at odds with each other	Father and mother interact—complementing each other
Affect:			
Control	Overcontrolled	Undercontrolled	Modulated
Appropriateness	Often inappropriate to content and behavior	Appropriate to behavior but often inappropriate to content	Appropriate to content and behavior
Intensity	Low	Sharp	Varied
Quality (overt)	Shallow, apathetic	Counterfeit, artificial	Believable with some depth
Type (covert)	Hostile, anxious	Depressive, self-punitive	Positive, warm
Interaction:			
Interpersonal	Forceful control of others	Teasing manipulation of others	Personal autonomy
Environmental	Controlling interaction of family with environment producing guilt	Manipulating interaction of family with environment producing shame and doubt	Coping interaction of family with environment producing pride
Goals	Conformity to external standards	Self-centered satisfaction	Mutual understanding and satisfaction
Characteristics	Skewed power struggle	Open conflict among members	Cooperation, empathy
Communication:			
Focus	Misses primary theme or fragments it	Shifts from primary to secondary themes	Follows primary theme
Continuity	Flow disruptive and fragmented	Shift in flow between several themes	Flows with logical relevance
Clarity	Blurred—clarity never reached	Wandering—clarity reduced	Sharp, cohesive—clarity maintained

231

Table 3

Characteristics of Family Discussion of Four Questions
from Revealed Differences Test *

Characteristics	Schizophrenic	Delinquent	Normal
Interaction time (minutes)	33.6	49.7	51.4
Total times family members spoke	591	813	614
Overlaps per minute †	1.3	1.4	0.6
Interruptions per minute ‡	4.1	3.8	3.1
Pauses per minute §	0.6	0.2	0.8

* Values shown are means.

† An overlap was defined as occurring when two or more people continued to speak simultaneously.

‡ An interruption was defined as the speech of one member's being interrupted by another before completion of the thought or utterance, but not in response to a pause.

§ Only pauses longer than 3 seconds were included.

tapes and verbatim typescripts—for a series of 5 objective characteristics as shown in Table 3.

The results do not achieve statistical significance, as tested by an analysis of variance; however, the patterns of the differences are consistent with the transactional observations listed in Table 2. The impression from the transactional observations, that the N families are more organized, productive, and coherent seems substantiated by their longer interaction time, fewer overlaps and interruptions, and more frequent pausings. The D families, also productive, showed considerably more undisciplined, competitive activity, as indicated by the greater total number of times the members spoke, more overlaps per minute, and fewer number of pauses. S family interactions were the least productive, as reflected by the fact that the members spoke the shortest length of time and the least number of times. The schizophrenic group, like the delinquent group, had a high rate of interruptions and twice the rate of overlaps that the normals had. The schizophrenic index interrupted least and was the least productive as compared to all other S family members and the other indexes. Thus the S index was not overtly a major contributor to the interactional disruption seen in these families. In the N families the father was significantly more potent in initiating discussion $(P<.001)$*

* All P values expressed are two-tailed.

than other members of his family (supportive of clear parental role differentiation), whereas the fathers of the S group were only slightly more active than the mother and control. There was no such difference between D family members in initiating discussion, thus supporting the observation that the fathers abdicate the leadership role and no other family member occupies it.*

In addition to the objective analysis of the Revealed Difference protocol a global, impressionistic estimation of communication clarity was made. The results were rank-ordered, thus revealing the S families to be the least clear, the D's next and the N's most clear. These results and their correlation with other data will be evaluated in the discussion.

Object Sorting Test

The Object Sorting Test, scored by blind raters, was used to assess the degree of clarity of conceptual abstraction in the individual members of the three diagnostic groups (Table 4). A high "zero" score indicated clear conceptual abstraction. The mean "zero" score for the N indexes and controls was significantly higher than that for the S indexes and the D indexes. There were no significant differences between the S index and S control group, the D index and D control group, and the N index and N control group or between the S controls, D controls, and the N indexes and controls. Thus the expected impairment of conceptual abstraction was present in the S indexes; however, unexpectedly, the D indexes showed considerable impairment.

When the scores for the 57 subjects who took the test were placed in rank order, the N indexes and controls, N parents, S controls, and D controls had predominantly high (clear con-

---

* This observation may be related to the fact that the age difference between the older D fathers and relatively younger D mothers (7.8 years) was significantly greater ($P < .05$) than the difference for the N parents (2.2 years) and S parents (2.6 years). In the D families the older fathers and younger indexes produced a discrepancy in age (36 years) that significantly differentiated this group ($P < .05$) from the N (28.4 years) and S groups (28.6 years).

Table 4

"Zero" Scores of Indexes and Controls on Object Sorting Test

Group	Mean "Zero" Score
Schizophrenic:	
Indexes (N = 5)	9.4 *
Controls (N = 3)	14.7
Delinquent:	
Indexes (N = 5)	10.6 †
Controls (N = 4)	12.5
Normal:	
Indexes (N = 5)	14.2
Controls (N = 5)	14.2

* $P < 0.01$ S indexes vs. N indexes + N controls.
† $P < 0.01$ D indexes vs. N indexes + N controls.

ceptualization) scores, while the S and D indexes and the S parents and D parents had lower "zero" scores. The mean scores for these two groupings differed significantly $(P<.01)$. There was no correlation with age or educational level of subject except that the S and D parents contributed a significantly greater proportion of pathologically low scores $(P<.05)$.

Further, the parents in the N group scored higher in conceptual ability than the parents in either the schizophrenic or delinquent group. The mean values for the parents' "zero" scores, total impairment scores, and the number of failures are listed in Table 5. The significantly lower "zero" score for the D parents was accompanied by a significantly higher number of failures, and a high total impairment score. In general, persons who had a high "zero" score (clear conceptual abstraction) were found to have a low impairment score. Rank-order comparison of the two pro-

Table 5

Object Sorting Scores for Parents *

Parent group	"Zero" Score	Failures	Lovibond Impairment Scores [15] Level of impairment 1	2	3	Total impairment (loaded) score
Schizophrenic	9.2	2.3	2.8	2.8	1.2	12.0
Delinquent	7.5 †	5.1 ‡	2.7	3.1	0.4	10.1
Normal	12.2	2.0	2.0	2.1	0.3	7.1

* Mean values.
† $P < 0.05$ between D + N groups.
‡ $P < 0.06$ between D + N groups.

duced a significant negative correlation $(rho=-.43, P<.01)$. There was no other significant difference between groups by analysis of variance.

Thematic Apperception Test

A classification of the unidentified, randomized TAT stories of the 30 parents by an independent trained rater significantly differentiated the three diagnostic groups $(P<.001,$ Table 6). In

Table 6

TAT Responses by Parents
Types of Parent-Child Interaction
(Blind Rating) *

| | Types of parent-child interaction † | | | | | |
Parent groups	A	B	C	Nonratable	No parent-child interaction	Total
Schizophrenic	5	15	20	9	31	80
Delinquent	13	25	3	3	36	80
Normal	41	4	3	6	26	80

* Categories differentiate diagnostic groups $(X^2 = 78.15, 6dF, P < .001)$.
† For a description of these categories, see the accompanying text.

category A stories, which were most commonly told by the N group, parents allowed children to act with a measure of autonomy, demonstrated understanding of the child's need and right for self-expression, and saw children as capable of achieving success with adequate striving. Yet children were not necessarily described as automatically obedient or paragons of virtue. Throughout the different card contexts, whether the child was perceived as young, adolescent, or grown-up, parental help was available when needed, and communication was open. The parental figures in these stories displayed a basic trust in the child's skill and abilities. Opportunities for self-expression for the child were provided by the parents; but the children, preferring other activities, acted in an autonomous way—however, without guilt or fear that the parent-child relationship would be disrupted. Disciplinary views were firm and reasonable rather than harsh. Serious or dramatic crises between the parent and child were not described.

235

The over-all response was flexible, empathic, and highly child-oriented, and it provided an allowance for the child's self-differentiation.

In the category B Stories, as told predominantly by the D parents, the involvement of the parents with the children appeared superficial and impersonal, although the parents were depicted as strictly demanding, coercive, and punitive. The parents appeared to be superficially "proper" and "respectable" and displayed a characteristic attitude of need for immediate submission as a goal rather than a consideration of the child's needs, abilities, present situation, or long-range benefits.

In all age-contexts there was an absence of the child-oriented attitude found in the parents of the normals. When the young child did not submit to parental rules, privileges were denied, and at times physical punishment was threatened. When the grown child did not live up to the parental standards, he was rejected rather than advised, and the parents were described as moralizing rather than as giving moral support. Self-assertion by the grown child was often viewed in terms of the parent's own welfare rather than the child's future prospects.

In many stories parents perceived the adolescent and grown children as behaving in socially undesirable ways, and serious conflicts were at the core of the stories' plots. The little communication that was described usually involved quarreling, followed by voluntary or forced separation of the child from the parent. Disciplines described were harsh and inflexible, leaving little opportunity for autonomy. Children were seen as superficially cooperative, partly in order to avoid punishment and partly to bargain for privileges, thus appearing to manipulate rather than to cope with the environment. Little basic trust in the child's ability was revealed. Success tended to be attributable to a quality such as the child's looks, and none of the parents described success as achieved by adequate work.

The parent-child interaction in category C, as described predominately by the S parents, was intense and more personal, but was seen in terms of parental-need satisfaction rather than in terms of the child's needs. Children of all age groups were visualized as an extension of the parents—seen as their property, so to speak—and not allowed self-expression or autonomy. The disciplines described in these stories often swung from harsh demands to bribery and cajoling of the child, thus taking attention away from the child's own decision-making. Crises often were centered around hurt and confused feelings rather than any type of acting-out behavior in the children, as seen in the stories of D parents. Hurt and unresolved feelings often appeared in the stories where adult children strove for self-assertion. In response to the heavy and often confusing parental demands described in these stories, children were seen as bewildered, either momentarily or for extended periods of time. In contrast to the stories of the D parents, these children were rarely seen as acting out or as superficially compliant but as thrust into an apathetically inactive position. Many of the stories were blurred and fragmented by switching the plot in a manner that obscured the main issue of these stories.

Independent blind judgments made for clarity of thought, as expressed in the 300 TAT stories for the 30 parents, were correlated at a significant level with "zero" scores of the Object Sorting Test ($rho=.468$, $P<.01$). Thus, those parents who had clear conceptual abstractions on the Object Sorting Test had relatively clear stories in the TAT, while those parents with conceptual impairment in object sorting had fragmented or blurred TAT stories.

DISCUSSION

We have described family patterns which appear to be typical for each group and those which differentiate the three groups. Though there are differentiating patterns, there is overlap between the groups; additionally, within a group each family had its own unique variation. We do not believe these family patterns to be primarily either a reaction to the presence of a psychologically disturbed child in S and D families, or a parallel but unrelated phenomenon. The disordered behavior of the S and D indexes and the healthy coping in the N offspring appear to be integral parts of these significant, long-standing behavior patterns.* The above patterns of behavior, which differentiate the three groups, are seen most clearly in the triad composed of the parents and the index. In the S and D families interactions seen in the triad composed of the parents and the control are quite distinct and different from those which are characteristic of the parent-index triad, and may prove on further analysis to be quite similar to the relationships in the control and index triads of the N families.†

Based on our data, we believe that there are characteristics of the N parents and their interaction with each other and their children that promote and maintain psychological health in their children. Consequently, for a full understanding of schizophrenic or delinquent psychopathology one should consider the absence of these health-promoting characteristics noted in the N families, as well as the presence of the more obvious pathological factors which are unique to the S and D families.

Further discussion and comparison of the results fall into three major categories, presented below.

Family Organization and Roles

The D families seemed to lack organization and clear role differentiation. This led to an unstable relationship in which it was uncertain who would be the father, who would be the mother, who would dominate or be the leader, since each person was operating in conflict with the others, alternately competing for or abdicating his appropriate role. Thus there were no fixed roles, and it remained unclear as to who was responsible for carrying out those activities necessary for stability and continuity in the

* These conclusions are supported by historical and interview material from family members to be detailed in a subsequent report.

† The factors affecting this issue have been explored by William Pollin, et al.[16]

family. It appeared as though the index child was more involved in this competitive, conflict-ridden, unstable relationship with his parents than was his control sibling. The lack of role differentiation was supported by the fact that there was no difference between the D family members in initiating discussion of a question in the Revealed Differences Test. The differentiation was clearest in the N family where the father was most active in initiating discussion, the mother, next, and the children least. The S father was slightly less active than the N father; the S mother, in contrast to the D mother, was no more active than the S control, while the S index was inactive. These data support the observation of clear role differentiation and expectation in the N family and the relative absence of it in the S and D families.

In contrast to the D families' unstable organization, the S parents, operating from a position of power and control, seemed to be locked in a rigid relationship to each other and to the index. The consequent struggle and stalemate of techniques which have been described by Lidz and Wynne [17] frequently lead to role distortion, isolation, or domination. The flexible empathic and complementary relationships we observed in the N families are lacking in the S and D families. These different relationships for the three groups of families were also highlighted in the three differentiating TAT categories.

Communication Patterns and Thought Disorder

Data from the three different tests suggest that in the S and D families there were both individual disturbances in thought process and impaired communication at the family level. In the S families our findings were similar to those of other investigators in that the parents as well as their schizophrenic offspring demonstrated reduced conceptual clarity as measured by the Object Sorting Test.[18] Furthermore, the communication impairment that was observed in the S families in the Revealed Differences Test was similar to that described for families of schizophrenics by other investigators.[19]

239

Reduced clarity is shown by the D families in the Revealed Differences Test. This appeared to result in part from the individual family members' interjecting into the discussion related but personalized themes which were followed to the detriment of the primary task. Clarity was further reduced by frequent interrupting.

The schizophrenics and their parents had low "zero" scores (poor abstract conceptualization) on the Object Sorting Test. An unexpected finding was that the delinquents and their parents also had as low or lower "zero" scores on the Object Sorting Test, indicating a significant impairment of conceptual abstraction. The Object Sorting "zero" scores of the S and D control siblings (with a mean of 13.4) were comparable to the "zero" scores of the N index and control siblings (with a mean of 14.2). Thus, on this measure the S and D control siblings were more similar to the N siblings than to the index sibling in their own families.

Object Sorting Test responses of the D parents demonstrated that they frequently failed to give a scorable answer (Table 5), but rather responded with "They don't belong together," or, "I don't know." This, or course, reduced their "zero" score and may have masked a thought disturbance. It is equally plausible to suggest that such a response might have developed from a lack of involvement and a refusal to take the test seriously. There is evidence, however, to suggest that to some degree this failure represents a masking of impaired conceptual abstraction. It was found that there was a marked negative correlation ($rho=0.82$, $P<.01$) between the number of failures and the total impairment score. Thus in the D group, those parents with low impairment had the greater number of failures and those parents with high impairment had the fewer number of failures.

In an effort to further evaluate the communication disturbance in the S and D parents, the TAT stories from all parents were blindly rated for clarity or fragmentation. There was a significant correlation ($P<.01$) between reduced clarity in the TAT and low "zero" scores on the Object Sorting Test (D and S parents) and clarity in the TAT stories and high "zero" scores—

clear conceptual abstraction—on the Object Sorting Test (N parents). Impairment of communication on a family level may be related to impairment of conceptual abstraction in individual family members. Evidence supporting this thesis is that ranking of families for clarity of communication in the Revealed Differences Test was positively correlated with the sum of the parents' "zero" scores on the Object Sorting Test (rank order correlation $P<.05$). Some caution must be exercised in evaluating this association since the judgment of the clarity of communication in the Revealed Differences Test, although done without knowledge of the Object Sorting scores, was not a blind rating; and although the TAT rating was blind, it was a global, impressionistic judgment.

There was relatively little evidence of communication impairment at the individual or family level in the N families. To the extent that the communication impairment and thinking disorders—as measured by the above tests—are similar for the S and D parents, these findings suggest that (1) disordered thinking is not unique to the schizophrenic and his parents, and (2) such disorders of thinking in the parents may be necessary but not sufficient to cause the schizophrenic symptomatology in their offspring. Other factors, which may include rigidity in the family structure, suppression of affectual and individual expression, incongruence of messages, and biological factors, might be necessary to cause the schizophrenic psychopathology.

Symptomatology and Parent-Child Interaction

A conflictual interaction in the interdependent triad of the schizophrenic and his parents has been noted by Bowen.[20] Jackson has pointed out that the schizophrenic symptomatology serves a homeostatic function within the family of schizophrenics.[21] Rosen has described psychotic, schizophrenic symptomatology as an "acting in." [22] Johnson and Szurek state that the delinquent acts out the thinly repressed wishes and impulses of his parents.[23] A hypothetical extension of these observations as drawn from our data is that the schizophrenic may not be *allowed* the verbal and motoric acting of conflict that the delinquent is *allowed*. The schizophrenic may have 'available' only an internalized expression of conflict—"acting in."

The responses to TAT cards may be interpreted on a number of different levels.[24] Although the latent content of the responses is of interest to us, we chose to limit our interpretation in this paper to the manifest content and its logical extension. The three modal patterns derived from the TAT stories of the three groups of parents may serve to elucidate parent-child interaction and symptomatology within each diagnostic group.*

The Revealed Differences Test provides another source of data for description of the family relationships. It differs from the TAT in being an observable interaction of the family members which represents an ongoing relationship. In contrast, the TAT stories reflect parent-child and family patterns as expressed by a single member. However, we found the two sources of data to be complementary when compared within each of the three diagnostic groups.

Some support for the above hypothetical considerations may be found in the following: In the Revealed Differences Test interaction, the S family organization was seen as rigid, roles were inflexibly maintained, affect was overcontrolled, and interpersonal interaction was closely bound to external standards and was characterized by forceful control of others. In the D families there was loose, unstable family organization, shifting of the family roles, undercontrol of affect, and an open conflict among family members. Further, the TAT data described in detail above similarly tend to confirm the above formulation and the Revealed

---

* Singer and Wynne found differing TAT responses that characterized the parents of schizophrenics and neurotics.[25] The social class level for the D group was almost one level lower than for the N and S groups (although this was not a statistically significant difference). Even though studies demonstrate that there is no correlation between the social desirability of a TAT theme and the frequency of appearance of a theme in the stories, the possibility remains that the effects of social class on child rearing attitudes and practices may partially explain some of the differences between the data for the D families and those for the other family groups.[26]

Differences Test observation. In the TAT data from the S parents, discipline was seen as harsh. Parent-child interaction was intense but was mainly in terms of parental-need satisfaction, and the child was often seen as inactive and as an "extension" of the parents. In the stories of the D group, parent-child interaction was superficial and impersonal. The demand was for expedient action, and when the parental "standards" were not met, the child was automatically rejected.

Both the observed interaction of the N families in the Revealed Differences Test and the TAT findings reveal the presence of warmth and empathy, the promotion of autonomy, complementarity between the parents, and encouragement for differentiation of the child. These are consistent with descriptions by other investigators of healthy adolescents and their families.[27]

This paper has presented only a small part of our study of three matched groups of five families each, composed of father, mother, an index sibling, and a control sibling. In these families, the index sibling is either schizophrenic, a nonschizophrenic delinquent, or nonschizophrenic and nondelinquent: and the control sibling is neither schizophrenic nor delinquent. While we have studied these families with an extensive battery of psychiatric and psychological test procedures, here we have reported only on our use of three structured techniques—the Revealed Differences Test, Object Sorting Test, and TAT.

Similar and complementary data were derived independently from the TAT and the Revealed Differences Test, describing characteristic modal interactional patterns for each family. The Object Sorting Test was used for an objective assessment of conceptual thinking, and yielded significantly higher "clear conceptualization" scores for the members of the "normal" families and for the control siblings in the "delinquent" and "schizophrenic" families than for the parents and indexes of the "delinquent" and "schizophrenic" families. Thus, thought disorder was not found to be limited to parents of schizophrenics, but also appeared in parents of offspring of a contrasting psychopathology—juvenile delinquency. There was also evidence in the families of schizophrenic and delinquent offspring of a communication impairment.

Further results showed that the family organization of the delinquent offspring was unstable, and roles were not reliably executed by the parents. In contrast, the family of the schizophrenic was rigidly stable, but often with resultant isolation or distortion. The families of normal offspring exhibited a flexible relationship with a consistency of family organization and reliability of role fulfillment.

It also appeared that in the "normal" families affect expression was predominantly genuine, and expressed freely and without anxiety. In the families with a schizophrenic offspring, warmth was lacking and affect was overcontrolled, but anxiety and hostility were nonetheless expressed frequently. In the families with a delinquent offspring, affect was quite artificial and uncontrolled.

Family interaction and the pathology of the offspring are more understandable when attention is paid to what "healthy" elements are absent from the families with schizophrenic and delinquent children, as well as to the presence of unique "pathogenic" factors in such families. The significantly different parent-child interaction as seen in the TAT productions of the three diagnostic groups, supplemented by the differences in family transactional behavior, are clearly correlative with the differing symptomatology in each group. These data support, but do not prove, the hypothesis, that differing patterns of interaction between parents and child are causally related to the development of psychopathology and the establishment and maintenance of mental health.

CHAPTER NINE

INDIVIDUAL THINKING AND
FAMILY INTERACTION, II. A STUDY
OF PATTERN RECOGNITION AND
HYPOTHESIS TESTING IN
FAMILIES OF NORMALS, CHARACTER
DISORDERS, AND SCHIZOPHRENICS * †

DAVID REISS

Recent clinical and experimental studies of families of schizophrenics have suggested that family interaction may have a critical role in shaping and maintaining the disorders of thinking and perception in schizophrenia. This is a report of one of a series of laboratory experiments that have been designed and executed to answer part of the general question of the relationship of family process to individual thinking.[1] Specifically, we asked three related questions: (a) Can it be shown, in the laboratory, that family interaction can influence some form of perceiving and thinking in its members? (b) In what way does this influence occur? (c) Are there special forms of such a relationship, between family interaction and thinking, in families of schizophrenics?

The present study was stimulated by the work of Wynne and Lidz and their associates.[2] Both have used experimental measures

* This study was carried out while the author was a Research Fellow in the Laboratory of Social Psychiatry, Massachusetts Mental Health Center and was supported by grants from The Milton Fund, Harvard University and the Medical Foundation, Boston. Present address: National Institute of Mental Health, Bethesda, Maryland.

† *Reprinted from the* Journal of Psychiatric Research, *5:193-211, 1967.*

of perceptual and cognitive function in family members of schizophrenics. They found that parents of schizophrenics typically displayed bizarre categorization of objects, failed to maintain persistent and goal-oriented sets and attention deployment, had delayed or absent perceptual closure leading to the experience of perceptual meaninglessness, and could not maintain consistent or appropriate relationships with the experimenter. Both groups of investigators inferred that the parents' performance in the experimental situation was characteristic of their enduring cognitive and interpersonal styles. They reasoned that parents' interactions with their children were pervaded by the same problems of attention deployment, perceptual meaninglessness, and inconsistent interpersonal distance. They further hypothesized that somewhere in the course of their development, offspring of these parents acquired the same disordered attentional styles, classificatory systems, and interpersonal deficits, which become the core of their schizophrenic illness. However, these investigators did not systematically specify the links between interaction of parents and offspring and the induction of cognitive and perceptual deficits in the latter, nor did they study this directly. The present study was designed to determine the presence and nature of some of the links between family interaction and perceptual and cognitive change in its members.

As the cognitive function for study in the present experiment, we selected pattern-concept formation. Previous studies have suggested that defects in pattern recognition and perceptual closure are characteristic of many schizophrenic patients.[3] Experimental studies of this kind, on perceptual and cognitive functioning, have made considerable headway towards defining a central psychologic defect in schizophrenia.[4] The methods used in the present study are based in part on a study by Bruner of concept attainment in normals.[5] He showed that the way individuals search for information about a particular concept, their strategies of hypothesis testing, is a critical step in concept attainment. We assumed that the process of hypothesis testing plays an equally critical role in concept attainment in schizophrenic patients and their families.

246

Therefore, if family interaction interferes with concept attainment in its members, it might do so by affecting their hypothesis-testing strategies. In the present experiment, we told families what kind of concept they were to attain and gave each member a small amount of information about a particular concept. Then we required the family to work together to construct hypotheses, confirmed or infirmed by the experimenter, in order to learn more about the concept. We assumed that this collaborative effort represented a significant sample of family interaction and its effects upon hypothesis testing. After the collaborative hypothesis testing was complete, we measured the character of the pattern concepts attained by each individual. We found that families of schizophrenics, as compared with other families in the study, showed defects in both collaborative hypothesis testing and in pattern concepts attained by individual members. We made a number of objective qualitative assessments of the hypotheses tested and concepts attained to determine whether the defects in concepts in family members might reasonably be ascribed to the characteristics of the collaborative hypothesis testing in which they participated.

SUBJECTS

The experimental sample consisted of three groups: five families of normals, five of character disorders, and five of schizophrenics. We used four members of each family: the parents, patient, and sibling nearest in age (but not always of the same sex as the patient). The families of normals were obtained through church and college lists; no individual in any of these families had ever had a psychiatric hospitalization. The child whose name appeared on the list that was used to locate the family was designated as the "patient control." The character-disorder patients were all hospitalized for clinical problems centering around inability to control impulsive behavior; they showed no evidence of schizophrenia at any psychiatric examination. The

247

schizophrenic patients had all shown gradual onset of increasing social withdrawal culminating in a definite psychotic attack or series of repeated attacks, all of which included severe associational disturbances, pervasive delusions and/or autistic and incoherent speech; four showed paranoid symptomatology. All patients were in full or partial remission at the time of the study. The character-disorder group was included to control the effects of psychiatric hospitalization on family performance in the test situation. The patients were males in two normal, two character disorder, and one schizophrenic family: the sibs were the same sex as the patient in five normal, two character disorder, and three schizophrenic families. In order to ensure that all subjects would understand the instructions, the selection criteria specified a restricted age range, fluency in English, and a minimum education. Thus, in all families, children were at least 15 years old and U.S.-born. The parents were all 60 years old or less, had completed high school, and all but two were U.S.-born. Table 1 shows that there were a significantly fewer number of subjects who had matriculated at college (whether graduated or not) in the character-disorder group.

The college-matriculated subjects were fairly evenly distributed among families within groups; there were at least two in each of the normal and schizophrenic groups and at least one in each character-disorder family. Table 1 also shows there was no sig-

Table 1

Comparison of Individual Members of Families of Normals,
Character Disorders, and Schizophrenics

Education	Number of subjects			
	N	CD	S	p *
High school	5	12	4	
College	15	8	16	.05

Generation	Mean age			
	N	CD	S	p †
Parents	51.6	46.4	52.9	n.s.‡
Children	20.3	19.0	21.0	n.s.

* Two-tailed chi-square test.
† Analysis of variance.
‡ Not significant.

nificant difference, across groups, between the mean age of parents or children.*

PROCEDURE

The family was seated in a series of connecting booths as illustrated in Fig. 1. The booths prevented subjects from seeing each

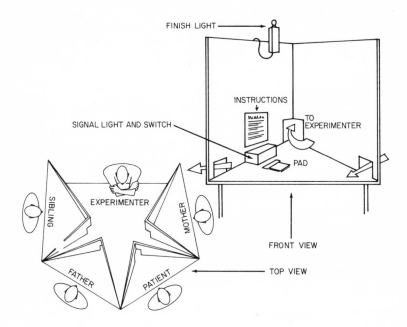

Fig. 1. Top view and subjects' view of the experimental apparatus.

* Each individual subject received several different tests of verbal and perceptual-motor intelligence. Although the collection and analysis of these data are not complete, present evidence suggests that the three groups of families were comparable on some measures of intelligence and not on others. These data are not reported here because the relationship between individual intelligence and performance in this experiment appears complex. Consequently, detailed analyses and discussion are required and will be presented in a later report.

other and the experimenter. Passageways permitted the passage of slips between each member and the experimenter.

Once the family was seated there were six steps to the procedure: (1) *Distribution of example sequences* from the experimenter to each subject; (2) *Distribution of the first private inventory* from the experimenter to each subject, the subjects' responses and return of inventories to the experimenter; (3) *Hypothesis testing* by each subject. Each subject had several turns to initiate this cycle which had several steps. (4) *Completion of hypothesis testing* by each subject at his discretion. (5) *Distribution of the second private inventory* by the experimenter to each subject and their responses and return of the inventories to the experimenter, and (6) *Return of the examples* by each subject to the experimenter.

Sample Task

This task was given first and designed to instruct the subjects in all of the above steps except 2 and 5.

1. *Distribution of example sequences.* The experimenter gave each subject a card containing four sequences of circles (C) and triangles. (T): C C C T, C C C C T T, C T T T, C C T T T T. The subjects were told that all four sequences shared a common pattern and that the objective of the puzzle was to recognize this pattern. The experimenter then showed the family another sequence C C C T C and said this did not have the same pattern although the difference between this and the other four was not made explicit.

2. This step was omitted in the sample task.

3. *Hypothesis testing.* Each subject had a chance to initiate the series of procedures in this step: mother went first followed by patient, father and sibling and then mother began again the cycle repeating until 4 (see below).

   a. Turn signal. A steady white light came on in a subject's booth to indicate it was his turn.

   b. Sequence construction. He was provided with a pad with

pages serially numbered. For each subject, every page of the pad had a letter identifying whether he was mother, patient, father, or sib. He was instructed to tear off the top slip and write down any sequence of circles and triangles he wished— as a way of guessing or hypothesizing about the correct pattern.

c. *Rating the sequence.* The subject passed his slip to the experimenter. If the sequence on it was written out according to the pattern of the examples ("An uninterrupted run of any number of circles followed by an uninterrupted run of any number of triangles") it was checked and a flashing white light came on in everyone's booth. If it were not, it was X'd and a flashing red light came on in everyone's booth.

d. *Distribution of the rated sequence.* The sequence just rated was passed through all booths for everyone to see in this way: the experimenter passed the slip with the sequence to mother (no matter who constructed the sequence); she passed it to patient who passed it to father; he passed it to sibling who passed it to the experimenter; he returned it to the subject who had constructed it. In this way each subject could learn about the pattern from trying out his sequences and, if he were attentive, from the trials of others in his family. Each subject, for his first turn in the sample task, was given a sequence to construct; thereafter, each made up his own. On her first turn, mother was told to construct C C T T C; after it had been passed through the family, they were told this sequence was wrong because it ended with a C. The patient was told to make up C T T T T; after it had been passed, the family was told this sequence was right because it began with a circle and ended with triangles. Father was told to make up C C C T T C T and sibling C C T T T, but the family was not told why the first was wrong or the second right.

4. *Completion of hypothesis testing.* When any subject felt he had discovered the correct pattern he could signal this by turning on his "finish light" (Fig. 1). He was required to take at least three turns before turning it on. After this, he still had to make up sequences each time that it was his turn, submit them to the

experimenter, and have them circulated among the rest of his family. However, the sequence submitted by the subject—after his finish light was on—would not be rated right or wrong. Although it was not made explicit, a subject would—presumably—submit only sequences he believed were correct after he had turned on his finish light. The hypothesis-testing step was over when all subjects had turned on their finish lights. If any of the subjects took more than ten turns before turning on the finish light, the experimenter stopped the hypothesis-testing step.

5. This step was omitted in the sample task.

6. The *subjects returned the examples* to the experimenter.

The subjects were permitted to ask questions about the experimental procedures during the sample task. If they asked questions about the characteristics of the pattern, they were told they should try to discover the answer themselves. Subject's performance in the sample task was not used as data. All families became quickly involved in the task, and the sequences they constructed showed they understood the instructions.

Experimental Tasks

Two experimental tasks, with procedures identical to each other, followed the sample task.

1. *Distribution of example sequences.* Each subject received one example sequence and was told it was constructed according to a pattern different from the preceding puzzle. In each experimental puzzle, the two examples given to the parents were constructed in a pattern different from the one used for the children's example. In experimental problem 1 the two patterns were: (a) "A sequence must begin with a C, to be followed by any number* of T's, and end with a C," and (b) "A sequence must begin with T, be followed by any number of C's, and end with a T." Parents received examples from the first patterns: CTC (father) and CTTTTTTTC (mother). Children received examples from the second: TCT (patient) and TCCCCCCCT (sibling). In prob-

---

* Any number was zero to infinity.

lem 2 the two patterns were: (a) "A sequence must begin with a C, be followed by an S (square), be followed by any number of T's, and end with an S," and (b) the same as pattern a of problem 1. Parents received examples of pattern a: $CSTTTTTT$-TS (mother) and $CSTS$ (father); and children received examples of b: $CTTTTTTTC$ (patient) and CTC (sibling). The two patterns to be learned in each problem were called *target patterns*, and all sequences that conformed to these patterns were called *target sequences*. The target pattern used to produce the parents' examples was called target-parent, and that used to produce the children's, target-child, symbolized T_p and T_c respectively. Two target patterns were used in each problem to detect responsiveness of both generations to each other in the hypothesis-testing step. It was assumed that at the start of the task, most individuals would test hypotheses like their examples. Because the examples given to the two generations differ, their initial hypotheses should also differ. If individuals are responsive to the performance of the other generation, they should be stimulated by them to construct hypotheses similar to the other generation's. If they are unresponsive, we assume they would continue, without much variation, to construct hypotheses very much like their own example. In most cases, the responsive individual would be expected to learn the concept of his example and the concept of the other generation's examples. The unresponsive individual, at best, would be expected to learn just the concept of his own example. Subjects were not told that each had received a different example.

2. *Distribution of the first private inventory.* The private inventory was distributed to each subject to determine what pattern he inferred from his example before he had a chance to participate in the collaborative hypothesis testing. The inventory was a sheet containing five sequences of the T_p type, five of the T_c type, and ten that were similar but not identical to T_p or T_c. The subject was instructed to check all those sequences he believed, in advance, might be rated as right. We assumed the subject's prediction corresponded to his inference of the pattern from his example. It was expected that no parents, at this point in the

task, would check sequences of the T_c type. However, after each member had a chance to observe what sequences others were constructing, a parent might check sequences of the T_c type, and vice versa. Individuals never learned about each other's performance on the private inventory. A more detailed description of the construction and scoring of the private inventory is in the Results section.

3. *Hypothesis testing.* This step was accomplished as in the sample task. If any subject made up a sequence of the T_p or the T_c type it was confirmed; all others were infirmed.

4. *Completion of hypothesis testing.* This was accomplished as in the sample task. When all finish lights were on, the slips containing the hypotheses were collected. Because they were serially numbered and each contained a letter identifying its author, they could be reassembled later in the order in which they had been constructed during the task.

5. *Distribution of the second private inventory* was accomplished in the same way as in step 2. This determined the pattern concept attained by each subject after completion of hypothesis testing.

4. *Return of the examples* by the subjects completed the puzzle.

RESULTS

In this section the performances of the groups of families are compared in three ways: (a.) Comparisons of their performance on the initial inventory permits inferences concerning the relative influence of problem-solving ability and family interaction on final performance; (b.) comparisons of change in performance from initial to final inventory which permit inferences concerning changes in individual pattern concepts during the task; and (c.) comparisons of the characteristics of hypotheses tested that permit inferences concerning the type of interaction in each group of families. We assumed that the performances of individual mem-

254

bers of the same family were too interdependent for the analysis to consider individual performance independent of family membership. Accordingly, our primary unit of analysis was the family as a whole; we considered our sample to consist of three groups of five families each, rather than sixty individual subjects.

There are two important reasons for comparing the performance of groups of families on the initial inventory. First, the quality of a subject's initial performance sets a logical limit on the kinds of changes that can occur in his performance as the result of collaborative work with his family in the testing phase. For instance, if a subject infers both target (correct) patterns from the single example presented to him initially, there is no possibility that he can learn the second patterns in the course of testing. Therefore, to make meaningful comparisons between families— in terms of changes from initial to final inventories—we need to know that all families had the same possibilities for change. Secondly, comparability of family members' performance on the initial inventory permits more certain inferences about the short-term effects of family interaction on individual pattern recognition. We assumed that a family member's performance on the initial inventory reflected his individual capacities more accurately than did his performance in the testing phase or on the final inventory; the latter two were probably partially or entirely dependent on short-term effects of family influence. Therefore, if families' performance is comparable on the initial inventory— but not on the final—we may infer that there are corresponding differences in the effect of family influence and interaction. However, if families also differ on the initial inventory, we do not know whether differences on the final inventory are due to inequality of competence of individual members or inequalities of interaction between members.

The comparability of groups of families on the initial inventories of problems 1 and 2 is shown graphically in Fig. 2. On the basis of sequences he selected as correct on the initial inventory, each subject was placed in one of four categories according to criteria described later in this section. (a.) *Both-target*: Subject appears to have learned pattern concept of examples given to him and to the other generation. (b.) *One-target*: Subject appears to have learned concept of his own example. (c.) *Probe*: Subject learned a concept similar but not identical to that of his example (these approximate concepts are described below). (d.) *Not ascertainable*: The subject learned a peculiar concept or was be-

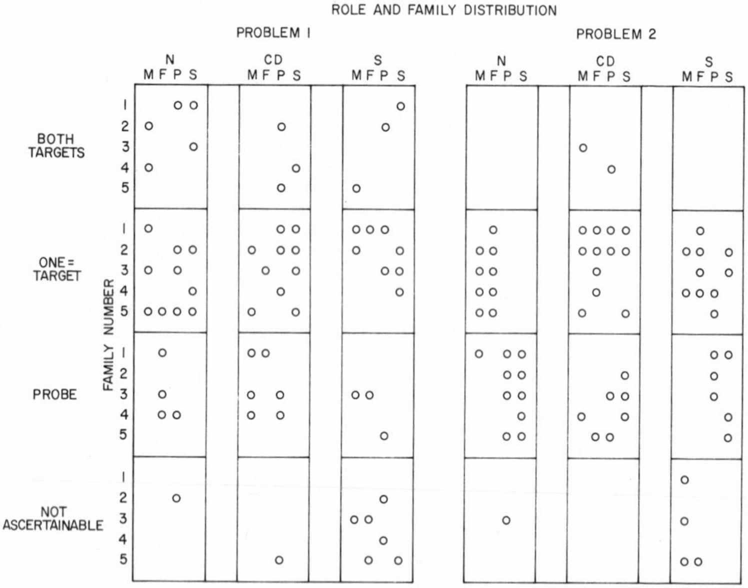

ROLE AND FAMILY DISTRIBUTION

PROBLEM 1 — PROBLEM 2

(Columns: N [M F P S], CD [M F P S], S [M F P S] for each problem)

Row groups by Family Number (1–5): BOTH TARGETS, ONE = TARGET, PROBE, NOT ASCERTAINABLE.

Fig. 2. Comparability of performance on the initial private inventory of problems 1 and 2. Each circle corresponds to the score obtained by one subject in problem 1 and 2. Circles are positioned in the cells according to the subject's performance, role, and family membership.

having randomly. Each of the diagrams in Figure 2 is divided into fifteen large cells, and each of these cells is subdivided into five rows, one for each family, and four columns, one for each role. The inventory performance of each subject is indicated by a circle that is positioned on the diagram according to the subject's group (normal, character disorder, or schizophrenic), family, role, and performance. This diagram can be used to compare families by showing the distribution of various types of inventory performance within each family and by indicating the performance of role players. In both problems, individuals scored as one target or probe seem to be evenly distributed through families in all groups. On problem 1, there is a tendency in most families, in all three groups, for one target performance to be distributed among the children and probe performance among the parents; the reverse appears to be true in problem 2. On problem 1, a number of individuals achieved both targets and these are fairly evenly distributed in families of all three groups. Only two individuals achieved both-target initially in problem 2. In general, the groups of families were quite comparable. The major difference between groups of families was the distribution of not-ascertainable performance patterns. These were distributed almost exclusively in families of schizophrenics: in 4 of the 5 families on problem 1 and 3 families on problem 2. All subjects scored as one-target or probe, except one, accepted the probe or target like their own example (e.g., all fathers rated as one-target or probe preferred either the T_p, $P1_p$ or $P2_p$ subsets). This implies that, on the initial inventory, individuals had a preference for sequences with structure similar to their own example.

The method for categorizing subject's performance on the initial inventory was based on the following rationale.

At the start of the task a number of inferences about patterns, from a single example of a correct sequence, are logically acceptable; in fact, subjects do make a number of different inferences at the start of each problem. Therefore, a more comprehensive comparison between families—at the start of each task—would

257

include a comparison not only of the number of individuals in-
ferring the target patterns but a comparison of the number
achieving various other pattern concepts as well. In the experimental trials and previous work, one kind of performance was
very common: subjects would recognize only one of the several
attributes of the sequential pattern of their example. This was
manifest in their performance on the private inventory where
they accepted: (a.) all sequences with one or both target patterns,
and (b.) an additional group of sequences that shared only one
structural features with the target sequences. For example, a subject might receive the example $CTTTTTTC$; he might notice
that it began and ended with a circle but fail to notice the uninterrupted run of triangles in the middle. Thus, he would accept
on the private inventory: (a.) all the correct sequences of the
pattern "begin with a C, followed by any number of T's and end
with C"; and (b.) all other sequences on the inventory that began
and ended with C (e.g., $CTCTCTC$). In pre-experimental trials,
most subjects who did not learn one of the target-pattern concepts inferred, in each of the two problems, one of four more
inclusive pattern concepts similar to the one described above. We
refer to these commonly-attained over-inclusive pattern concepts
as *probe patterns*.

The private inventory was constructed to distinguish between
subjects who inferred the target patterns and those who inferred
one of the probe patterns; a small group of subjects who did not
appear to attain either a target or probe pattern remained as unclassifiable. Each private inventory was composed of seven groups
or subsets of sequences. There were two *target subsets*. One set
contained T_p sequences; the other contained T_c sequences. For
example, the T_p subsets in problem 1 contained sequences such
as $CTTC$ and $CTTTTC$. There were four *probe subsets*. Each
probe subset contained a target subset plus two or three additional
sequences that shared one or two—but not all—of the features
of the sequential pattern of the target sequences. There were two
probe subsets that contained one T_p subset and two that con-

tained the T_c subset. For example, in problem 1, these two probe subsets contained target subset T_p: (a.) A subset whose sequences all began with T or C followed by any number of T's and ending in C; this subset as defined contained all the sequences of the T_p subset and others that were not a member of this set (for example, TTC and $TTTTTC$). (b.) A subset whose sequences began with C followed by T's or C's and T's in any order and ending in C; as defined, this subset contained the T_p sequences and some that were not members of this group or members of probe subset 1 (for example, $CTCTC$). Probe subsets are designated by the symbol P ($P1$ or $P2$) with the same subscript as the target subset they include. The two probe subsets described in this paragraph were designated as $P1_p$ and $P2_p$, respectively. In addition to two target subsets and four probe subsets, each inventory contained a seventh subset—the *both-target subset*—which was a disjunction of the two target subsets. Although the sequences used in the final inventory were grouped in the same subsets as on the initial inventory, they were not identical to those in the initial inventory. Therefore, the subject was required to make a fresh set of decisions at the conclusion of the problem. The subsets used on private inventories in problems 1 and 2 are described in Table 2. Four types of subjects can be distinguished by each inventory—those who show a selection preference on the inventory for sequences from ($a.$) the both-target subset—the subject was assumed to have learned both target patterns; (b.) either-target subset—he is assumed to have inferred only one target pattern; (c.) one of the four probe subsets—he is assumed to have inferred a probe pattern; and (d.) none of these—the subject's concept is not ascertainable (he may have attained some undiscoverable concept or his choice performance was random). If a subject accepted all the sequences in one of the seven defined subsets—and rejected all the rest—his preference would be clear and unmistakable and he could be assigned to either the both-target, one-target, or probe category. However, two other types of choice performances were common:

TABLE 2
Formal Descriptions of Subsets on the Sequence Inventory

Name of subset	Sequential pattern
Problem 1:	
Target: parent, T_p	Must begin with a *circle*, to be followed by any number * of *triangles*, and end with a *circle*
Probe 1: parent, P_{1p}	Must begin with a *triangle or a circle*, to be followed by any number of *triangles*, and end with a *circle*
Probe 2: parent, P_{2p}	Must begin with a *circle*, to be followed by any number of *triangles or circles* in any order, and end with a *circle*
Target: child, T_c	Must begin with a *triangle*, to be followed by any number of *circles*, and end with a *triangle*
Probe 1: child, P_{1c}	Must begin with a *triangle or circle*, to be followed by any number of *circles*, and end with a *triangle*
Probe 2: child, P_{2c}	Must begin with a *triangle*, to be followed by any number of *triangles or circles* in any order, and end with a *triangle*
Problem 2:	
Target: parent, T_p	Must begin with a *circle*, to be followed by a *square* to be followed by any number of *triangles*, and end with a *square*
Probe 1: parent, P_{1p}	Must begin with a *circle*, to be followed by a *square or a triangle*, to be followed by any number of *triangles* (if square precedes) or any number of *circles* (if triangle precedes), and end with a *square* (if triangle precedes) or a *triangle* (if circle precedes)
Probe 2: parent, P_{2p}	Must contain at least one *square*
Target: child, T_c	Same as T_p in problem 1
Probe 1: child, P_{1c}	Must begin with a *circle*, to be followed by any number of *squares* or any number of *triangles*, and end with a *circle*
Probe 2: child, P_{2c}	Must not contain any *squares*.

---

* Any number = zero to infinity.

(a.) Subjects who accepted sequences from only one of the defined subsets but did not accept the whole subset. If a subject selected a sufficient number of sequences, he was categorized as if he had accepted the whole set. In order to be assigned to the both-target category, he had to accept an equal number of T_c and T_p sequences and accept a minimum of four from the whole subset. This minimum number was determined in this way. We regarded the probability of a subject accepting a single sequence, from the both-target subset, by chance alone, as 0.5 since there were 10 sequences in this subset and a total of 20 sequences on the inventory. Thus, if he accepted only 2 sequences on the inventory and these 2 were from the both-target subset, the probability that his performance could be due to chance alone would be 0.25. We set 0.2 as the maximum probability level. Since we specified that a subject must select an equal number of T_c and T_p sequences, the next highest value to consider is four sequences from the both-target subset. The probability here is 0.06 (0.5 x 0.5 x 0.5 x 0.5), which falls below our level; and, therefore, the subject is categorized as having attained both targets.* There were 5 sequences in each one-target set and 7 or 8 in each probe set, and the probability of accepting one sequence in the set by chance alone was regarded as $5/20=0.25$ and $7/20=0.35$, respectively. Thus, accepting at least two sequences for a one-target or a probe subset permitted a subject to be classified in one or the other. Since all probe subsets contained one target subset, we had to specify that a subject must accept at least two of the sequences from the non-target portion of the probe subset before being classed in the probe category.

(b.) Subjects who accepted sequences from one of the defined

* The method of multiplying probabilities assumes that subject scans the whole inventory and then selects at the same time all sequences he believes are correct. Hence, the probability of selecting any sequence in the subset is the same as selecting any other. This would not be true if the subject went through the inventory one sequence at a time and serially accepted or rejected sequences. The assumption underlying the present statistical usage seems the simplest and corresponds to the way many subjects were observed making their selections. It may be in error for some subjects and require revision as we learn more about selection performance on tasks of this kind.

sets and fewer number from one or more of the other sets. For example, consider a subject who accepted as correct eight sequences; six of these were from the both-target subset and two were from other subsets. Although he showed a preference for the both-target subset, it was possible that this apparent preference was due to chance alone. To determine the likelihood of this, we again assumed that the probability of accepting one sequence from the both-target subset by chance was 0.5 and asked what is the probability of accepting as many as 6 of 8 from the both-target subset by chance alone. We used a binomial expansion formula:

$$\text{Probability} = \sum_{i=0}^{x} \binom{N}{i} P^i Q^{N-i}$$

where N=total number of sequences accepted (8 in this example)

X=number of accepted sequences in the preferred subset (here 6 from the both-target subset)

P=number of sequences in the preferred subset divided by 20 ($10/20$=0.5 in this example)

and Q=1–P. The probability for this example is 0.145; since this is lower than the arbitrary level of 0.2, the subject was placed in the both-target category. The same computations were done for subjects showing preference for a one-target or probe subset. One problem arises when a subject accepts target and non-target sequences from the same probe subset. For example, a subject who accepts all 5 sequences with the pattern "C, any number of T's, C" and also accepts the sequences $CTCTC$ and $CTCCCC$ could be classified as attaining one target (5 out of 7 choices are targets with the probability of getting one target by chance at 0.25) or as one probe (7 out of 7 choices are probes with probability of one by chance at 0.35). In this kind of instance, where at least two sequences were accepted from the non-target portion, the subject was classified in the probe category. In other instances where subjects could be classified into more than one category the order of preference was: (i) both-target; (ii) one-target; (iii) probe. All subjects who could not be classed in any of these three were categorized as "not ascertainable."

CHANGE IN CONCEPT FORMATION DURING
COLLABORATIVE FAMILY TESTING

Figure 3 presents data comparing groups of families according to their change in performance from the initial to final inventory. The same method of diagraming is used here as in Fig. 2. Since there were no significant differences between groups in problem 1

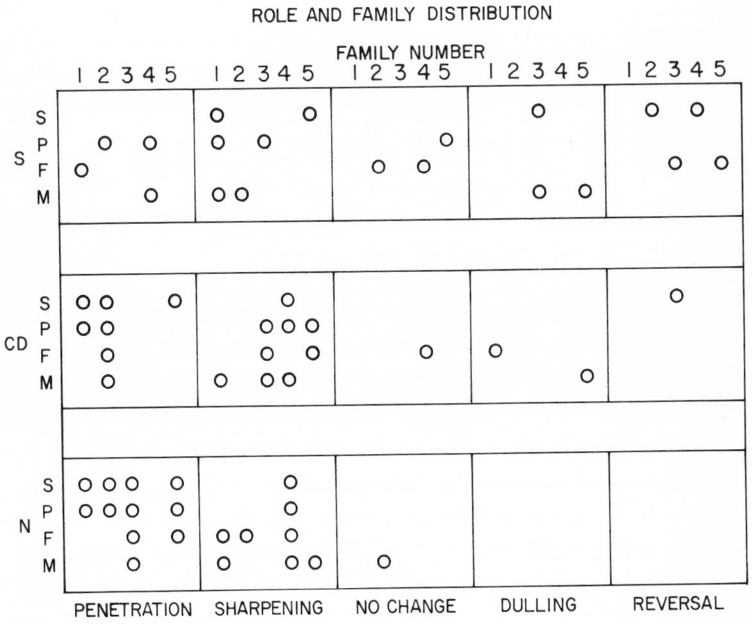

ROLE AND FAMILY DISTRIBUTION

FAMILY NUMBER

Fig. 3. Change in pattern concept from initial to final inventory for problem 2. Each circle corresponds to the score obtained by one subject and is positioned according to the subject's performance, role, and family membership.

only data from problem 2 are shown. Each subject was classified according to the type of change he showed from the first to the second inventory using classificatory criteria described later in this section. (a.) *Penetration*: Subject appears to have learned the pattern concept of his own example on the first inventory and to have learned both target patterns by the time he was given the second inventory. (b.) *Sharpening*: The subject appears to have improved his grasp of the concept of his own example but has not learned the other generation's target pattern. (c.) *No change*: No significant change in pattern concept is in evidence. (d.) *Dulling*: Subject appears to have a more hazy idea of concept of his example and does not learn the other generation's target concept. (e.) *Reversal*: Subject appears to have learned the target pattern of his own example at the start of the task but completely, or nearly so, surrenders this concept in favor of the target pattern of the other generation by the end of the task.

The diagram shows that penetration and sharpening were fairly evenly distributed in families of normals and character disorders; five of these families showed all four members achieving penetration or sharpening and the remaining five showed three members achieving this. In only one family of a schizophrenic did all four members achieve sharpening or penetration and in this family only one achieved penetration. In the remaining families not more than two individuals achieved sharpening. However, in four of the five schizophrenic families at least two individuals achieved no change, dulling, or reversal; neither of the other two groups had families with more than one member with no change, dulling, or reversal. Furthermore, four of the families of schizophrenics showed an individual with reversal, only one of the character-disorder families did so, and none of the normal families showed dulling or reversal. Children in families of normals usually achieved penetration, whereas their parents achieved sharpening. There was no clear-cut distinction in performance—by roles—in the other two groups of families except the patients in families of schizophrenics, who showed no deterioration of pattern concepts.

264

The criteria used for classifying subjects were: *

1. *Penetration.* (*a*) The subject accepted at least two T_h sequences on the first inventory *and*(*b*) accepted no fewer T_h sequences on the final than on the initial inventory *and*(*c*) he accepted more T_h than T_t sequences on the first inventory *and*(*d*) increased the number of T_t sequences accepted on the final inventory by three or more *and*(*e*) he accepted more target than non-target sequences on both inventories.

2. *Sharpening.* (*a*) The subject accepts at least two sequences on the first and second inventories *and*(*b*) he accepts one or no T_t sequences on either inventory, or the increase in T_t sequences was less than three, *and*(*c*) the ratio of target to non-target sequences was increased.

3. *No change.* Subjects who do not meet criteria described above and below were classified here.

4. *Dulling.* The criteria for this category are the same as for sharpening except that the ratio of accepted target to non-target sequences decreases from initial to final inventory.

5. *Reversal.* (*a*) The subject accepts fewer T_h and more T_t on the second than on the first inventory, *and*(*b*) on the first inventory, he accepted more T_h than T_t *and*(*c*) on the second, he accepted more T_t than T_h *and*(*d*) the change in number of T_t and T_h accepted—from the first to second inventory—is three or more, *and*(*e*) on both inventories he accepted more target than non-target sequences.

FAMILY PERFORMANCE IN THE COLLABORATIVE
TESTING OF SEQUENCES

During the period of collaborative testing of sequences each family member knew what sequences other members were testing and whether these sequences were confirmed or infirmed; this was in contrast to the administration of the private inventory where family members knew nothing of each other's performance. The raw data for this analysis was the complete array of sequences tested by each family in each problem reassembled in the order in which they were constructed and tested.

1. *Focus.* During the testing phase, the sequential pattern of

* An additional convention of notation is used: $T_h =$ sequences with the target pattern of the subject's own example; $T_t =$ sequences with target pattern of the other generation's

265

the sequences an individual constructs may be determined by the patterns he observes in sequences tested by others. We developed two measures that were assumed to reflect two aspects of this form of influence or interaction. The first—the *focus-sequence* measure—was an attempt to measure the degree to which individuals rather blindly copied the form of sequences that had been tested in the immediately preceding turns by others; we assumed that such copying did not mean that the subject understood the idea behind the sequences that he was copying. The second—the *focus-idea* measure—was developed to measure the degree to which an individual recognized and utilized the ideas behind others' sequences to construct his own sequences.

a. *Focus-sequence.* The focus-sequence score, for each individual, was the proportion of sequences he tested (before turning on the finish light) that were similar in pattern to at least one sequence tested by another in the immediately preceding turn. Objective criteria for the judgment of similarity are described later in this section. The data are presented in Table 3. The tabular format is the same for the following three tables, has been designed to provide a quick grasp of interrelated findings, and permits easy comparison of the present data with findings in closely related studies using the same format.[6] The *family score* is derived from the performance of the whole family irrespective of individual contributions to the family total. Details of score computation are reported at the end of this section. Nonparametric statistical tests were done on sum of ranks and are described in the footnote to Table 3. Table 3 shows that for focus-sequence, family scores showed the normal group lowest and the schizophrenic highest except on problem 2 where the latter were in the middle. The statistical difference between the groups is not strong. However, the finding is of great relevance because the direction of group differences is exactly opposite to that obtained with the focus-idea analysis to follow;

Table 3

Focus-sequence Scores, Relative Magnitude of Sum of Ranks *

Problem	N	Family score CD	S	P		Role	N.	Within-role across-group CD	S	P		Role	Within-family across-role N	CD	S
1 + 2		L	M	H	n.s.†	Mother		L	H	M	0.20	Mother	LM/HM	H	H
1		L	H	M	n.s.	Father		M	H	L	n.s.	Father	LM/HM	LM	LM
2		L	H	M	n.s.	Patient		M	L	H	0.05	Patient	H	L	HM
						Sib		L	M	H	n.s.	Sib	L	HM	L
												W	0.07	0.20	0.34
												P	n.s.	n.s.	n.s.

* Note on tests of significance: (1) p values listed for family scores and within-role analyses were obtained by two-tailed Kruskal-Wallis analysis of variance. (2) Brackets in the family score and within-role analyses refer to two tailed p values for the Mann-Whitney test: •••• = p < 0.22; —— = p < 0.10; ——— = p < 0.056; —— = p < 0.020. (3) In the within-family analysis W = Kendall's coefficient of concordance and p = its significance. (4) In the within-family analysis, brackets refer to two-tailed p values for the sign test: —•—— = p < 0.10. (5) The relative magnitude of the sum of ranks is indicated: H = high; HM = high middle; M = middle; LM = low middle; L = low.

† Not significant.

this contrast has considerable theoretical interest and will be examined in the Discussion section. The *within-role across-group* analysis compared the individual performance of the same role players from the same group of families with the same role players in each of the other two groups of families. Table 3 shows that patients in schizophrenic families had higher focus-sequence scores than patients in families of character disorders and patient controls in normal families. The *within-family across-role* scores compared the individual performance of one set of role players with each of the other three sets of role players within the same group of families. Table 3 shows there was no significant difference between sets of role players in any of the three groups of families.

A detailed description of scoring follows:

Focus-sequence score. This score was the proportion of total sequences tested that were rated as similar in pattern to at least one

267

sequence tested by another in the immediately preceding turn. We used the target and the probe sequential-pattern descriptions specified in Table 2 * to make objective judgments of similarity between the subject's sequences and the immediately preceding ones. This method employed the formal application of structural rules rather than subjective judgments of similarity. For each problem all sequences tested were divided into seven mutually exclusive subsets: Two target subsets, four non-target probe subsets (each of these four containing all the sequences tested that had one of the probe patterns, but not either of the target patterns) and a set of non-classifiable sequences (whose pattern did not conform to any of the target or probe patterns for that problem).† Non-classifiable sequences were rated as dissimilar to preceding sequences. Other sequences were rated similar if they and one of the preceding three were in the same subset. For instance, on her third turn, in problem 2, mother tested this sequence: $CSSC$ (this is in the non-target portion of Pl_c subset); on the immediately preceding turn, patient had tested $CTTTTC$ (T_c); father had tested $CSSSSSC$ (non-target of Pl_c) and sibling $TCCT$ (nonclassifiable). Mother's sequence would be rated as similar to father's since both were in the non-target portion of Pl_c probe subset.

Statistic comparisons. Examples will clarify the computation of family within-role and across-role comparisons. (a.) *Family score.* This score was calculated as follows: for each individual we determined the number of sequences tested that were similar to another member's on the immediately preceding turn; the number of sequences so rated for all four members was totaled and divided by the total number of sequences tested by the family before finish lights were turned on. This is the family score. For instance, if mother in family X tested eight sequences of four of which were similar, father seven with three similar, and patient and sibling each tested six with two similar, then the family score would be the total number of similar sequences (eleven) divided by the total number of sequences tested (twenty-seven), yielding the family score of 0.408. The family scores for all fifteen families were ranked with the rank of 1 assigned to

---

* Since $P2_p$ $P2_c$, in problem 3, were too inclusive for this purpose, we constructed somewhat less inclusive ones to replace them: $P2_p$—"Must begin with a C, to be followed by any number of T's, C's, or S's in any order and end with S;" $P2_c$—"Must begin with a C, to be followed by any number of T's, C's or S's in any order and end with a C."

† The proportion of sequences tested that were non-classifiable were: normals 17 percent ($N = 181$): character disorder, 14 percent ($N = 187$), and schizophrenics, 24 percent ($N = 176$) where N equals total number of sequences tested by families in each group.

the family with lowest family score and 15 to the highest. The sum of family ranks was obtained for each group. Comparisons across groups of families were made on the basis of these sums of ranks. Family scores were derived from performance on problem 1, problem 2, and on both problems combined. (b.) *Within-role across-group.* This compared a set of role players in one group with the same set of role players in each of the other two groups. *Individual scores* were used. For instance, if mother tested eight sequences, four of which were similar, her individual score would be 0.500. The individual scores for all fifteen mothers, obtained in this way, were ranked, and the sums of ranks were obtained and statistically compared across groups just as the family scores. This was done for fathers, patients, and siblings as well. (c.) *Within-family across-role.* This also used individual scores, but individuals were ranked in comparison to other role players within their own families. For instance, in family X, the individual scores were mother, 0.500, father, 0.429, and patient and sibling, 0.333. Patient and sibling, therefore, tied for ranks 1 and 2; father is ranked 3 and mother 4; i.e., the highest rank, 4, goes to the highest similarity score, 0.500. For each group of families, the ranks received by each role player were summed. Within each group the sums of ranks for role players were computed and statistically compared, as described in the footnote to Table 3. To summarize, the within-role across-group analysis determined whether role players in one group of families were significantly different from the same role players in other groups; the within-family across-role analysis determined whether a role player—in each of the three experimental groups— differed significantly from other role players in his family. Both analyses are based on performance in problems 1 and 2 combined.

    b. Focus idea. It was assumed that once an individual apprehends another's idea and decides to use it for himself, it will determine his performance—to some extent—for the rest of the task. Thus, an idea may be apprehended early in the task and still determine performance late in the task. Comparisons of tested sequences with those in immediately preceding turns, as done for the focus-sequence analysis, would not reveal these remote effects. In the present analysis, we determined the proportion of sequences tested before the finish light that were likely to have been responses to apprehending another's idea. There were many different ideas or hunches about correct

269

patterns that might be apprehended from another throughout the task. We selected one transmittable or apprehensible idea for scoring. An individual could learn from the other generation to test sequences like the other generation's and unlike his own. Rationale and scoring methods are discussed in detail at the end of this section. The focus-idea score was the proportion of total sequences tested that had a pattern similar to the other generations' target pattern.

The data are in Table 4. The form of presentation is the same as in Table 3. The family-score analysis shows the normal families to be significantly higher than the families of schizophrenics. Although the significance is weak, the finding is notable in that it is directly opposite in direction to the focus-sequence analysis. Both the patients and siblings in families of schizophrenics are significantly lower than their counterparts in families of normals, and the schizophrenic siblings are significantly lower than the character-disorder siblings as well. The within-family analysis shows that the children are significantly higher than are parents, in families of normals and character disorders, along this dimension.

Details of the method for deriving focus-sequences scores follows. In problem 1 we assumed that parents would get the idea from their

Table 4
Focus-idea Scores, Relative Magnitude of Sum of Ranks *

Problem	Family scores				Role	Within-role across-group				Role	Within-family across-role		
	N	CD	S	P		N	CD	S	P		N	CD	S
1 + 2	H	M	L	n.s.	Mother	H/M	L	H/M	n.s.	Mother	L/LM	LM	LM
1	H	M	L	n.s.	Father	M	L	H	n.s.	Father	L/LM	L	L
2	H	M	L	n.s.	Patient	H	M	L	n.s.	Patient	HM	HM	HM
					Sib	M	H	L	0.20	Sib	H	H	H
										W	0.87	0.84	0.20
										P	0.01	0.01	n.s.

* See Table 3 for note on statistical tests and symbols.

270

example that acceptable sequences must begin and end with circles. If they tested a large number of sequences that began and ended with triangles, we assumed that this reflected: (a.) their observing their children-testing sequence of *TT* type, and (b.) "getting the idea" behind the tested sequences of the children and trying out some themselves. We assumed the reverse for children. For parents, the "focus-idea" score was the portion of total sequences tested that began and ended with triangles; for children, it was the proportion of tested sequences that began and ended with circles. In problem 2 we assumed that parents would get the idea from their example that acceptable sequences could have squares and would learn from sequences tested by their children that acceptable sequences may also have no squares; we assumed the reverse for the children. In problem 2, the focus-idea score for parents was the proportion of their tested sequences that contained no squares; for the children it was the proportion that contained squares. For any and all individuals, testing sequences unlike their examples may reflect their individual inventiveness or willingness to try out a wide range of ideas. They might test sequences unlike their examples in the absence of any influence from other members. The critical question is whether a disposition to test such sequences in the absence of influence from others is more heavily distributed in one group of families than in others. Since the initial private inventory is assumed to measure an individual's preference for sequential patterns—in the absence of influence from other members—we would expect it to show evidence of any major inequalities among groups. However, there were no major differences between groups in this respect (Fig. 2).

2. *Risk.* A second form of family influence on individual performance in these tasks arises from the individual's willingness to risk having his sequences judged incorrect. For example, an individual's concern may derive from one or more sources; some individuals may fear chagrin before their family, whereas others may fear that their incorrect performance might confuse the family. The present measures do not determine the meaning—to the individual—of the risk of being wrong but assess his willingness to assume this risk. We assumed there were two important ways an individual could reduce this risk. In the first, an individual could use whatever knowledge he had about the target pattern or patterns to make up only correct sequences; in this case he

271

would construct almost no incorrect sequences and thus avoid what we have termed *infirmed-hypothesis* risk. We have seen that a large number of individuals perceive at least one pattern at the outset of the task and that there was no difference, in this respect, between groups of families (Fig. 2). Presumably this percept could be used to avoid constructing incorrect sequences. Secondly, an individual could avoid risk by paying close attention to which sequences tested by others were rated as correct. He would be particularly careful never to test a sequence dissimilar to one tested in the immediately preceding turn if the preceding sequence were rated correct (not changing a good hypothesis in midstream): he would be avoiding what we have termed *midstream risk*.

a. *Infirmed-hypothesis risk.* The score was the portion of sequences constructed by the subject—prior to turning on the finish light—that were wrong. Data are presented in Table 5. The family-score analysis shows normal families significantly higher than families of schizophrenics. Children in families of schizophrenics were significantly lower than other children, whereas fathers of schizophrenics were significantly higher than were other fathers. The children were significantly higher than were the parents in families of normals and character disorders.

Table 5

Infirmed Hypothesis Risk, Relative Magnitude of Sum of Ranks *

Problem	Family score				Role	Within-role across-group				Role	Within-family across-role		
	N	CD	S	P		N	CD	S	P		N	CD	S
1 + 2	H	M	L	n.s.	Mother	H	M	L	n.s.	Mother	L	LM	L
1	H	M	L	n.s.	Father	M	L	H	0.20	Father	LM	L	HM
2	H	M	L	0.20	Patient	M	H	L	0.20	Patient	HM	H	LM
					Sib	H	M	L	0.05	Sib	H	HM	H
										W	0.93	0.93	0.13
										P	0.01	0.01	n.s.

* See Table 3 for note on statistical tests and symbols.

b. Midstream risk. The measure was the proportion of sequences tested—prior to turning on the finish light—that were rated as "high risk" according to the following criteria. (1) The sequence was judged as to whether or not it was similar in sequential pattern to the immediately preceding one (e.g., sibling's fifth sequence tested was compared with father's fifth). Scoring details are described at the end of this section. (2) It was judged as high risk if it were similar and the preceding sequence was wrong or it was dissimilar and the preceding sequence was right. If the individual in the preceding turn had turned on his finish light, his sequence would, of course, not have been confirmed or infirmed. Therefore, the sequence being rated was compared with the sequence tested two turns previously. If three members had stopped testing, the remaining member's sequences would be compared with his own immediately preceding sequence.

Data are presented in Table 6. The family scores showed families of normals were significantly higher than families of schizophrenics, with families of character disorders in between. This is the same direction of differences as the infirmed-hypothesis risk measure despite the marked differences in how these risk measures are computed. The within-role analysis shows only weak differences between groups of role players; children in families of schizophrenics are lower than children in other families, whereas

Table 6
Midstream Risk, Relative Magnitude of Sum of Ranks *

Problem	Family score N CD S P				Role	Within-role across-group N CD S P				Role	Within-family across-role N	CD	S
1 + 2	H	M	L	n.s.	Mother	M	H	L	n.s.	Mother	HM	H	LM
1	H	L	H	n.s.	Father	H	L	M	n.s.	Father	LM	L	H
2	H	M	L	n.s.	Patient	H	M	L	n.s.	Patient	H	LM/HM	L
					Sib	M	H	L	n.s.	Sib	L	LM/HM	HM
										W	0.07	0.41	0.12
										P	n.s.	n.s.	n.s.

* See Table 3 for note on statistical tests and symbols.

fathers of normals are higher than fathers of character disorders. There are no significant differences between role players within families in any of the three groups. In sum, these data suggest that members of families of schizophrenics copy each other's performance only if the others are successful.

For midstream risk scoring we used the same criteria for judging the similarity of sequences constructed by subjects as in the focus-idea measure: In problem 1, all sequences that began and ended with C were placed in one group and all that began and ended with T were placed in another. This left an unclassifiable group which did not begin and end with the same figure (for example, $CTTTT$). These were assigned to one of the two groups according to who constructed them; for parents, these unclassifiable sequences were assigned to the group beginning and ending with C, for children, to the group beginning and ending with T. In problem 2, the tested sequences were also divided into two groups: one contained all sequences with squares and the other contained all sequences without squares. A sequence was rated similar to its predecessor if it was in the same group.

DISCUSSION

There were two important sets of findings that distinguished the groups of families: findings drawn from pattern-concept changes as measured by the private inventories and from measurements of the hypotheses tested. For pattern concepts, the most significant finding was that families of schizophrenics showed deterioration of pattern concepts, in the course of the task, whereas families of normals showed improved pattern concepts. More particularly, normal families showed a capacity to learn one pattern concept at the start of the task and acquire a second concept by the end of the task—or at the very least improve the accuracy of the pattern concept initially attained. Families of schizophrenics were also able to attain a concept similar or identical to those of normal families at the beginning of the task, but this concept often appeared to become more hazy or to be surrendered in favor of another by the end of the task. Learning of two concepts was very infrequent in the schizophrenic group. The major differences between groups was obtained on problem 2; our assumption is that problem 2 was more difficult and hence revealed the difference between groups of families more clearly than did problem 1, although it is possible that our failure to obtain differences on both problems means that the differences between groups are unreliable.

For hypothesis testing, the most significant findings were that families of normals tested a diversity of hypotheses and appeared willing to assume the risk of constructing incorrect hypotheses. Families of schizophrenics tested a narrower range of hypotheses, very much like their initial example, and were less willing to take a risk.

The findings for character disorders were often between normals and schizophrenics. By use of all the dimensions they could be distinguished from both normals and schizophrenics. This suggests that the normal-schizophrenic differences obtained in this study were not simply a result of the latter group containing a child who had been psychiatrically hospitalized.

Based on the foregoing results our hypotheses are that: (a.) characteristics of hypothesis testing for each group of families reflects styles of interpersonal interaction characteristic for that group of families, and (b.) this characteristic type of hypothesis testing determines the changes in pattern concept observed.

With respect to hypothesis (a.), an alternative explanation is that the hypothesis testing style primarily reflects individual perceptual and cognitive abilities and has little to do with the individual's characteristic involvement with his family. This might be tested by regrouping our subjects into foursomes of unrelated persons. An individual's style of hypothesis testing should be the same in his family, or the group of unrelated persons, if the alternate hypothesis is true. However, direct observations of family interaction have reported phenomena similar to our findings and give some support to hypothesis (a.). For example, the high degree of copying each other's performance (focus-sequence scores) and the low degree of actual sharing of ideas (focus-idea scores) seems similar to Wynne's findings of pseudomutuality.[7]

275

With respect to hypothesis (b.), an alternative explanation is that an individual's characteristic style of hypothesis testing has little to do with the change in pattern concept in the course of the task. If this were true we should be unable to predict the qualitative change in an individual's pattern concept from the type of hypotheses he tests. Such predictive studies must be part of future methodologic innovation, but data from the present study shed some light on the problem. From their hypothesis testing, we can infer that individuals in normal families stimulate each other to try out a wide range of hypotheses even though this involves taking a greater risk. Logically, we would expect that hypothesis testing of this kind would frequently result in learning both concepts. We found that penetration, the learning of the second concept, is most frequent in normal families. This would seem to support hypothesis (b.). However, families of schizophrenics characteristically test a narrow range of hypotheses; and most of these are correct. Logically, we would not necessarily expect that dulling and reversal—characteristic for these families— would follow from this type of hypothesis testing. For example, subjects who show reversal seem to have a special affinity for the concept of the other generation. As a sign of this affinity, we would expect that reversal subjects would test a proportion of hypotheses drawn from the other generation's concepts considerably greater than the median for all subjects, 0.33. The four subjects who showed reversal had scores of 0.14, 0.33, 0.50, and 0.78. Thus, for the first two, there was no prediction in the hypothesis tested that they had a special affinity. Dulling and reversal both imply that the subject loses grasp and/or confidence, of the pattern concept he initially attained, but this loss is not clearly reflected in the schizophrenic families' hypothesis testing style. We might be able to clarify the role of hypothesis testing in concept change by: (i) studying a broader range of characteristics of hypothesis testing, and (ii) designing a "no-hypothesis" experimental situation where subjects were given the first inventory, performed unrelated tasks collaboratively, and then were given a second inventory.

One additional finding merits discussion. Patients in schizophrenic families showed no deterioration of pattern concepts, in striking contrast to other role players in the same group of families. However, they seem to have less improvement than do patient controls in normal families despite the fact that they begin the task with the attainment of somewhat higher-grade pattern concepts (one-targets and probes vs. probes and not ascertainables for the patient controls in families of normals). This relative failure might be regarded as a short-term cognitive deficit induced by family interaction in schizophrenic patients. However, it is not very dramatic and seems to indicate that the present experiment does not shed much light on the factors that make the schizophrenic patient the "sick one" in his own family. Rather, we get a picture of his family working together in a cautious and restrained way that leads to impairment in perception in the parents and sibs as much as the patient himself.

SUMMARY

The present study investigated the relationship between family interaction and individual pattern recognition in five families of normals, five families of character disorders, and five families of schizophrenics. Following a period of family interaction, members of normal families showed improvement in pattern recognition and members of families of schizophrenics showed deterioration or no change; and members of character-disorder families were in between. During the period of family interaction, members of normal families were independent and adventuresome in testing their pattern concepts, whereas members of families of schizophrenics were cautious and copied each other's performance but showed little pooling of ideas. These findings support the hypothesis that family interaction can influence perceptual process in its individual members in a short time and points to some particular relationships between family interaction and individual perception.

Part III

COMMENTARIES

RESPONSES OF THE THEORISTS
TO E. G. MISHLER AND N. E. WAXLER
"FAMILY INTERACTION AND SCHIZOPHRENIA:
A REVIEW OF CURRENT THEORIES" *

Gregory Bateson

THE AUTHORS HAVE been generous and—so far as this was possible—have been understanding in their critique of "double bind"
theory. They say with some justice that the phrasings of the
theory are sometimes ambiguous. They might have gone further
and said that (like much of psychoanalytic theory) the double
bind theory of schizophrenia is *slippery*—so slippery that perhaps
no imaginable set of empirical facts could contradict it.

The fact of the matter is that many of the "theories" of psychoanalysis, and those which I have contributed to the discussion of
schizophrenia, are really not theories in the ordinary sense, but
are more like new languages or perhaps new epistemologies. A
language can be confusing or enlightening. It can be convenient
or clumsy. But it cannot, in itself, be true or false.

I am sure that what Wynne says in his language could be
translated into my language and then it would look like things
that I have said or might have said.

I am less sure that this is true of what Lidz says, perhaps be-
cause I have had less opportunity for personal discussion with
Lidz than with Wynne. Certainly there are many concepts in
Lidz's theory which I would not know how to translate without

* *Reprinted from "Critical Evaluations,"* International Journal of Psychiatry,
2:415-428, 1966.

consulting him. In principle, double bind theory invokes the *formal* characteristics of constellations of ideas and/or experiences. Lidz's explanations tend to be in more episodic terms. He invokes content where I would invoke form, but if by "incest" (for example) he means a constellation of ideas and experiences characterized by the sorts of contradiction which seem to me to be pathogenic, then we agree.

Before asking which of various languages or epistemologies is to be preferred, we must answer first the major pragmatic question "for what?" Indeed it is very doubtful whether any complex human creation can ever be understood until this question has been answered.[1] We need to know what larger problems are to be illuminated or what purposes served by a language before we can judge of its value.

I cannot presume to answer this major question for Lidz and Wynne, but it may be useful to try to say what I was after in the constructing of "double bind" theory.

Let me say first that, while I have cared for several schizophrenic patients, I have never been intellectually interested in *them*. The same is true of my work with native peoples in New Guinea and Bali. Always my intellectual focus has been on general principles which were illustrated or exemplified in the data. I want to know: What sort of universe is this? How may it best be described? What are the *necessary* conditions and limitations of experience, communication, pattern, and order?

Insofar as I have succeeded in showing that the phenomena of schizophrenia are derivable from such basic premises as that the name is different from the thing named, I feel I know a little more about how natural history is limited and shaped. I can assert that if there be other learning entities of human complexity in other planets, then these entities must either sporadically exhibit phenomena analogous to schizophrenia or must have specific means of preventing these phenomena. The theories of Wynne and Lidz cannot be extended in this way.

There are formal truths of organization and communication as pervasive as the 2nd Law of Thermodynamics. It is these that I have tried to illuminate with the "double bind" theory. My "language" is still crude but was designed for this purpose.

Unfortunately, but necessarily, there is a basic formal truth about all abstract premises, namely the more abstract the premise, the more likely it is to be self-validating.[2] The organism which has once learned that it can do nothing to influence the course of external events is likely to live a life in which experience will continually reinforce this fatalism. By the same token, if we engage in experiments to study the wave forms of light, we shall continually reinforce our belief in the wave theory.

This basic truth about abstract premises is doubly relevant to the present discussion. The circumstance that abstract premises tend to be self-validating leads organisms to assimilate such premises into the deepest and most rigid structures of the mind or brain. Simple consideration of adaptive economy shows that it must always pay to save the more flexible and more conscious parts of the mind for the least predictable and most changeable truths.[3] The more constant premises or truths are more economically stored in the less flexible and more basic parts of the organism. It is the thesis of double bind theory that schizophrenic or related symptoms tend to appear when these abstract premises are violently or continually disturbed. These are the premises about identity, or, looking at the other side of the coin, we may call them the premises about love, hate, and dependency, and all other styles of relationship.

But the same truth about abstract premises has another and more sinister bearing upon the theory: the theory itself is highly abstract and, to this extent, is itself likely to be self-validating. The more abstract the premise, the less it can tell us about concrete details of the phenomena which we may encounter. It thus becomes excessively difficult to test the premises or the theory against empirical fact. To this is due the inevitable "slipperiness" of the theory.

Personally, I do not believe that the theory is at present subject to rigorous empirical testing. At best it can be vividly exemplified or illustrated by the phenomena of schizophrenia, humor, religion, art, and the like. To make rigorous testing possible, it will be necessary to learn a great deal more than we at present know about the nature of biological communication, the methods of coding of non-verbal communication, both between organisms and within the organism. We need to know also the implications of these coding methods for psychic and adaptational economy. To this end, I am currently devoting myself to the study of cetacean and other animal communication.

Theodore Lidz

I APPRECIATE THE attention that the reviewers have given the work that my colleagues and I have carried out and the high evaluation they have given it. Their task was difficult and, as might be anticipated, I might take issue with various interpretations and comments.

Perhaps the critical issue concerns their understanding of what we were trying to do. The authors criticize us for various theoretical inconsistencies between papers, refer to us as "theorists," and seem to imply that we had formulated a theory about the family's part in the production of schizophrenics, and then set out to test the theory. To some extent this is what Bateson, Jackson, *et al.* did. Our start was very different. We were following a lead based on clinical observation that schizophrenic patients we had treated always had grown up in seriously disturbed family settings. This observation may seem obvious now, and it is even taken for granted by many, but it was a new concept at the time. If it proved to be correct, the next questions concerned what factors in the family might be significant to the etiology of schizophrenia. For example, was it simply that the "schizophrenogenic mother" created an unstable family? As we investigated one facet of family interactions after another—separating them arbitrarily but never forgetting the essential unity of the family—the problem became increasingly complicated. We were primarily interested in establishing facts, for if we were wrong, we would not only mislead ourselves, but, perhaps, many other investigators and therapists. Theory was necessary to sort out the data. However, no suitable theory concerning the functions of the family in personality development and maldevelopment existed. What the reviewers are reviewing is the gradual emergence of a theory—including some tentative explorations that were not pursued further for various reasons. I believe that the reviewers would find more consistency if they constantly bore in mind that we have not been interested in family interaction as such, but in the family's functions in the personality development and integration of its offspring. It also seems to me that the similarities between our findings and those of Wynne *et al.* are more remarkable than the differences. We are clearly describing the same phenomena, even if sometimes in somewhat different terms.

One puzzling aspect of the review is the minimal attention given to our own efforts to present a coherent theory based on our findings in our paper, "Family Studies and a Theory of Schizophrenia." Perhaps the reviewers rightly believe that we neglected salient aspects of our work. In any event, we wrote:

As every area of interaction in these families was found to be faulty in some respect, the question arose if something were not fundamentally wrong with the capacities of these parents to establish families capable of providing the essentials for the integrative development of their offspring. The emphasis of the hypothesis directing the analysis of the data shifted from asking not only what had gone wrong early in the lives of these patients, but also what had been lacking. . . .

Although the deficiencies and distorting influences of the parents and the families they created were many and differed from family to family, when a child's developmental needs are taken as the focus of attention, they could be grouped into three categories: 1. Deficiencies of parental nurturance—which we shall relate to the patient's difficulties in achieving adequate autonomy; that is, to attain sufficient independence, boundaries, and responsibility for the Self, 2. The failures of the family as a social institution that directs the integrated development of the child by channeling drives and by providing conflict-free areas and roles appropriate to the offspring's age and sex into which he can grow, and motivating him to do so. The deficiencies in the family structure will be related to the faulty structuring of the patient's personality—to achievement or maintenance of an integrated ego structure, and 3. The defects in transmitting the communicative and other basic instrumental techniques of the culture to the child. . . . Recognition of the relationship of words and their meanings to ego functioning—the capacity to direct the Self into the future—clarifies the connection between the aberrant conceptual thinking and the ego disorganization of schizophrenic patients. Until recently only the first of these three sets of factors, parental nurturance, has received any appreciable attention in psychoanalytic theories of personality development, or been considered of potential moment in the genesis of schizophrenia.

In any case, the reader can survey our work and our findings in the book *Schizophrenia and the Family* which has now been published.[4]

Lyman C. Wynne

MISHLER AND WAXLER have performed a valuable function through their painstaking effort to understand, evaluate, and compare various views of the families of schizophrenics. The theories considered have much in common: a sustained interest in the actual behavior, transactions, and relationships within family units; the conceptualization of the family as a meaningful unit which can be strategically studied in relation to psychopathology; an interest in clinical observations which are more comprehensive than the traditional history-taking from one parent and psychotherapy with the individual identified patient; the discard of earlier simplistic notions of causality, such as the "schizophrenogenic mother"; and the use of the preliminary, clinically derived theories as a base for more systematic empirical investigations.

This review comes at a time when there appears to be a general, though implicit, recognition that the phase of preliminary theory building is, by and large, over. This phase has been superseded during the last few years by a very energetic and healthy trend to more systematic investigations in which new research methods are being scrutinized. As I see the general trend in this field, and certainly in our program at NIMH, the current emphasis is upon the empirical evaluation of *specific* concepts and upon the testing of selected *specific* hypotheses. A few of the recent experimental studies of family interaction which illustrate this shift of emphasis are mentioned in the concluding section by Mishler and Waxler. Further aspects of this trend have been recently reviewed by Framo [5] and were discussed by a variety of investigators in a recent research conference sponsored by the American Psychiatric Association.[6]

Most substantial revisions of present theories will, I expect, wait upon new findings from current systematic empirical research. An exception is that more conceptualization and hypothesis-formation is needed (and will soon be forthcoming) on the problem of boundaries between nuclear family units and the extended family, community, and broader culture and social structure. Interactional studies of families of schizophrenics have mainly been carried out with middle-class, white American and northern European families for whom the concept of the nuclear family (parents and children) as a relatively isolated and autonomous social unit has been generally, but too often uncritically, accepted. In our NIMH work, we are greatly interested in considering modifications of theory that may be necessary for families of different kinds and in studying families of schizophrenics using a cross-cultural and cross-class frame of reference.

Future changes in theories stemming from work with the families of schizophrenics will, I believe, not only change our ideas about family-patient relationships but also our conceptualization of the schizophrenias. Working with schizophrenics in the transactional setting of the family has raised numerous important questions about the adequacy of traditional formulations of the concept of schizophrenic disorders. I feel confident that from this work significant and generally acceptable contributions to our understanding of the origins, development, course, and varieties of the schizophrenias will emerge. However, there is still a great deal of work which needs to be done to connect interactional family studies empirically and conceptually with relevant recent developments in experimental psychology, especially learning theory and cognitive psychology, to cross-cultural and to epidemiological work, and to studies of the genetics and biology of persons labeled schizophrenic. Perhaps the review could usefully have discussed the extent to which the various theories differently lend themselves to further research.

In our research at NIMH, at least, we are greatly interested in facilitating the exploration of such connections between family studies and other approaches. For example, we are greatly interested in studying attentional and cognitive difficulties, which we have observed clinically in the families of schizophrenics, with experimental methods now becoming available. Other issues can most appropriately be tackled by applying the family study approach to special populations, such as is being done in our program at NIMH under Drs. Pollin and Stabenau in which detailed studies are made of families of genetically identical twins who are discordant for schizophrenia. Longitudinal studies and adoption studies are other approaches which can be usefully tied together with newer methods for evaluating family interaction. Such work will undoubtedly clarify limits and qualifications for the formulations which could not be fully specified in the earlier theoretical presentations.

Unlike some of my fellow family researchers, I strongly believe that progress will be greatly facilitated by taking seriously the concept of heterogeneity among schizophrenics, and, as Margaret Thaler Singer and I have emphasized, the concept of heterogeneity among the *families* of different kinds of schizophrenics. Some ways of subclassifying schizophrenics are dependent upon data of the premorbid and developmental history; other distinctions are related to sex and birth order of the offspring; other subclasses can be defined in terms of cognitive style, patterns of expression of affects, and modes of interpersonal relating.

One of the points about the current theories of our NIMH group which perhaps is not accurately conveyed in the review is that we do not regard identity crises as especially pivotal in the so-called "process" schizophrenics with a long history of skill deficits and with an insidious onset. The problem of identity crises is much more relevant to the acute reactive schizophrenics who have a breakdown and disintegration of previously relatively well-developed and differentiated ego functions. Identity crises involve difficulties of integration, typically a fragmentation in the case of acute schizophrenics, of the personality organization. Those schizophrenics with what we have called "amorphous" forms of thinking, a poor premorbid history, and an insidious onset have typically not become well-differentiated enough to have the issue of identity integration versus identity disintegration be a central one. In the "Pseudo-Mutuality" paper of 1958, identity problems were emphasized because that paper dealt with acute reactive schizophrenics.[7] In our later work, which has included the study of many families of so-called process or nuclear schizophrenia, the identity crisis aspect of the earlier formulations is not so applicable. This is just one of the many ways in which the variety of family and variety of subclass of schizophrenic needs to be carefully considered in order to avoid generalizations which are too sweeping and which are incorrect for portions of the schizophrenic population.

There are a few minor points of wording in the paper which I regard as inaccurate: in one section, the authors state that in all of the formulations shared family defenses would be considered "as inherently unstable." As the authors themselves indicate in subsequent examples, many of these defensive family patterns are exceedingly stable; indeed, there is enduring resistance to change despite drastic maturational and other shifts in individual family members.

Mishler and Waxler incorrectly attribute to our thinking this statement: "These styles of communicating meaning are assumed to be characteristic of the family as a whole, not simply the thought patterns of one parent." To the contrary, the same style of communicating may not be shared by both parents or all offspring. For example, we have described how certain family members, especially those who are emotionally split off from another part of the family, may be psychologically ostracized and considered as alien by another part of the family.[8] The communica-

286

tion style of the two parents is sometimes quite different; it is the transactional "fit" or lack of fit of the parents with each other and with each of the offspring which we feel deserves special attention. Depending upon the type of pattern involved, it is possible to make predictions about whether *similar* behavior is likely to have evolved through identification processes or *different,* complementary, behavior is apt to have been stimulated through the impact, for example, of a highly erratic, intrusive parent. We have found suggestive evidence that the parents of schizophrenics tend to augment actively or to acquiesce passively with the communication deviances and defects of one another. If *one* of a pair of parents is deviant in ways similar to the parents of schizophrenics, but the other parent counteracts or identifies actively those deviances, then even the sickest offspring is apt to be neurotic or borderline rather than frankly schizophrenic.[9]

The authors slip up in failing to make a distinction which we feel is important: they attribute to us the idea that "basic meaninglessness" exists in the family relationships of schizophrenics. We have emphasized that these are *feelings* of meaninglessness or pointlessness as *subjectively* experienced by the persons themselves. Commonly, in these families there is "a disbelief in the possibility of connected, subjectively meaningful, and satisfying experience. . . . The families of the amorphous schizophrenics often appear to have no stake in looking for meanings. . . . The families of fragmented schizophrenics often have profound skepticism about achieving meaning but end up with identifiable, albeit peculiar or narrow, reductionistic kinds of meanings." [10] From the vantage point of the outside, emotionally detached observer, these *feelings* of meaninglessness or of aridity of meaning may not be recognized or appreciated.[11]

Especially in research on schizophrenia, it is necessary constantly to distinguish and evaluate with separate standards: (1) subjective experience and meaning as organized by the patient and family members themselves; (2) the organization and meaning of behavior which is attributed to the patient and family by the researcher. Both conceptual and methodological confusion have resulted from shifting unwittingly from one frame of reference to the other. We have tried to specify which frame of reference we are using at a given time as consistently as we can.

Considering the numerous vantage points and levels of consideration which have been applied to the study of family interaction processes in schizophrenia, I feel that the authors are appropriately cautious in their concluding comments when they note that "the theories cannot be compared directly with each other" even though each of them contains hypotheses and concepts within itself that lead easily into empirical study. Even though many of the viewpoints that have been expressed so far in the literature may be appropriately regarded as "artful constructions," rather than scientific theories, my observation and expectation is that current empirical investigations are leading into the evaluation of various specific issues which can and will contribute to scientific theories of these complex matters which are more fully comprehensive. I am completely in accord with the expectation of the authors that such work will "result in an increased understanding not only of schizophrenia but of normal human behavior as well."

John P. Spiegel

THOUGH IT IS obvious that the review article fulfills an important function in the development of a field of science, the precise nature of its function is not clear. Nevertheless, it seems beyond doubt that one of its functions is that of a monitoring device which becomes important when a field is just getting started, or when, having made a certain amount of progress, it appears to be in trouble. During such times, investigators want to look around, to see where they have been and where they are going. They may want to question the basic assumptions underlying their efforts in order to make sure that it is worthwhile going on. At these moments, they work hard to ascertain what their basic assumptions are, and what their implications may be. Differences on this point may well account for the surprising disparity in the amounts of optimism or pessimism with which various reviewers regard their subject matters.

Topics in the area of the behavior disorders are chronically beset by stubborn difficulties, and the problem of schizophrenia is one of the most troublesome of the lot. It has, accordingly, given rise to a huge number of optimistic and pessimistic review articles, survey-type books, and conferences. Taken as a whole, the array features a broad spectrum of attitudes running from despair to enthusiasm. The review article by Mishler and Waxler, under consideration here, is a good example of qualified optimism. But it is interesting to note that a previous article coauthored by Mishler,[12] reviewing the relation between sociocultural factors and the epidemiology of schizophrenia, gives evidence of near despair. There, the authors said, "Writing a concluding section for a review of studies of the social etiology of schizophrenia is like talking to the relatives of the deceased after returning from a funeral. Other than platitudes, there is little that can be suggested that would remedy, alleviate, or eliminate the trouble." [13] Though they did, nevertheless, conclude with some hopeful suggestions, the dismal outlook of that article contrasts strongly with the generally cheerful view of the current studies. "There is some likelihood," we are now told, "that, guided by this new view of the phenomenon, such studies will result in an increased understanding not only of schizophrenia but of normal human behavior as well."

I subscribe neither to the bleak pessimism of the first review (neither did the official commentators, though for a mixed bag of reasons) nor to the optimism of the current article. It seems idle, however, to respond to such optimism-pessimism quotients simply by registering agreement or disagreement or by listing studies which the reviewer might have included as arguments for a different position on a presumptive hopefulness scale. Something more basic than the preferences of the individual investigator is at stake. But if there is a more basic issue behind these attitudes, what is it?

Some help with this question can be derived from the work of Kuhn on the nature of scientific progress.[14] A historian of science, Kuhn has postulated a sequence of stages in the development of any mature field of science. The stages are based upon the presence and the state of functioning of a "scientific paradigm" which can be defined as a particularly coherent tradition of research accepted through consensus within the scientific community. Examples are Ptolemaic versus Copernican astronomy, and Aristotelian versus Newtonian versus Einsteinian dynamics. The paradigm includes laws, concepts, theories, applications, and instrumentation and provides the general model from which they are developed.

Once a paradigm model has become established within a scientific community, according to Kuhn, "normal science" can take place. Though the paradigm itself, and its accepted theories, explains an impressive segment of the relevant phenomena, numerous puzzles are always left over. Over time, "normal" scientific procedures directed toward solving the puzzles create a group of "anomalies"—facts which no longer fit any theory generated by the paradigm. Then, a crisis develops, revolutionary theories are created, rejected theories are recovered, and controversy reaches extraordinary intensity until a new paradigm is gradually accepted.

The novel paradigm enables scientists to "see" new phenomena, to accept as "factual" what had previously been dismissed as trivial, and to return to the procedures of "normal science." Before the crisis is resolved, however, every effort is made to fit the anomalous observations into received views by the expansion, elaboration, and articulation of existing theory. In short, contrary to the popular conception, scientists are conservative, and tend to adhere to a tradition for as long as they possibly can.

The period of crisis, according to Kuhn, resembles in some ways the first or "preparadigm" phase of the development of a science. At this stage various potential paradigms compete with each other but none attains general acceptance. Rather, each one, with its embedded facts, technical terms, laws, theories, and methods, gives rise to a "school of thought" generously supplied with its professionals, its journals and texts, and its public audiences, the latter often in the role of partisans. Each "school" sharply challenges the basic assumptions of the others, though all direct their research—or important parts of it—to the same set of empirical phenomena. Within the schools, some practitioners ignore the existence of the other schools, some engage in public controversy, and some try to keep a foothold in one or more of the other schools (disciplines) while hoping for ultimate "unification" or "integration."

Few observers will disagree that the social and behavioral sciences are in the "preparadigm" stage of development. And most observers, it can be assumed, would agree on the major paradigms competing for attention in any particular department or subspecialty of these sciences. Where schizophrenia is concerned, for example, there would probably be consensus that a biological (genetic, neurophysiological, endocrinological) paradigm asserts its claim in competition with a psychological paradigm (personality, theory, learning theory, psychoanalysis, or all vaguely lumped together under the label "clinical theory") which is itself in competition with a "family interaction" paradigm (or small group process or communications theory) and with a sociocultural paradigm.

One of the chief features of a paradigm is the way in which it colors the views of the research workers associated with it. The same empirical phenomena appear in a wholly different light when looked at from the point of view of one or another of the competing approaches. For example, to the person doing research in the biological area, schizophrenia boils down to a problem in the molecular composition of the genes which influences the physiology of the central nervous system so that neuronal messages arrive at erroneous destinations. To the psychoanalyst and to clinicians of other schools of psychology, the same behavior is seen mainly in the light of failures in the course of emotional and cognitive development. For those investigating family interaction, schizophrenia appears as a perfectly natural part of intensely distorted family relationships and communication processes. To the social scientist, schizophrenia is a matter of mismatched and conflicting directives for appropriate behavior associated with segments of the society undergoing rapid change or some other form of social stress. To be sure, there may be some overlap between the neighboring paradigms but, on the whole, each approach lays down its own imperatives as to how the behavior in question is to be understood.

Now the reason for making these distinctions is not for the sake of asserting the claims of one paradigmatic approach over any of the others. My own view is that the coordination and articulation of all the paradigms is required in order to make much headway, and I have attempted to explore some of the theoretical and methodological features of a coordinated (interdisciplinary) program of investigation.[15] My purpose at this juncture, however, is to point out the need in any one study (or review of studies) of separating the significance of a paradigm from the significance of a theory (or set of theories) generated by that paradigm. There is some question, as I shall show shortly, whether such a separation can be effectively pursued in the absence of an articulation of paradigms. Nevertheless, it is important to keep simultaneously in view both the influence of the paradigm on the phenomena to be observed and the support given by a particular substantive theory for the causal relationships governing those phenomena.

If the influence of a paradigm on a phenomenon is examined in the virtual absence of any substantive theory, then the various elements included within the paradigm are denoted as "factors" or "variables." This is what takes place in the usual "empirical" study. But the empiricist's "factor" is the theorist's "process." As soon as a theoretical formulation is incorporated within the investigation, the "factor" as a static item is transformed into a dynamic process of cause-and-effect. This distinction does not make it more or less correct to call something observed a "factor" or a "process." What it is called depends upon how it is used. But until a "factor" included as an item in a paradigm can be converted into a "process" called for by a particular theory, its significance as a "factor" remains difficult to determine. And, for this reason, the relevance of the paradigm to the phenomenon in question remains in doubt.

In the Mishler and Scotch review, "Sociocultural Factors in the Epidemiology of Schizophrenia," the relevance of the sociocultural paradigm is examined in the near absence of any explanatory theory. The review takes up in succession the studies devoted to establishing the relevance of one or another social "factor" thought to have an influence on the incidence, prevalence, and etiology of schizophrenia: social class, social mobility, social ecology, migration, culture change, and total community characteristics. As a result of the caution and the strict logic with which the authors carry out their analysis of the findings of the various studies, all of these "factors" come off very badly. Either the findings are contradictory or incommensurate or the methods by which they were obtained are unsatisfactory. Still, so powerful is the influence of the paradigm itself that the authors are reluctant to accept their own judgment. For example, in concluding the section on cultural change, they say, "In summarizing this section, we agree with the consensus that a relationship has not yet been demonstrated between the culture and schizophrenia. There are various possible explanations for this. Most logical, but most difficult to accept, is the possibility that no such relationship exists. More acceptable to social scientists is the likelihood that the relationship is too complex, or too distant, or both, making it extremely difficult to study."

It seems to me that the problem is more manageable than this assessment indicates. If the relation of cultural "factors" to schizophrenia is so difficult to study, the problem consists of the absence of observation and theory linking the cause to the effect through a number of intervening steps. Even the much-noted instability in the use of the diagnostic label "schizophrenia," from one culture (or subculture) to another, must be placed within a cultural context which accounts for one or another usage, and thus relates the culturally determined "process" of diagnosis and treatment to the behavior denoted as "schizophrenia."

293

As presently executed, epidemiological studies are too micro-scopic, too empirical, and too "culture-bound" (to Western cate-gories of thought). In the absence of fine-grained, theoretically constructed, interconnections of cause to effect (plus the transac-tional reverberation of the effect back upon the cause) epidemio-logical studies are a waste of time. To have established this point so clearly is a valid contribution of the Mishler and Scotch re-view. But this conclusion passes no judgment on the *relevance* of the sociocultural paradigm to the phenomenon of schizophrenia. It is a comment, for the most part, on the way in which the paradigm has been used.

One may ask why the sociocultural paradigm has generated so little substantive theory and why existing theory is so little used. My answer would be that little progress in theory-building or theory-using can take place in the absence of a better articulation of the paradigmatic models among themselves.[16] How can one talk about the cultural determinants of schizophrenia without bringing the cultural aspects of the behavior into a firm relation with the psychological aspects of the behavior, and, *at the same time*, with the family aspects of that behavior? If these various types of processing (including the biological) go on simulta-neously, do we not need theoretical constructs which specify how one kind of process is related to another? Do we not also require research designs which make room for the reciprocal influence of one paradigm upon another—not just the influence of the cul-ture on schizophrenia but the effect of the culture on the family, of the family on the schizophrenic process in the individual, and of the reciprocal effect of that schizophrenic process in the family member upon the family and perhaps back upon the culture?

If it is agreed that these assumptions apply to the previous review of the sociocultural "factors," then they apply equally to the present Mishler and Waxler review of family "process." In dealing with family interaction process, Mishler and Waxler re-verse the previous strategy. Here the relevance of the paradigm is not called into question in any serious way and we are no longer confronted with "factors." What is examined is the status of a group of interrelated theories which this paradigm has generated. Family interaction is assumed to be a significant determinant of schizophrenic behavior. The question that is asked is what substantive theory accounts best for the process.

This strategy has both advantages and disadvantages. On the plus side, we are presented with reasonably clear accounts of the various theories—a feat in itself, considering their tendency to change over time. Further, the degree of clarity or vagueness in each formulation is well laid out, and the degree of overlap and discontinuity between the theories is nicely set forth. The differences in the explanatory strength—proceeding from cause to effect—in the various theories is exhibited. Finally, we are left with the clear impression that the processes specified by the theories can be operationally tested. This feature is, perhaps, the chief cause for the optimism with which the review concludes.

Operational testing requires all theoretically specified "processes" to be reconverted into "factors" through appropriate coding procedures; samples of family interaction are then examined for the presence or absence of such factors (double-bind, rigid or amorphous roles, etc.). The conversion of process into factors or variables is a part of "normal science" insofar as it yields ascertainable and quantifiable data. Yet, the unexamined questions with respect to the relevance of the paradigm itself now produce an equivocal situation.

We are to assume, for example, that there is a specifiable schizogenic process in a family leading to the outcome of schizophrenia in one (or more) family members. But what is the significance of the outcome, or dependent variable? Is it necessary to assume, for the sake of logic, that there is a neurotogenic process in the family which leads to a neurosis in a family? Is there a manic-depressogenic factor? Is there a different causal process leading to psychosomatic illness, juvenile delinquency, sexual perversion, and other discrete outcome variables? Is mental health the outcome of a still different family interaction process?

If the paradigm of family interaction process enters into each of these outcomes in a different way, then do we require a different set of theoretical variables for each of the different processes?

The logic of such inquiries leads us to two alternatives. Either we need a different (and not-as-yet-worked-out) set of theories for each of the different outcomes or we must carefully separate the family interaction process paradigm from the biological, the sociocultural and the psychological paradigms, while studying the effect of their interrelations with each other upon the various outcomes. In either case, there is a great deal of theory-building to be done. If different clinical outcomes are to be attributed wholly to the family process paradigm, then one probably needs to discern new processes (or different combinations of already specified processes) by studying samples of families containing neurotic, delinquent, sexually deviant, and psychosomatically ill members as the index case. If the paradigms themselves are to be separated out and studied for their mutual influence, then the research samples and the methods used must be chosen in such a fashion that the influence of each can be observed in some isolation from the others.

Actually, the family-interaction-process studies reported on in this review are unsatisfactory in terms of either of these alternatives. They have not been directed at an investigation of the clinically available range of outcomes, but have focused exclusively on schizophrenia as an outcome (sometimes with a "normal" control group). At the same time, they have neither excluded the psychological paradigm nor have they kept it separate from the family process model. At times—for example, in the case of the Lidz group—sociocultural "factors" have been introduced in an *ad hoc*, unsystematic fashion. In all cases, but in various fashions, the investigators have assumed that the family interaction leads to an unfavorable change in the psychological processing in the schizophrenic child and that its origin lies in an unfavorable psychological constellation in one or both parents. Due to the lack of separation of the paradigms, this assumption cannot be tested. But it is at least theoretically possible that the origin of

296

double-binds, skewed roles, amorphous communications, etc., lies in an incompatability of cultural values and role definitions as learned by the parents.

The lack of attention to paradigm relevance constitutes a serious deficiency in all the theories reviewed in the Mishler and Waxler article. One culture's skewed family relations may represent another's culture's design for family living. Amorphous communications, in some areas at least, may represent a challenge to a child of a certain biological type, while representing a defeat for another. Pseudomutuality may block a child's psychological growth in the first three years of life and be handled with humor or going-along-with-the-game in an older child.

These criticisms, however, do not detract from the value of the conceptual formulations themselves. The investigators in all the groups reviewed deserve credit for constructing concepts and hypotheses which can be approached through the observation of ongoing family behavior—as the authors of the review point out. Every style of research creates new problems as it begins to solve old ones. Though none of the theories discussed in the review are as yet in a finished state, I agree with Mishler and Waxler that it is fruitful to compare them with each other and to use experimental methods to determine their range of applicability. But if such experimental designs do not take systematically into account the influence of the sociocultural area, on the one side, and of the psychological and biological, on the other, they may well lead to results as inconclusive as those which have emerged from the previous epidemiological studies.

CHAPTER NOTES

CHAPTER I

Family Interaction Processes and Schizophrenia:
A Review of Current Theories

Elliot G. Mishler and Nancy E. Waxler

[1] Reviews of much of this work may be found in V. Sanua, "Sociocultural Factors in Families of Schizophrenics: A Review of the Literature," *Psychiatry*, 24:246-265, 1961; and J. Spiegel and N. Bell, "The Family of the Psychiatric Patient," in Silvano Arieti (ed.), *American Handbook of Psychiatry*, Vol. I, Basic Books, New York, 1959, pp. 114-149.

[2] A recent paper by W. W. Meissner, "Thinking About the Family— Psychiatric Aspects," *Family Process*, 3:1-40, 1964, also attempts a review and critique of these and other theories of family relationships. The two papers overlap in the territory covered but differ considerably in point of view and in the framework used for the comparative analysis of these theories.

[3] See the comments by P. Watzlawick, "A Review of the Double-Bind Theory." *Family Process*, 2:132-153, 1963.

[4] G. Bateson, D. Jackson, J. Haley and J. Weakland, "Toward a Theory of Schizophrenia," *Behavioral Science*, 1:251-264, 1956, pp. 253-254.

[5] G. Bateson, "Cultural Problems Posed by a Study of Schizophrenic Process," in A. Auerback (ed.), *Schizophrenia: An Integrated Approach*, Ronald, New York, 1959, p. 133.

[6] Bateson et al., 1956, *op. cit.*, p. 259.

[7] G. Bateson, "Minimal Requirements for a Theory of Schizophrenia," *Archives of General Psychiatry*, 2:477-491, 1960, p. 477.

[8] See, for example, the comments on cultures caught in double binds in Bateson, "Cultural Problems Posed by a Study of Schizophrenic Process."

[9] J. Haley, *Strategies of Psychotherapy*, Grune & Stratton, New York, 1963.

[10] *Ibid.*, p. 160.

[11] *Ibid.*, p. 366.

[12] J. Haley, "The Family of the Schizophrenic: A Model System," *Journal of Nervous and Mental Disease*, 129:357-374, 1959 (a), p. 372.

[13] J. Haley, "An Interactional Description of Schizophrenia," *Psychiatry*, 22:321-332, 1959 (b), p. 325.

[14] H. Searles, "The Effort to Drive the Other Person Crazy—An Element in the Aetiology and Psychotherapy of Schizophrenia," *British Journal of Medical Psychology* (1) 32:1-18, 1959.

298

[15] R. Laing, *The Self and Others: Further Studies in Sanity and Madness*, Quadrangle Books, Chicago, 1961, p. 89.

[16] *Ibid.*, p. 91.

[17] *Ibid.*, p. 93.

[18] *Ibid.*, p. 90.

[19] D. D. Jackson, personal communication.

[20] T. Lidz, *The Family and Human Adaptation*, International Universities Press, New York, 1963, p. 53.

[21] T. Lidz, A. Cornelison, S. Fleck, and D. Terry, "The Intrafamilial Environment of Schizophrenic Patients: II. Marital Schism and Marital Skew," *American Journal of Psychiatry.*, 114:241-248, 1957, p. 244.

[22] *Ibid.*, p. 246.

[23] *Ibid.*, p. 243.

[24] T. Lidz, S. Fleck, Y. Alanen, and A. Cornelison, "Schizophrenic Patients and Their Siblings," *Psychiatry*, 26:1-18, 1963, p. 10.

[25] J. Spiegel, "The Resolution of Role Conflict Within the Family," *Psychiatry*, 20:1-16, 1957.

[26] Lidz, 1963, *op. cit.*, p. 72.

[27] *Ibid.*, p. 96.

[28] *Ibid.*, p. 101.

[29] M. Bowen, "Family Relationships in Schizophrenia," in Auerbach, *op. cit.* and "A Family Concept of Schizophrenia," In D. Jackson (ed.), *The Etiology of Schizophrenia*, Basic Books, New York, 1960, pp. 346-372; M. Bowen, R. Dysinger, and B. Basamania, "Role of the Father in Families with a Schizophrenic Patient," *American Journal of Psychiatry*, 115:1017-1020, 1959.

[30] W. Brodey, "Some Family Operations and Schizophrenia," *Archives of General Psychiatry*, 1:379-402, 1959.

[31] L. Wynne, I. Ryckoff, J. Day and S. Hirsch, "Pseudo-Mutuality in the Family Relations of Schizophrenics," *Psychiatry*, 21:205-220, 1958, p. 205.

[32] *Ibid.*, p. 215.

[33] L. Wynne and M. Singer, "Thinking Disorders and Family Transactions," paper presented at the American Psychiatric Association, May, 1964, p. 10.

[34] M. Singer and L. Wynne, "Thought Disorder and the Family Relations of Schizophrenics; III. Methodology Using Projective Techniques," dittoed, 1963, p. 14.

[35] *Ibid.*, p. 20.

[36] *Ibid.*, p. 9.

[37] *Ibid.*, pp. 27-28.

[38] *Ibid.*, p. 27.

[39] L. Wynne, personal communication.

[40] Wynne et al., 1958, *op. cit.*, p. 207.

[41] *Ibid.*, p. 211.

[42] *Ibid.*

[43] T. Lidz and S. Fleck, "Family Studies and a Theory of Schizophrenia," mimeographed, 1964, p. 4.

[44] Bateson, 1960, *op. cit.*, p. 487.

[45] Bateson, 1959, *op. cit.*, pp. 133-134.

[46] J. Perceval, *Perceval's Narrative*, Gregory Bateson (ed.), Stanford University Press, Stanford, Calif., 1961.

[47] *Ibid.*, pp. xi-xii, xiv.

[48] Haley, 1959(b), pp. 326-327.

[49] Haley, 1960, *op. cit.*, 466-467.

[50] Haley 1959(a), *op. cit.*, p. 369.

[51] L. Wynne and M. Singer, "Thought Disorders and Family Relations of Schizophrenics: II. A Classification of Forms of Thinking," *Archives of General Psychiatry* 9:199-206, 1963, p. 200.

[52] Wynne et al., 1958, pp. 215-216.

[53] Wynne and Singer, 1964, p. 7.

[54] Wynne and Singer, 1963.

[55] L. Wynne and M. Singer, "Thought Disorders and the Family Relations of Schizophrenics," dittoed, 1962, p. 71.

[56] Wynne and Singer, 1964, p. 9.

[57] L. C. Wynne and M. T. Singer, "Thought Disorders and Family Relations of Schzophrenics: I. A. Research Strategy," *Archives of General Psychiatry*, 9:191-198, 1963.

[58] *Ibid.*, p. 3.

[59] Lidz, 1963, *op. cit.*, p. 91.

[60] Lidz et al., 1963, p. 3.

[61] Lidz, 1963, *op. cit.*, pp. 73, 92.

[62] Lidz and Fleck, 1964, *op. cit.*, p. 5.

[63] *Ibid.*, p. 20.

[64] See, for example, B. Z. Locke, M. Kramer, C. E. Timberlake, B. Pasamanick and D. Smeltzer, "Problems in Interpretation of Patterns of First Admissions to Ohio State Public Hospitals for Patients with Schizophrenic Reactions," *Psychiatric Research Reports*, 10:172-196, 1958, p. 175; and E. G. Mishler and N. Scotch, "Sociocultural Factors in the Epidemiology of Schizophrenia," *International Journal of Psychiatry*, 1:315-343, 1965, p. 318.

[65] Yi-chuang Lu, "Mother-Child Role Relations in Schizophrenia: A Comparison of Schizophrenic Patients with Non-Schizophrenic Siblings," *Psychiatry*, 24:133-142, 1961, and "Contradictory Parental Expectations in Schizophrenia," *Archives of General Psychiatry*, 6:219-234, 1962; Bowen, 1959, *op. cit.*; Brodey, 1959, *op. cit.*

[66] G. Bateson, "The Biosocial Integration of Behavior in the Schizophrenic Family," in N. Ackerman, F. Beatman, and S. Sherman (eds.), *Exploring the Base for Family Therapy*, Family Service Association of America, New York, 1961, pp. 116-122, p. 118.

[67] Bateson, 1959, p. 128.

[68] *Ibid.*, p. 136.

[69] Haley, 1959(a), p. 371.

[70] *Ibid.*, p. 373.

[71] *Ibid.*, p. 372.

[72] H. Searles, "Positive Feelings in the Relationship Between the Schizophrenic and His Mother," *International Journal of Psychoanalysis*, (6) 39:569-586, 1958; and "The Effort to Drive the Other Person Crazy—An Element in the Aetiology and Psychotherapy of Schizophrenia," 1959, *op. cit.*, pp. 1-18.

[73] For example, see Lidz, 1963, *op. cit.*, pp. 39-76.

[74] Lidz et al., 1963, pp. 2-3.

[75] T. Lidz, A. Cornelison, S. Fleck and D. Terry, "The Intrafamilial Environment of the Schizophrenic Patient: I. The Father," *Psychiatry*, 20:329-342, 1957(a), p. 342.

[76] Bateson, 1960, pp. 485-486.

[77] *Ibid.*, p. 486.
[78] Wynne and Singer, 1964, pp. 13-20.
[79] Lu, 1962, p. 229.
[80] Brodey, 1959, *op. cit.*
[81] Wynne and Singer, 1963, p. 61.
[82] A. Farina, "Patterns of Role Dominance and Conflict in Parents of Schizophrenic Patients," *Journal of Abnormal and Social Psychology*, 61:31-38, 1960.
[83] F. Strodtbeck, "The Family as a Three-Person Group," *American Sociological Review*, 19:23-29, 1954.
[84] D. Caputo, "The Parents of the Schizophrenic," *Family Process*, 2:339-356, 1963.
[85] R. F. Bales, *Interaction Process Analysis*, Addison-Wesley, Cambridge, Mass., 1950.
[86] F. Cheek, "The 'Schizophrenogenic Mother' in Word and Deed," *Family Process*, 3:155-177, 1964, and "A Serendipitous Finding: Sex Roles and Schizophrenia," *Journal of Abnormal and Social Psychology*, 69:392-400, 1964.
[87] J. Haley, "Research on Family Patterns: An Instrumental Measurement," *Family Process*, 3:41-65, 1964.
[88] E. G. Mishler and N. E. Waxler, "Interaction in Families of Schizophrenics: An Experimental Study," paper presented at the American Sociological Association, September, 1964.

CHAPTER II

Patterns of Role Dominance and Conflict in Parents of Schizophrenic Patients

Amerigo Farina

[1] Frieda Fromm-Reichman, "Notes on the Development of Treatment of Schizophrenia by Psychoanalytic Psychotherapy," *Psychiatry*, 11:263-273, 1948; J. N. Rosen, *Direct Analysis*, Grune & Stratton, New York, 1953.
[2] S. Arieti, *Interpretation of Schizophrenia*, Robert Brunner, New York, 1955; E. A. Ellison and D. Hamilton, "The Hospital Treatment of Dementia Praecox. Part II., *American Journal of Psychiatry*, 106:454-461, 1949; D. L. Gerard and J. Siegel, "The Family Background in Schizophrenia," *Psychiatric Quarterly*, 24:45-73, 1950; M. L. Kohn and J. A. Clausen, "Parental Authority Behavior and Schizophrenia," *American Journal of Orthopsychiatry*, 26:297-313, 1956; T. Lidz, A. Cornelison, S. Fleck, and D. Terry, "The Interfamilial Environment of the Schizophrenic Patient," *Psychiatry*, 20:329-342, 1957(a); Suzanne Reichard and C. Tillman, "Patterns of Parent-Child Relationships in Schizophrenia," *Psychiatry*, 13:247-257, 1950.
[3] E. H. Rodnick and N. Garmezy, "An Experimental Approach to the Study of Motivation in Schizophrenia," in M. R. Jones (ed.), *Nebraska*

Symposium on *Motivation*, University of Nebraska Press, Lincoln, 1957, pp. 109-183.

[4] M. K. Opler, "Schizophrenia and Culture," *Scientific American*, 197:103-110, 1957.

[5] H. E. Frazee, "Children Who Later Became Schizophrenic," *Smith College Studies in Social Work*, 23:125-149, 1953; D. Friedlander, "Personality Development of 27 Children Who Later Became Psychotic," *Journal of Abnormal and Social Psychology*, 40:330-335, 1945; Gerard and Siegel, *op. cit.*; T. Lidz, A. Cornelison, S. Fleck and D. Terry, "The Interfamilial Environment of the Schizophrenic Patient.: II. Marital Schism and Marital Skew," *American Journal of Psychiatry*, 114:241-248, 1957(b); Trude Tietze, "A Study of Mothers of Schizophrenic Patients," *Psychiatry*, 12:55-65, 1949.

[6] J. D. Matarazzo, G. Saslow and S. B. Guze, "Stability of Interaction Patterns during Interviews: A Replication," *Journal of Consulting Psychology*, 20:267-274, 1956.

[7] F. L. Strodtbeck, "Husband-Wife Interaction over Revealed Differences," in A. P. Hare, E. F. Borgatta and R. F. Bales (eds.), *Small Groups*, Knopf, New York, 1955, pp. 464-472; V. Cervin, "Relationship of Ascendant-Submissive Behavior in Dyadic Groups of Human Subjects to Their Emotional Responsiveness," *Journal of Abnormal and Social Psychology*, 54:241-249, 1957.

[8] L. Phillips, "Case History Data and Prognosis in Schizophrenia," *Journal of Nervous Mental Disease*, 117:515-525, 1953.

[9] Rodnick and Garmezy, *op. cit.*

[10] E. S. Schaefer and R. Q. Bell, "Parental Attitude Research Instrument (PARI)," unpublished manuscript, Laboratory of Psychology, National Institute of Mental Health, 1955.

[11] P. W. Jackson, "Verbal Solutions to Parent-Child Problems," *Child Development*, 27:339-349, 1956.

[12] P. W. Jackson, "Verbal Solutions to Parent-Child Problems and Reports of Experience with Punishment," unpublished doctoral dissertation, Columbia University, New York, 1955, and *ibid.*

[13] Jackson, 1955, *op. cit.*

[14] A. Farina, "Patterns of Role Dominance and Conflict in the Interaction of Parents of Schizophrenic Patients," unpublished doctoral dissertation, Duke University, Durham, N. C., 1958.

[15] A. R. Jonckheere, "A Distribution-free K-sample Test against Ordered Alternatives," *Biometrika*, 41:133-145, 1954.

[16] H. B. Mann and D. R. Whitney, "On a Test of Whether One of Two Random Variables is Stochastically Larger than the Other," *Annals of Mathematical Statistics*, 18:50-60, 1947.

[17] N. Garmezy, A. Farina and E. H. Rodnick, "The Structured Situational Test: A Method for Studying Family Interaction in Schizophrenia," *American Journal of Orthopsychiatry*, 30:445-452, 1960.

[18] Patricia N. Naka, "Shirley's Babies after Fifteen Years: A Personality Study," *Journal of Genetic Psychology*, 73:175-186, 1948.

[19] O. H. Mowrer, *Learning Theory and Personality Dynamics*, Ronald, New York, 1950, p. 596.

[20] Lidz et al., 1957(b), *op. cit.*

[21] R. R. Sears, M. H. Pintler, and P. S. Sears, "Effect of Father Separation on Preschool Children's Doll Play Aggression," *Child Development*, 17:219-243, 1946.

CHAPTER III

The Parents of the Schizophrenic

Daniel V. Caputo

[1] J. L. Despert, "Prophylactic Aspect of Schizophrenia in Childhood," *Nervous Child*, 1:199-231, 1942; D. L. Gerard and J. Siegel, "The Family Background of Schizophrenia," *Psychiatric Quarterly*, 24:47-73, 1950; J. Kasanin, E. Knight and P. Sage, "The Parent-Child Relationship in Schizophrenia," *Journal of Nervous and Mental Disease*, 79:249-263, 1934; T. Lidz, "Schizophrenia and the Family," *Psychiatry*, 21:21-27, 1958; T. Tietze, "A Study of the Mothers of Schizophrenic Patients," *Psychiatry*, 12:55-65, 1949.

[2] J. Block, V. Patterson, J. Block, and D. D. Jackson, "A Study of the Parents of Schizophrenic and Neurotic Children," *Psychiatry*, 21:387-397, 1958; Despert, *op. cit.*; Gerard and Siegel, *op. cit.*; C. T. Prout and M. A. White, "A Controlled Study of Personality Relationships in Mothers of Schizophrenic Male Patients," *American Journal of Psychiatry*, 107:251-256, 1950; Tietze, *op. cit.*

[3] A. T. Boisen, *The Exploration of the Inner World*, Willett, Clark, Chicago, 1936.

[4] A. Hoffer, H. Osmond and J. Smythies, "Schizophrenia: A New Approach. II. Result of a Year's Research," *Journal of Mental Science*, 100:29-45, 1954.

[5] W. R. Garner, H. W. Hake and C. W. Erikson, "Operationism and the Concept of Perception," *Psychological Review*, 63:149-159, 1956.

[6] D. M. Levy, "Maternal Over-protection and Rejection," cited by Kasanin et al., *op. cit.*

[7] Gerard and Siegel, *op. cit.*

[8] *Ibid.*

[9] T. Lidz, A. R. Cornelison, D. Terry and S. Fleck, "The Intrafamilial Environment of the Schizophrenic Patient: I. The Father," *Psychiatry*, 20: 329-342, 1956.

[10] Block et al., *op. cit.*

[11] Lidz, et al., *op. cit.*, p. 340.

[12] C. E. Osgood, G. J. Suci, and P. H. Tannenbaum, *The Measurement of Meaning*, University of Illinois Press, Urbana, 1957.

[13] D. R. Peterson, personal communication, 1960.

[14] R. F. Bales, *Interaction Process Analysis*, Addison-Wesley, Cambridge, Mass., 1950.

[15] W. L. Warner, M. Meeker and K. Eells, *Social Class in America*, Harper, New York, 1960.

[16] E. S. Schaefer and R. Q. Bell, "Parental Attitude Research Instrument (PARI)," unpublished manuscript, Laboratory of Psychology, National Institute of Mental Health, 1955.

[17] Gerard and Siegel, *op. cit.*

[18] Lidz et al., *op. cit.*

[19] V. D. Sanua, "Sociocultural Factors in Families of Schizophrenics," *Psychiatry*, 24:246-265, 1961.

[20] H. E. Frazee, "Children Who Later Became Schizophrenic," *Smith College Studies in Social Work*, 23:125-149, 1953.

[21] M. I. Kohn and J. A. Clausen, "Parental Authority Behavior and Schizophrenia," *American Journal of Orthopsychiatry*, 26:297-313, 1956.
[22] A. Farina, "Patterns of Role Dominance and Conflict in Parents of Schizophrenic Patients," *Journal of Abnormal and Social Psychology*, 61:31-38, 1960; E. H. Rodnick and N. Garmezy, "An Experimental Approach to the Study of Motivation in Schizophrenia," in M. R. Jones (ed.), *Nebraska Symposium on Motivation*, University of Nebraska Press, Lincoln, 1957, pp. 109-184.
[23] O. H. Mowrer, *Learning Theory and Personality Dynamics*, Ronald, New York, 1950.

Resolution of Intrafamilial Role Conflict in Families of Schizophrenic Patients.
I: Thought Disturbance

Paul M. Lerner

[1] L. C. Wynne, I. M. Ryckoff, J. Day, and S. Hirsch, "Pseudo-Mutuality in the Family Relations of Schizophrenics," *Psychiatry*, 21:205-220, 1958.
[2] T. Lidz, A. Cornelison, S. Fleck, and D. Terry, "The Intrafamilial Environment of the Schizophrenic Patient. VI. The Transmission of Irrationality," *Archives of Neurological Psychiatry*, 79:305-315, 1958.
[3] W. Becker, "A Genetic Approach to the Interpretation and Evaluation of the Process Reactive Distinction in Schizophrenia," *Journal of Abnormal and Social Psychology*, 53:229-236, 1956.
[4] F. L. Strodtbeck, "Husband-Wife Interaction Over Revealed Differences," *American Sociological Review*, 15:468-473, 1951.
[5] L. C. Wynne and M. T. Singer, "Thought Disorders and Family Relations of Schizophrenics: I. A Research Strategy, II. A Classification of Forms of Thinking," *Archives of General Psychiatry*, 9:191-206, 1963.
[6] Becker, *op. cit.*
[7] H. Werner, "The Concept of Development from a Comparative and Organismic Point of View," in D. B. Harris (ed.), *The Concept of Development: An Issue in the Study of Human Behavior*, University of Minnesota Press, Minneapolis, 1957; H. Friedman, "Perceptual Regression in Schizophrenia: An Hypothesis Suggested by the Use of the Rorschach Test," *Journal of Projective Techniques*, 17:171-185, 1953; E. L. Siegel, "Genetic Parallels of Perceptual Structuralization in Paranoid Schizophrenia: An Analysis by Means of the Rorschach Technique." *Journal of Projective Techniques*, 17:151-161, 1953; L. Hemmendinger, "Perceptual Organization and Development as Reflected in the Structure of Rorschach Test Response," *Journal of Projective Techniques*, 17-162-170, 1953.
[8] T. Parsons and R. F. Bales, *The Family*, Free Press, New York, 1955; J. P. Spiegel, "The Resolution of Role Conflict within the Family," *Psychiatry*, 20:1-16, 1957; Lidz et al., *op. cit.*; Wynne et al., *op. cit.*

9 P. M. Lerner, "Resolution of Intrafamilial Role Conflict in Families of Schizophrenic Patients," unpublished doctoral dissertation, University of Illinois, Urbana, 1964.

10 Spiegel, *op. cit.*

11 *Ibid.*

12 N. Ackerman, *The Psychodynamics of Family Life*, Basic Books, New York, 1958.

13 Lidz et al., *op. cit.*

14 Spiegel, *op. cit.*; A. Farina, "Patterns of Role Dominance and Conflict in Parents of Schizophrenic Patients," *Journal of Abnormal and Social Psychology*, 61:31-38, 1960.

15 Spiegel, *op. cit.*

16 Farina, *op. cit.*

17 Lidz, et al., *op. cit.*

:8 Wynne and Singer, *op. cit.*

19 Wynne et al., *op. cit.*

20 Ackerman, *op. cit.*

21 Becker, *op. cit.*

22 Wynne et al., *op. cit.*

Parents with a Schizophrenic Child: The Pathogenic Triad Introduction

Elliot G. Mishler and Nancy E. Waxler

1 E. G. Mishler and N. E. Waxler. "Family Interaction and Schizophrenia: Alternative Frameworks of Interpretation," presented to the conference on the Transmission of Schizophrenia sponsored by the Foundations' Fund for Research in Psychiatry, Dorado, Puerto Rico, June 26-30, 1967b.

2 E. G. Mishler and N. E. Waxler. "Family Interaction Patterns and Schizophrenia: A Multi-level Analysis," In the *Origins of Schizophrenia*, (Proceedings of the First Rochester International Conference on Schizophrenia), Excerpta Medica Foundation, Netherlands, 1967a.

3 T. Lidz and S. Fleck. "Family Studies and a Theory of Schizophrenia." Reprinted as Ch. XX in *Schizophrenia and the Family*, T. Lidz, S. Fleck, and A. R. Cornelison (eds.). International Universities Press, New York: 1965.

4 W. Goldfarb. *Childhood Schizophrenia*. Harvard University Press, Cambridge, Mass.: 1961, p. 19.

5 J. O'Rourke. "Field and Laboratory: A Study of Family Groups in Two Experimental Cultures," Sociometry, 27:422-435, 1963.

6 F. Cheek. "The 'Schizophrenogenic Mother' in Word and Deed," *Family Process*, 3:155-177, 1964a. "A Serendipitous Finding: Sex Roles and Schizophrenia," *Journal of Abnormal and Social Psychology*, 69:392-400, 1964b.

7 H. L. Lennard, M. R. Beaulieu and N. Embrey, "Interaction in Families with a Schizophrenic Child" in this volume, pp. 139-169, p. 156.

CHAPTER V

Interaction in Families with a Schizophrenic Child

Henry L. Lennard, Arnold Bernstein, and Maurice R. Beaulieu

[1] Adapted and revised from H. L. Lennard, Maurice R. Beaulieu, and Nolen G. Embrey, "Interaction in Families with a Schizophrenic Child" *Archives of General Psychiatry*, Feb., 1965, Vol. 12, pp. 166-183.

[2] N. W. Ackerman, *Family Focused Therapy of Schizophrenia*, Jewish Family Service, N.Y., 1959, mimeographed; G. Bateson, D. Jackson, J. Haley and J. Weakland, "Toward a Theory of Schizophrenia," *Behavioral Science*, 1:251-264, October 1956; M. Bowen, "Family Concept of Schizophrenia," in D. D. Jackson (ed.), *The Etiology of Schizophrenia*, Basic Books, New York, 1960; W. Goldfarb, L. Sibulkin, M. Behrens and H. Jahoda, "Parental Perplexity and Childhood Confusion," in A. H. Esman (ed.) *New Frontiers in Child Guidance*, International Universities Press, New York, 1958, pp. 157-176; T. Lidz, A. Cornelison, S. Fleck and D. Terry, "Intrafamilial Environment of Schizophrenic Patients: II. Marital Schism and Marital Skew," *American Journal of Psychiatry*, 114:241-248, 1957; L. C. Wynne, I. Ryckoff, J. Day and S. Hirsch, "Pseudo-Mutuality in Family Relations of Schizophrenics," *Psychiatry*, 21:205-220, 1958.

[3] J. N. Morris writes, ". . . the epidemiologist . . . can sometimes ask questions which the clinician also asks, and get different (maybe better, maybe worse) information in reply. Often, the epidemiologist may ask questions that cannot be asked in clinical medicine at all." (J. N. Morris, *Uses of Epidemiology*, E.&S. Livingstone, Ltd., Edinburgh, Scotland, 1957.)

[4] R. F. Bales, *Interaction Process Analysis: Method for Study of Small Groups*, Addison-Wesley Press, Cambridge, Mass., 1950.

[5] Rather than repeat the phrase "families with a child diagnosed as schizophrenic," we shall use the briefer expression, "schizophrenic families," throughout the paper. This does not imply that other family members have been diagnosed likewise.

[6] H. L. Lennard, A. Bernstein, E. B. Palmore, and H. C. Hendin, *Anatomy of Psychotherapy*, Columbia University Press, New York, 1960.

[7] Work done by Dr. Lennard with Dr. N. Ackerman in the Department of Psychiatry, Jewish Family Service, New York.

[8] The significance of locating new variables worth pursuing is underlined in a slightly difference context by Levinson, "It is often the aim in process studies to examine in a microscopic way what is going on . . . with the aim of deriving variables for further study." (D. Levinson, *Research in Psychotherapy*, H. H. Strupp and L. Luborsky (ed.), American Psychological Association, Inc., Washington, D.C., 1962, p. 197.)

[9] M. Bowen, *op. cit.*

[10] For more information about coding methodology, see Lennard and Bernstein, *op. cit.*

[11] The study of family interaction patterns in schizophrenic families often has as its objective the identification of those patterns which support and maintain the illness of one of the family members or the characterization of one of the family members as "ill." For example, Bateson writes: "These families seem to be stable with relation to the descriptive statement 'this family con-

tains a schizophrenic.' If the identified patient shows sudden improvement, the behavior of the others will change in such a way as to push him back into schizophrenic behavior." (G. Bateson, "Biosocial Integration of Behavior in the Schizophrenic Family," in N. W. Ackerman, F. Beatman, and S. Sherman, (ed.), *Exploring The Base for Family Therapy*, Family Service Association of America, New York, 1961, p. 118.) Another illustration of this position is the recent work of Dan Miller, which explores most skillfully the pressures operating in families to maintain the identified patient as "patient." Miller is working mainly with families with a child who has a serious reading disability. (G. A. Miller and G. A. Heise, "Problem Solving by Small Groups Using Various Communication Nets," *Journal of Abnormal and Social Psychology*, 46:327-336, 1951.)

[12] A number of investigators (for example, Bateson, Bowen, Goldfarb, Haley, Jackson, Lidz, and Wynne) have proposed that the mode of familial interaction is the significant factor (alone or in combination with genetic and other unspecified variables) which leads to the development of thinking and behavioral processes labeled as schizophrenic. For instance, Haley writes: "A logical hypothesis about the origin of schizophrenic behavior, when the behavior is seen in communications terms, would involve the family interaction of the patient. If a child learns to relate to the people in a relationship with parents who constantly induce him to respond to incongruous messages, he might learn to work out his relationships with all people in those terms. It would seem to follow that the control of the definition of relationships would be a central problem in the origin of schizophrenia." (J. Haley, "Interactional Description of Schizophrenia," *Psychiatry*, 22:321-332, November 1953.)

[13] N. W. Ackerman suggests that "the family environment in the 'sick' families may remain essentially unaltered through the years." In that case, he states, "the personality of the child is fixed by the time he reaches six years and thereafter changes very little . . . but if the family environment itself changes considerably over the passage of years, the ongoing interrelations . . . bring about considerable modification of the emerging personality of the child. . . ." (N. W. Ackerman, Lectures at the Academy of Medicine, March 1960, unpublished data.) The work of Lyman Wynne and collaborators is very relevant here. Wynne's concept of pseudo-mutuality refers to expectational stability (or rigidity) in schizophrenic families. Wynne's work not only suggests stability of family processes in such families, but considers such stability as inappropriate and as symptomatic of the family disturbance itself. (L. C. Wynne et al., 1958, *op. cit.*)

[14] It should be noted that the same complex problems do not arise in exploring the hypothesis that *current* intrafamily patterns contribute towards maintaining the illness of a family member.

[15] Students of paralinguistic and kinesic interaction such as R. Birdwhistle have claimed that characteristic patterns of such interaction are revealed within a few minutes or less. (See for example: R. E. Pittenger, C. F. Hockett and J. S. Danehy, *First Five Minutes: Sample of Microscopic Interview Analysis*, Paul Martineau, Ithaca, New York, 1960.)

[16] J. Haley, "Family Experiments: New Type of Experimentation," *Family Process* 3:41-65, 1962.

[17] Unreliability in diagnosis of schizophrenia is estimated as quite high by Don Jackson. (D. D. Jackson, "Critique of Literature on Genetics of Schizophrenia," in *The Etiology of Schizophrenia*, Basic Books, New York, 1960.)

[18] W. Goldfarb, *Childhood Schizophrenia*, Harvard University Press for Commonwealth Fund, Oxford, 1961.

[19] J. Haley, 1962, *op. cit.*

[20] One can also capitalize on the special situation created by the research by paying special attention to the reactions of family members to the recording and observation. In a still-to-be-completed study on another group of schizophrenic families (the children of which are in daily treatment center) one of the mothers spent a few minutes looking for the location of the tape recorder in the room, only to remark to the son, some time later, that she was not at all "worried about being recorded."

[21] G. Bateson, 1956, *op. cit.*

[22] N. Bell. Personal communication to the authors.

[23] H. L. Lennard, "Analysis of Family Conflict," in N. W. Ackerman et al. (ed.), *Exploring The Base for Family Therapy*, Family Service Association of America, New York, 1961.

[24] In a study involving a small number of families in each group, when, furthermore, sample homegeneity is doubtful, the median appears to be a better measure of trends than means. However, means are presented whenever median and mean are close.

[25] N. Epstein and W. Westley, "Patterns of Intra-Familial Communication," *Psychiatric Research Reports*, 11:1, 1959.

[26] S. Fleck et al., "Some Aspects of Communication in Families of Schizophrenic Patients," paper read before the American Psychiatric Association Meeting, Philadelphia, 1959.

[27] Epstein and Westley, *op. cit.*

[28] T. Lidz and S. Fleck, "Schizophrenic Human Integration and Role of Family," in D. Jackson (ed.), *The Etiology of Schizophrenia*, Basic Books, New York, 1960.

[29] T. Parsons and R. F. Bales, *Family, Socialization and Interaction Process*, Free Press, Glencoe, Ill, 1955, pp. 91-94.

[30] Fleck et al., 1959, *op. cit.*

[31] *Ibid.*

[32] H. Bruch, "Falsification of Bodily Needs and Body Concept in Schizophrenia," *Archives of General Psychiatry*, 6:18-24, January 1962.

[33] Another speculative, though intriguing, notion is offered by Bateson (in a personal communication), who sees in the mode of current handling of a child's effort to "enter" familial interaction a reflection and a repetition of the original intrusion of the child at birth into the parental relationship.

[34] Using data made available at the Department of Psychiatry of the Jewish Family Service (in collaboration with N. W. Ackerman) and data made available by Frances Cheek.

[35] The significance of this parameter is stressed by Bettelheim who states that his work demonstrates "how important it is that from birth on the child gets responses from the environment that encourages his spontaneous moves toward the world; he should not be ignored or overpowered." (*New York Times Magazine*, January 12, 1967.)

[36] Bruch, *op. cit.*

[37] R. Laing, *Self and Others*, Tavistock Press, London, 1961.

[38] Bruch, *op. cit.*

[39] *Ibid.*

[40] Fleck, 1963, *op. cit.*

[41] Lidz and Fleck, *op. cit.*
[42] Bowen, *op. cit.*

CHAPTER VI

The Father of the Schizophrenic
The Function of a Peripheral Role

Frances E. Cheek

[1] D. Gerard and J. Siegel, "The Family Background of Schizophrenia," *Psychiatric Quarterly*, 24:47, 1950; L. Hajdu-Gimes, "Contributions to the Etiology of Schizophrenia," *Psychoanalytic Review*, 27:421-438, 1940.
[2] H. E. Frazee, "Children Who Later Became Schizophrenic," *Psychiatric Quarterly*, 25:125, 1953; S. Reichard and C. Tillman, "Patterns of Parent-Child Relationships in Schizophrenia," *Psychiatry*, 13:247, 1950.
[3] S. Fleck, T. Lidz and A. Cornelison, "Comparison of Parent-Child Relationships of Male and Female Schizophrenic Patients," *Archives of General Psychiatry*, 8:1-7, 1963.
[4] M. Bowen, R. H. Dysinger and B. Basamania, "The Role of the Father in Families with a Schizophrenic Patient," *American Journal of Psychiatry*, 115:1017-1020, 1959; J. L. Despert, "Schizophrenia in Children," *Psychiatric Quarterly*, 12:366-371, 1938; Gerard and Siegel, *op. cit.*; B. Rank, "Adaptation of the Psychoanalytic Technique for the Treatment of Young Children with Atypical Development," *American Journal of Orthopsychiatry*, 19:130-139, 1949; C. W. Wahl, "Some Antecedent Factors in the Family Histories of 568 Male Schizophrenics of the U. S. Navy," *American Journal of Psychiatry*, 113:201-210, 1956.
[5] L. Wynne, I. Ryckoff, J. Day and S. Hirsch, "Pseudo-Mutuality in the Family Relations of Schizophrenics," *Psychiatry*, 21:205-220, 1958.
[6] E. F. Borgatta and R. F. Bales, "A Systematic Study of Interaction Process Scores, Peer and Self-Assessments and Other Variables," *Genetic Psychological Monographs*, 65:219-291, 1962.
[7] T. Parsons, *The Social System*, Free Press, Glencoe, Ill., 1951, chaps. 6, 7.
[8] F. E. Cheek, "Family Interaction with Schizophrenics," unpublished doctoral dissertation, Columbia University, New York, 1962.
[9] F. E. Cheek, "The 'Schizophrenogenic Mother' in Word and Deed," *Family Process*, 3:155-177, March, 1964.
[10] F. E. Cheek, "A Serendipitous Finding, Sex Roles and Schizophrenia," *Journal of Abnormal and Social Psychology*, 69:392-400, 1964.
[11] F. E. Cheek, "Family Interaction Patterns and Convalescent Adjustment of the Schizophrenic, *Archives of General Psychiatry*, 13:138-147, 1965.
[12] Parsons, *op. cit.*
[13] Borgatta and Bales, 1962, *op. cit.*
[14] J. P. Guilford, *Fundamental Statistics in Psychology and Education*, McGraw-Hill, New York, 1950, p. 47.
[15] J. D. Matarazzo, G. Saslow and S. B. Guze, "Stability of Interaction Patterns During Interviews: A. Replication," *Journal of Consulting Psychology*, 20:267-274, 1956.

[16] E. F. Borgatta and R. F. Bales, "Interaction of Individuals in Reconstituted Groups," in P. Hare, E. F. Borgatta and R. F. Bales, *Small Groups*, Knopf, New York, 1955 pp. 379-395.

[17] J. F. O'Rourke, "Field and Laboratory: The Decision-making Behavior of Family Groups in Two Experimental Conditions," *Sociometry*, 26:422-435, December, 1963.

[18] J. Haley, "Family Experiments: A New Type of Experimentation," *Family Process*, 2:265-293, September, 1962.

[19] H. Lennard, "Characteristics of Interaction Patterns in Families with a Schizophrenic Child," paper read before the American Psychiatric Association meeting, St. Louis, May, 1963.

[20] Parsons, 1951, *op. cit.*

[21] T. Parsons and R. F. Bales, *Family Socialization and Interaction Process*, Free Press, Glencoe, Ill., 1955.

[22] *Ibid.*, p. 257.

CHAPTER VII

Family Interaction with Schizophrenics and Their Siblings

Shlomo Sharan (Singer)

[1] M. A. Bowen, "A Family Concept of Schizophrenia," in D. D. Jackson (ed.), *The Etiology of Schizophrenia*, Basic Books, New York, 1960, pp. 346-372; T. Lidz, *The Family and Human Adaptation*, International Universities Press, New York, 1963.

[2] G. Bateson, "Minimal Requirements for a Theory of Schizophrenia," *Archives of General Psychiatry*, 2:477-491, 1960; T. Lidz, S. Fleck, Y. Alanen and A. Cornelison, "Schizophrenic Patients and Their Siblings," *Psychiatry*, 26:1-18, 1963.

[3] S. Fleck, T. Lidz and A. Cornelison, "Comparison of Parent-Child Relationships of Male and Female Schizophrenic Patients," *Archives of General Psychiatry*, 8:1-7, 1963; J. Haley, "The Family of the Schizophrenic: A Model System," *Journal of Nervous and Mental Disease*, 129:357-374, 1959.

[4] Bowen, *op. cit.*; T. Lidz, A. Cornelison, S. Fleck and D. Terry, "The Intrafamilial Environment of the Schizophrenic Patient. IV. Parental Personalities and Family Interaction," *American Journal of Orthopsychiatry*, 28:764-776, 1956.

[5] W. M. Brodey, "Some Family Operations of Schizophrenia: A Study of Five Hospitalized Families Each with a Schizophrenic Member," *Archives of General Psychiatry*, 1:379-402, 1959.

[6] Yi-Chuang Lu, "Mother-Child Role Relations in Schizophrenia," *Psychiatry*, 24:133-142, 1961, and "Contradictory Parental Expectation in Schizophrenia," *Archives of General Psychiatry*, 6:219-234, 1962; C. T. Prout and M. A. White, "The Schizophrenic Sibling," *Journal of Nervous and Mental Disease*, 123:162-170, 1956.

[7] Lidz, *op. cit.*

[8] A. Farina and R. Dunham, "Measurement of Family Relationships and Their Effects," *Archives of General Psychiatry*, 9:64-73, 1963.

[9] D. V. Caputo, "The Parents of the Schizophrenic," *Family Process*, 2:339-356, 1963, p. 354.

[10] F. Cheek, "The 'Schizophrenogenic Mother' in Word and Deed," *Family Process*, 3:155-177, 1964.

[11] J. Haley, "Family Experiments: A New Type of Experimentation," *Family Process*, 3:41-65, 1962.

[12] H. L. Lennard, M. R. Beaulieu, and N. G. Embrey, "Interaction in Families with a Schizophrenic Child," *Archives of General Psychiatry*, 12:166-183, 1965.

[13] Lidz, *op. cit.*

[14] M. Roman and G. Bauman, "Interaction Testing: A Technique for the Psychological Evaluation of Small Groups," in M. Harrower (ed.), *Creative Variations in the Projective Techniques*, Charles C. Thomas, Springfield, Ill., 1960, pp. 93-138.

[15] D. Wechsler, *The Measurement of Adult Intelligence*, Williams & Wilkins, Baltimore, 1944, and *The Wechsler-Bellevue Intelligence Scale. Form II*, Psychological Corporation, New York, 1946.

[16] T. Mills, "Power Relations in Three-person Groups," *American Sociological Review*, 18:351-357, 1953.

[17] R. F. Bales, *Interaction Process Analysis*, Addison-Wesley, Cambridge, Mass., 1950.

[18] Caputo, *op. cit.*; Cheek, *op. cit.*; Farina and Dunham, *op. cit.*

[19] J. Block, V. Patterson, J. Block and D. D. Jackson, "A Study of Schizophrenic and Neurotic Children," *Psychiatry*, 21:387-397, 1958.

[20] Lennard et. al, *op. cit.*

[21] Lidz, *op. cit.*

[22] *Ibid.*

[23] Cheek, *op. cit.*

[24] G. Handel, "Psychological Study of Whole Families," *Psychological Bulletin*, 63:19-41, 1965.

Parents, Patient and Sibling: The Family Triad.

Introduction

Elliot G. Mishler and Nancy E. Waxler

[1] A. H. Buss and P. J. Lang, "Psychological Deficit in Schizophrenia: I. Affect Reinforcement, and Concept Attainment," *Journal of Abnormal Psychology*, 70:2-24, 1965; P. J. Lang and A. H. Buss, "Psychological Deficit in Schizophrenia: II. Interference and Activation," *Journal of Abnormal Psychology*, 70:77-106, 1965.

CHAPTER VIII

A Comparative Study of Families of Schizophrenics, Delinquents, and Normals

James R. Stabenau, Joe Tupin, Martha Werner, and William Pollin

[1] J. Kasanin, E. Knight and P. Sage, "The Parent-Child Relationship in Schizophrenia," *Journal of Nervous and Mental Disease*, 79:249-263, 1934;

Gerard and J. Siegel, "The Family Background of Schizophrenia," *Psychiatric Quarterly*, 24:47-73. 1950; S. Reichard and C. Tillman, "Patterns of Parent-Child Relationships in Schizophrenia," *Psychiatry*, 13:247-257, 1950; T. Lidz, A. R. Cornelison, S. Fleck and D. Terry, "The Intrafamilial Environment of the Schizophrenic Patient. II. Marital Schism and Marital Skew," *American Journal of Psychiatry*, 114:241-248, 1957; Y. O. Alanen, "The Mothers of Schizophrenic Patients," *Acta Psychiatrica Neurological Scandinavian Supplementation*, 124, 33:1-359, 1958; L. C. Wynne, I. M. Ryckoff, J. Day and S. Hirsch, "Pseudo-Mutuality in the Family Relations of Schizophrenics," *Psychiatry*, 21:205-220, 1958; M. Bowen, "A Family Concept of Schizophrenia," in D. D. Jackson (ed.), *The Etiology of Schizophrenia*, Basic Books, New York, 1960; T. Lidz, S. Fleck, Y. Alanen and A. Cornelison, "Schizophrenic Patients and Their Siblings," *Psychiatry*, 26:1-18, 1963.

[2] G. Bateson, D. D. Jackson, J. Haley and J. Weakland, "Toward a Theory of Schizophrenia," *Behavioral Science*, 1:251-264, 1956; T. Lidz, A. Cornelison, D. Terry and S. Fleck, "Intrafamilial Environment of the Schizophrenic Patient, VI. The Tranmission of Irrationality," *A.M.A. Archives of Neurology and Psychiatry*, 79:305-316, 1958; J. Haley, "The Family of the Schizophrenic: A Model System," *Journal of Nervous and Mental Disease*, 129: 357-374, 1959.

[3] J. Haley, "An Interactional Description of Schizophrenia," *Psychiatry*, 22:321-332, 1959; S. Fleck, "Family Dynamics and Origin of Schizophrenia," *Psychosomatic Medicine*, 22:333-344, 1960; L. C. Wynne and M. T. Singer, "Thought Disorder and Family Relations of Schizophrenics," *Archives of General Psychiatry*, 9:191-206, 1963.

[4] A. M. Johnson, M. E. Giffin, J. Watson and P. G. S. Beckett, "II. Observations on Ego Functions in Schizophrenia," *Psychiatry*, 19:143-148, 1956; D. D. Jackson, "A Note on the Importance of Trauma in the Genesis of Schizophrenia," *Psychiatry*, 20:181-184, 1957.

[5] W. Pollin, J. R. Stabenau, and J. Tupin, "Family Studies with Identical Twins Discordant for Schizophrenia," *Psychiatry*, 28:60-78, 1965.

[6] I. Kaufman, H. Durkin, Jr., T. Frank, L. W. Heims, D. B. Jones, Z. Ryter, B. Stone and J. Zilbach, "Delineation of Two Diagnostic Groups among Juvenile Delinquents: The Schizophrenic and the Impulse-ridden Character Disorder," *Journal of the American Academy of Child Psychiatry*, 2:292-318, 1963.

[7] E. Silber, D. A. Hamburg, G. V. Coelho, E. B. Murphey, M. Rosenberg and L. T. Pearlin, "Adaptive Behavior in Competent Adolescents," *Archives of General Psychiatry*, 5:354-365, 1961.

[8] J. L. Titchener and M. Golden, "Prediction of Therapeutic Themes from Observation of Family Interaction Evoked by the Revealed Differences Technique," *Journal of Nervous and Mental Disease*, 136:464-474, 1963.

[9] D. Rapaport, R. Schafer, and M. Gill, *Diagnostic Psychological Testing*, I, The Year Book Publishers, Chicago, 1945.

[10] S. H. Lovibond, "The Object Sorting Test and Conceptual Thinking in Schizophrenia," *Australian Journal of Psychology*, 6:52-70, 1954.

[11] N. McConaghy, "The Use of An Object Sorting Test in Elucidating the Hereditary Factor in Schizophrenia," *Journal of Neurology, Neurosurgery and Psychiatry*, 22:243-246, 1959; T. Lidz, C. Wild, S. Schafer, B. Rosman and S. Fleck, "Thought Disorders in the Parents of Schizophrenic Patients: A Study Utilizing the Object Sorting Test," *Psychiatric Research Reports*, 1:193-200, 1962.

[12] M. Werner, J. Stabenan and W. Pollin, "The Use of the TAT in the Study of Families of Schizophrenics, Delinquents, and Normals," (in preparation).

[13] Wynne and Singer, *op. cit.*

[14] *Ibid.*

[15] Lovibond, *op. cit.*

[16] Pollin et al., *op. cit.*

[17] Lidz et al., 1957, *op. cit.*; Wynne et al., *op. cit.*

[18] Lovibond, *op. cit.*

[19] Bateson et al., *op. cit.*; Lidz et al., 1958, *op. cit.*; Haley, 1959, *op. cit.*

[20] Bowen *op. cit.*

[21] D. D. Jackson, "The Question of Family Homeostasis," *Psychiatric Quarterly* (1) 31:79-90, 1957.

[22] J. N. Rosen, "Acting-Out and Acting-In," *American Journal of Psychotherapy*, 17:390-403, 1963.

[23] A. M. Johnson and S. A. Szurek, "The Genesis of Antisocial Acting Out in Children and Adults," *Psychoanalytic Quarterly*, 21:323-343, 1952.

[24] M. B. Arnold, *Story Sequence Analysis*, Columbia University Press, New York, 1962; W. E. Henry, *The Analysis of Fantasy*, Wiley, New York, 1956; S. Fisher and D. Mendell, "The Communication of Neurotic Patterns over Two and Three Generations," *Psychiatry*, 19:41-46, 1956; M. I. Stein, *The Thematic Apperception Test. An Introductory Manual for its Clinical Use with Adults*, Addison-Wesley, Cambridge, Mass., 1955; M. Reznikoff, "Social Desirability in TAT Themes," *Journal of Projective Techniques*, 25:87-89, 1961; D. Reynolds, "Social Desirability in the TAT: A Replication and Extension of Reznikoff's Study," *Journal of Projective Techniques*, 28:78-80, 1964; L. Srole, T. S. Langer, S. T. Michael, M. K. Opler and T. A. C. Rennie, *Mental Health in the Metropolis. The Midtown Manhattan Study*, vol. 1, McGraw-Hill, New York, 1962, pp. 194-200.

[25] M. T. Singer and L. C. Wynne, "Differentiating Characteristics of Parents of Childhood Schizophrenics, Childhood Neurotics and Young Adult Schizophrenics," *American Journal of Psychiatry*, 120:234-243, 1963.

[26] Reznikoff, *op. cit.*, p. 35.

[27] E. B. Murphey, E. Silber, G. V. Coelho, D. A. Hamburg, and I. Greenberg, "Development of Autonomy and Parent-Child Interaction in Late Adolescence," *American Journal of Orthopsychiatry*, 33:643-652, 1963; S. J. Beck, "Families of Schizophrenic and of Well Children: Method, Concepts, and Some Results," *American Journal of Orthopsychiatry*, 30:247-275, 1960; W. A. Westley, *The Family in Contemporary Society*, International Universities Press, New York, 1958.

Individual Thinking and Family Interaction. A Study of Pattern Recognition and Hypothesis Testing in Families of Normals, Character Disorders, and Schizophrenics

David Reiss

[1] D. Reiss, "Individual Thinking and Family Interaction. I. Introduction to an Experimental Study of Problem-Solving in Families of Normals, Character

Disorders and Schizophrenics," *Archives of General Psychiatry*, 16:80-93, 1967, and D. Reiss, "Individual Thinking and Family Interaction. III. An Experimental Study of Categorization Performance in Families of Normals, Character Disorders and Schizophrenics," in preparation.

[2] T. Lidz, C. Wild, S. Schaefer, B. Rosman and S. Fleck, "Thought Disorders in Parents of Schizophrenic Patients: A Study Utilizing the Object Sorting Test," *Journal of Psychiatric Research*, 1:93-200, 1963; B. Rosman, C. Wild, J. Ricci, S. Fleck and T. Lidz, "Thought Disorder in the Parents of Schizophrenic Patients: A Further Study Utilizing the Object Sorting Test," *Journal of Psychiatric Research*, 2:211-221, 1964; M. T. Singer and L. C. Wynne, "Thought Disorder and Family Relations of Schizophrenics. III. Methodology Using Projective Techniques," *Archives of General Psychiatry*, 12:187-200, 1965; C. Wild, M. T. Singer, B. Rosman, J. Ricci and T. Lidz, "Measuring Disordered Styles of Thinking Using the Object Sorting Test on Parents of Schizophrenic Patients," *Archives of General Psychiatry*, 13:471-476, 1965; L. C. Wynne and M. T. Singer, "Thought Disorder and Family Relations of Schizophrenics. II. A Classification of Forms of Thinking," *Archives of General Psychiatry*, 9:199-206, 1963; L. C. Wynne and M. T. Singer, "Thought Disorder and Family Relations of Schizophrenics. IV. Results and Implications," *Archives of General Psychiatry*, 12:201-212, 1965.

[3] B. D. Cohen, R. Senf and P. E. Huston, "Perceptual Accuracy in Schizophrenia, Depression and Neurosis and Effects of Amytal," *Journal of Abnormal and Social Psychology*, 52:363-367, 1956; S. Snyder, D. Rosenthal and I. A. Taylor, "Perceptual Closure in Schizophrenia," *Journal of Abnormal and Social Psychology*, 63:131-136, 1961.

[4] A. H. Buss and P. J. Lang, "Psychological Deficit in Schizophrenia: 1. Affect Reinforcement and Concept Attainment," *Journal of Abnormal Psychology*, 70:2, 1965; J. Silverman, "The Problem of Attention in Research and Theory in Schizophrenia," *Psychological Review*, 71:352-379, 1964.

[5] J. S. Bruner, J. J. Goodnow and G. A. Austin, *A Study of Thinking*, Wiley, New York, 1956.

[6] D. Reiss, I., 1967, *op. cit.*, and III., *op. cit.*; Lang and Buss, *op. cit.*

[7] L. C. Wynne, I. M. Rychoff, J. Day and S. I. Hirsch, "Pseudo-mutuality in the Family Relations of Schizophrenics," *Psychiatry*, 21:205-220, 1958.

Responses of the Theorists

[1] R. G. Collingwood, *Principles of Art*, New York: Oxford University Press, 1938.

[2] J. Ruesch and G. Bateson, *Communication: the Social Matrix of Psychiatry*, W. W. Norton and Co., New York: 1951, Chap. VIII.

[3] G. Bateson, "The Role of Somatic Change in Evolution," *Evolution*, 17:529-539, 1963.

[4] T. Lidz, S. Fleck, and A. R. Cornelison, *Schizophrenia and the Family* International Universities Press, Inc., New York: 1966.

[5] J. L. Framo, "Systematic Research on Family Dynamics," in I. Böszörmenyi-Nagy and J. L. Framo, *Intensive Family Therapy*, New York: Harper & Row, 1965.

[6] American Psychiatric Association, *Psychiatric Research Report*, 20, February 1966.

[7] L. C. Wynne, I. M. Ryckoff, J. Day, and S. I. Hirsch, "Pseudo-Mutuality in the Family Relations of Schizophrenics," *Psychiatry*, 21:205-220, 1958.

[8] *Ibid.*; L. C. Wynne and M. T. Singer, "Thought Disorder and Family Relations of Schizophrenics: I. A Research Strategy," *Archives of General Psychiatry*, 9:191-198, 1963.

[9] M. T. Singer and L. C. Wynne, "Thought Disorder and Family Relations of Schizophrenics: IV. Results and Implications," *Archives of General Psychiatry*, 12:201-212, 1965, and "Communication Styles in Parents of Normals, Neurotics and Schizophrenics: Some Findings Using a new Rorschach Scoring Manual," American Psychiatric Association, *Psychiatric Research Report*, 20, February 1966.

[10] M. T. Singer and L. C. Wynne, "Thought Disorder and Family Relations of Schizophrenics: III. Methodology Using Projective Techniques," *Archives of General Psychiatry*, 12:187-212, 1965.

[11] L. Schaffer, L. C. Wynne, J. Day, I. M. Ryckoff, and A. Halperin, "On the Nature and Sources of the Psychiatrists' Experience with the Family of the Schizophrenic," *Psychiatry*, 25:32-45, 1962.

[12] E. G. Mishler and N. A. Scotch, "Sociocultural Factors in the Epidemiology of Schizophrenia," *International Journal of Psychiatry*, 1:258-293, 1965.

[13] *Ibid.*, p. 282.

[14] T. S. Kuhn, *The Structure of Scientific Revolutions*. The University of Chicago Press, Chicago, 1962.

[15] J. P. Spiegel and F. R. Kluckhohn, *Integration and Conflict in Family Behavior*, Report No. 27, Topeka, Kansas: Group for the Advancement of Psychiatry, 1954; J. P. Spiegel, "Interpersonal Influences Within the Family," in Bertram Schaffner, ed., *Group Process*, The Josiah Macy Jr. Foundation, New York: 1965, "The Resolution of Role Conflict Within the Family," *Psychiatry*, 20:1-16, 1957, "Some Cultural Aspects of Transference and Countertransference," in Jules H. Masserman, ed., *Individual and Family Dynamics*, Basic Books, New York: 1959, and "Conflicting Formal and Informal Roles in Newly Acculturated Families," in David Rioch, ed., *Disorders of Communication*, Vol. XLII, Research Publications, A R. N. M. D. Association for Research in Nervous and Mental Disease, New York: 1964; J. P. Spiegel and P. Machotka, *The Messages of the Body* (Cambridge, Mass.: Harvard University Press. In preparation.

[16] If one considers the totality of theory generated by the family paradigm as reported in the literature, the result is near-chaos. If one then tries to order the theories which articulate the family with the sociocultural and the psychological paradigms, the chaos is compounded. For a valiant attempt to produce some semblance of order out of the shambles of concepts and theories strewn across the literature, and which also attempts to allocate substantive theory to generative paradigm, *see* Reuben Hill, "Contemporary Developments in Family Theory," *Journal of Marriage and the Family*, 28:10-26, 1966.

INDEX

317